INSTRUCTOR GUIDE

Human Anatomy & Physiology
Laboratory Manual

INSTRUCTOR GUIDE

Human Anatomy & Physiology
Laboratory Manual

INSTRUCTOR GUIDE

Human Anatomy & Physiology
Laboratory Manual

CAT VERSION, Twelfth Edition
MAIN VERSION, Eleventh Edition
FETAL PIG VERSION, Twelfth Edition

ELAINE N. MARIEB, R.N., Ph.D.
Holyoke Community College

JEFF SCHINSKE
De Anza College

LORI A. SMITH, Ph.D.
American River College

PhysioEx™ 9.1 Exercises authored by
Peter Z. Zao, North Idaho College
Timothy Stabler, Indiana University Northwest
Lori A. Smith, American River College
Andrew Lokuta, University of Wisconsin–Madison
Edwin Griff, University of Cincinnati

PEARSON

Boston Columbus Indianapolis New York San Francisco Upper Saddle River
Amsterdam Cape Town Dubai London Madrid Milan Munich Paris Montréal Toronto
Delhi Mexico City São Paulo Sydney Hong Kong Seoul Singapore Taipei Tokyo

Editor-in-Chief: Serina Beauparlant
Senior Acquisitions Editor: Brooke Suchomel
Program Manager Team Lead: Nancy Tabor
Project Manager Team Lead: Mike Early
Project Manager: Arielle Grant
Production Project and Design Manager: Michele Mangelli
Compositor: Cenveo® Publisher Services
Supplement Cover Design: Cory Skidds
Main Text Cover Design: Tani Hasegawa
Manufacturing Buyer: Stacey Weinberger
Marketing Manager: Derek Perrigo

Cover Photo Credits: Pole Vaulter, Pete Saloutos/Getty Images; Sky, Gregor Schuster/Getty Images

Credits and acknowledgments borrowed from other sources and reproduced, with permission, in this textbook appear on the appropriate page within the text.

www.pearsonhighered.com

ISBN 10: 0-133-99925-4
ISBN 13: 978-0-133-99925-9
4 5 6 7 8 9 10—V056—18 17 16 15

Contents

Part One: Exercises

Part Two: Dissection Exercises

Part Three: PhysioEx™ Exercises

Appendices

Preface

Organization of This Instructor's Guide

The Instructor's Guide for *Human Anatomy & Physiology Laboratory Manuals*, Main Version, Eleventh Edition, and Cat and Fetal Pig Versions, Twelfth Editions by Elaine N. Marieb and Lori A. Smith, continues to feature a wealth of information for the anatomy and physiology laboratory instructor.

Each exercise in this manual includes detailed directions for setting up the laboratory; comments on the exercise (including common problems encountered); some additional or alternative activities; and answers to the pre-lab quizzes, activity questions, Group Challenges and the new "Why This Matters" questions that appear in the text of the lab manual. Answers to questions regarding student observations and data have not been included.

Answers to the lab manual Review Sheets follow each exercise. In some cases several acceptable answers have been provided. Answers to the dissection review questions are located in this guide with the dissection exercises.

Directions for use of the kymograph have been removed from the lab manual but appear in Exercise 14 in the Instructor's Guide. Several complete exercises incorporating PowerLab®, iWorx®, and Intelitool® computer data acquisition and compilation systems, as well as instructions for an older version of the BIOPAC® software can be downloaded from the Instructor Resource section of the new MasteringA&P website for the *Human Anatomy & Physiology Laboratory Manuals*, and may be duplicated for student use.

 The time allotment at the beginning of each exercise, indicated by the hourglass icon, is an estimate of the amount of in-lab time it will take to complete the exercise, unless noted otherwise. If you are using multimedia, add the running time to the time allotted for a given exercise.

 Suggested multimedia resources, indicated by the computer icon, are listed for each exercise. Format options include VHS, CD-ROM, DVD, website, and streaming webcast. Information includes title, format, running time, and distributor. The key to distributor abbreviations is in the Guide to Multimedia Resource Distributors, Appendix B. Street and web addresses of the distributors are also listed in Appendix B.

 Each exercise includes directions for preparing needed solutions, indicated by the test tube icon.

Trends in Instrumentation includes information about laboratory techniques and equipment, including information on PowerLab®, iWorx®, and Intelitool®. There are some suggestions about additional investigations using techniques and equipment not described in the laboratory manual.

The Laboratory Materials list in each exercise is intended as a convenience when ordering. Amounts listed assume a laboratory class of 24 students working in groups of 4. Information about several supply houses appears in Appendix A. *Note:* The information provided is not an exhaustive list of suppliers.

Laboratory Safety

Always establish safety procedures for the laboratory. Students should be given a list of safety procedures at the beginning of each semester and should be asked to locate exits and safety equipment. Suggested procedures may be found on the inside cover of the lab manual.

Special precautions must be taken for laboratories using body fluids. Students should use only their own fluids or those provided by the instructor. In many cases, suitable alternatives have been suggested. All reusable glassware and plasticware should be soaked in 10% bleach solution for 2 hours and then washed with laboratory detergent and autoclaved if possible. Disposable items should be placed in an autoclave bag for 15 minutes at 121°C and 15 pounds of pressure to ensure sterility. After autoclaving, items may be discarded in any disposal facility.

Disposal of dissection materials and preservatives should be arranged according to state regulations. Be advised that regulations vary from state to state. Contact your state Department of Health or Environmental Protection Agency or their counterparts for advice. Keep in mind that many dissection specimens can be ordered in formaldehyde-free preservatives; however, even formaldehyde-free specimens may not be accepted by local landfill organizations.

Lori A. Smith
American River College

Strategies for Learning the Language of Anatomy and Physiology

The number of new terms in anatomy and physiology (A&P) can feel overwhelming to students, but there are a wide variety of ways to study these terms effectively. The important part is for each student to find study strategies that work for her or him, and stop using strategies that don't work well. All too often students repeat strategies that do not work well for them, simply because they have a limited repertoire of strategies to employ. Below you will find a sampling of study strategies to introduce to students. Students should experiment with these strategies throughout the course and repeat the strategies they find most helpful. Encourage students to have patience with new techniques they try, since a new strategy might end up being perfect for them once they get the hang of it. Some instructors encourage this practice by providing lab participation points each week if students can show evidence that they have created a study aid based on one of these strategies or another effective study strategy they develop.

Teach Another Person about Anatomy

How It's Done:

1. Convince someone to listen to you for a few minutes and serve as your "student." A colleague from class will do, but often a friend or family member from outside the class will work just as well. For that matter, you could "teach" the material to a goldfish or a stack of papers in your room! The goal is not exactly to have another person learn, but rather to give you an opportunity to exercise additional parts of your brain while studying. By speaking and moving about, you will more actively engage your Broca's area, Wernicke's area, motor cortex, and auditory cortex while studying, regardless of whether anyone is actually listening or learning.

2. Open up your lab manual to the topic you are studying.

3. With minimal reference to the manual text (don't just have your "student" read from the manual!), explain to your "student" the most important points related to the topic of study. Point to your own body as necessary, or hold up a diagram from your manual to point out critical structures.

4. Field questions from your "student" and make note of areas about which you have difficulties explaining.

5. Review material about which you found it difficult to teach and steal another few minutes of time from your friend/family member to try teaching the topic again.

Advantages: As most college faculty know, the best way to find out if you understand a subject is to try to convey information about that subject to others. Teaching others not only reinforces learned material, but it also very quickly makes apparent areas that require further study.

Disadvantages: Some students may not be comfortable teaching others or even speaking aloud about A&P when alone. In addition, this method assumes students have enough knowledge such that they are able to isolate the most important material to "teach" and not just try to point out every word and diagram in the manual.

Sound-Alike Mnemonics

How It's Done:

1. Think of the vocabulary words from this exercise that you need to learn (e.g., *maxillary bone, parietal bones*)

2. Find other words you are familiar with that sound like the vocabulary words and also have some relationship to the meaning of the vocabulary words (e.g., *parietal/parental, maxillae/Godzilla*).

3. Rehearse those words as you study (e.g., "*Godzilla* had big teeth, so the *maxillae* must be part of your mouth that holds teeth" and "You have two *parents* that hover over you, so your *parietal* bones must come in a pair on top of your head").

Advantages: For some terms, these mnemonics can be very quick to create and easy to remember. This speeds up the learning process considerably for those terms. Furthermore, the sound-alike words need not be from the English language. Students might find appropriate sound-alike words in other languages, making this a potentially useful strategy for English language learners.

Disadvantages: For this technique to be effective, the sound-alike words must somehow lead students to the correct meaning of the vocabulary word. That is, it's not enough to just find a word that sounds similar to an A&P term. That word must be meaningful in relation to what the vocabulary word represents in A&P. This means it might not be possible to identify appropriate sound-alikes for every vocabulary word.

Concept Mapping

How It's Done:

1. Make a list of the key terms for a particular topic (generally all nouns).
2. Write two of the terms on a piece of paper and connect them with an arrow.
3. Write words on the arrow to show the relationship between the terms.
4. Add another term from the list and connect it with arrows to the terms already on the page.
5. Continue adding terms and arrows with descriptions until all words are connected.
6. Use the laboratory manual to look up any terms that seemed less familiar or could not be easily connected to the others.

Advantages: The process of making concept maps, especially when done as a review activity without notes, provides an excellent opportunity for learning and illuminating areas for further study. Once created, concept maps represent enduring study tools that succinctly display large amounts of information. The maps also make connections between anatomical and physiological terms explicit and easy to follow. For reference, databases of concept maps on A&P topics can be found online. Searching Google Images for "concept map" + the name of an A&P topic often returns examples that might help students become familiar with the process.

Disadvantages: Not all students have made concept maps before, so the process may be initially unfamiliar or uncomfortable. While some students are immediately drawn to concept mapping, others can become impatient with the process.

Creating (and Re-Creating) Labeled Sketches

How It's Done:

1. From memory, make a sketch of a structure/part from the topic being studied, such as a muscle fiber or the inner eye or the kidney.
2. Again from memory, label as many anatomical parts on that sketch as possible.
3. Check the lab manual and notes for accuracy and the absence of parts that should have been included. Correct the sketch as needed.
4. Repeat the process with the same structures later that day, the next day, or before tests.

Advantages: Students generally rely heavily on artwork from lab manuals and textbooks, but do not as often attempt to create their own artwork to describe their knowledge of anatomical structures. Students may not realize that, to a large extent, artistic ability is not a prerequisite for studying in this manner. Even less-than-attractive student sketches can be helpful to solidify whether students understand the relative positioning and sizes of parts. In that sense, it is the process of creating the sketch, rather than the quality of the end product, that helps students identify their own strengths and weaknesses in understanding anatomy.

Disadvantages: Numerous very close or extremely detailed structures may be difficult for students to diagram, unless their sketches are sufficiently large. This technique most easily allows for the study of structural features, and functional processes may be more difficult to sketch in a single diagram.

"Sticky Note" Labeling of Yourself or a Friend

How It's Done:

1. Write the name of each anatomical part you need to know (for example, the name of every blood vessel you need to learn) on a separate, small "sticky note."

2. Stick the notes on your own body (or on a friend) where you think the parts are found. You could instead stick the notes on an unlabeled diagram if the parts cannot easily be indicated on the surface of your body.

3. Check the lab manual for accuracy and make corrections.

4. Mix up the notes and try again.

Advantages: Students generally find this enjoyable, and they are never without their study aid (their own body!). Students can even recruit family or friends to serve as models for labeling.

Disadvantages: Since students are generally tested using models, specimens, or diagrams (not their own bodies), they must still be able to relate their knowledge back to those items for evaluation.

A&P Coloring Books

How It's Done:

1. Obtain an anatomy and physiology coloring book! The *Anatomy and Physiology Coloring Workbook: A Complete Study Guide,* Eleventh Edition, by Elaine Marieb (Pearson Education) is specifically designed to complement your laboratory manual.

2. The coloring workbook includes questions for self-testing in addition to drawing/coloring exercises using some of the same artwork found in your laboratory manual.

Advantages: This method allows students to review parts and terms in a visual format even if students themselves are not the best artists. It also uses the same artwork students find in their manuals. Color-coding parts helps some student's better grasp where exactly one part is in relation to the neighboring anatomical parts.

Disadvantages: Students could easily go about coloring in the parts without much noticing the names of those parts and other important information about those parts. Learning the parts well would probably require revising the artwork many times, and even then, students would likely need to study models/specimens in order to understand three-dimensional relationships between parts.

Jeff Schinske

De Anza College

Trends in Instrumentation

Robert Anthony and Alan Wade, Triton College
Peter Zao, North Idaho College
Susan J. Mitchell, Onondaga Community College

This section is designed for instructors interested in incorporating additional laboratory technologies and instrumentation into their anatomy and physiology courses. The following techniques will introduce students to some standard approaches and instrumentation currently used in clinical and research facilities. Although these techniques are used in various biology and chemistry laboratory courses, many students in basic anatomy and physiology are not routinely introduced to these skills. Rather than detailing specific laboratory procedures, this discussion will provide insight into some of the options for bringing technology into the introductory anatomy and physiology laboratory.

One of the standard methods available to medical technicians and researchers is computerized data acquisition. Currently available computer packages can measure and analyze various aspects of cardiac, reflex, muscle, and respiratory physiology. Other standard methods include chromatography, spectrophotometry, and electrophoresis. Applications of available computer data acquisition systems and clinical technologies for use in an anatomy and physiology laboratory are listed on the following pages. Included in each application are relevant exercises in the laboratory manual and a brief description of each possible application. A list of companies offering appropriate products is included in Appendix A.

Computerized Data Acquisition

Computerized equipment is commonly used to monitor patients in today's allied health areas. We have found that students appreciate the brief exposure to computers in our labs. Incorporating computer-based exercises into the lab also generates increased interest because most students realize that they will be using computers in their chosen professions.

Analog-to-digital converters can be used to create customized physiological data collection systems. Easy-to-use computer data acquisition systems include BIOPAC®, PowerLab®, Intelitool®, iWorx®, and Vernier® systems. The packages are designed for use in college-level courses and require minimal computer experience.

Directions for BIOPAC® are included in the lab manual. Exercises using PowerLab®, iWorx®, and Intelitool® can be downloaded from the Instructor Resource section of the MasteringA&P companion website for the lab manuals at www.masteringaandp.com. The Vernier system can be easily adapted to sections of Exercise 31.

General Tips for Computer Data Acquisition Systems Use in the Laboratory

The following ideas are general guidelines designed as an introduction to the operation of computer acquisition systems. Each system contains the software, equipment, and basic instructions needed to conduct the experiments on a computer.

Starting the Laboratory

- Prepare the laboratory for a computer-assisted data acquisition exercise by connecting the transducers and cables to the computer.
- Run through each exercise yourself so that you have a good idea of how much time is required to complete the activities in the given lab time period.

- You may wish to start the program so that the main menu is visible as the students sit down to work. If computer novices are left to start and prepare the system by themselves, their initial frustration may waste valuable lab time and detract from the experience.

- Once the program menu is up, students should be able to follow the exercise procedures without difficulty.

- It may be helpful to have an introductory lab designed to introduce the students to the general operation of the system.

Exercises Based on the PowerLab® System

Laboratory Exercises with PowerLab® instructions are available for download from the Instructor Resource section of MasteringA&P for the following lab exercises:

Exercise 14   Skeletal Muscle Physiology: Frogs and Human Subjects
Exercise 21   Human Reflex Physiology
Exercise 31   Conduction System of the Heart and Electrocardiography
Exercise 33   Human Cardiovascular Physiology: Blood Pressure and Pulse Determinations
Exercise 34   Frog Cardiovascular Physiology
Exercise 37   Respiratory System Physiology

Comments and tips specific to each exercise are included in the instructions.

Exercises Based on iWorx®

Laboratory Exercises with iWorx® instructions are available for download from the Instructor Resource section of MasteringA&P for the following lab exercises:

Exercise 14   Electromyography in a Human Subject Using iWorx®
Exercise 18   Electroencephalography Using iWorx®
Exercise 21   Measuring Reaction Time Using iWorx®
Exercise 31   Electrocardiography Using iWorx®
Exercise 33   Measuring Pulse Using iWorx®
Exercise 34   Recording Baseline Frog Heart Activity
Exercise 37   Measuring Respiratory Variations

Exercises Based on Intelitool® Systems

Laboratory exercises with Intelitool® instructions are available for download from the Instructor Resource section of MasteringA&P for the following lab exercises:

Exercise 14   Muscle Physiology
Exercise 21   Human Reflex Physiology
Exercise 31   Conduction System of the Heart and Electrocardiography
Exercise 37   Respiratory System Physiology

Comments and tips specific to each exercise are included on a separate Tips for Instructors page preceding each exercise.

Exercises in Cell Physiology and Clinical Chemistry

Modern cell physiology lab exercises frequently involve biochemical analysis of cellular components and products. A number of techniques can be used to detect and quantify the constituents of cells and body fluids. Some of the more commonly used clinical and research techniques include chromatography, spectrophotometry, and electrophoresis.[1]

Chromatography

Exercise 4: The Cell: Anatomy and Division Introduce molecular separation techniques when discussing the cell (or macromolecules).

Exercise 29: Blood Separate protein and lipid components during blood analysis.

Application

Chromatographic techniques have a number of applications in cell physiology and chemistry. Chromatography is used for separation and identification of components in mixtures containing amino acids, nucleic acids, sugars, vitamins, steroids, antibiotics, and other drugs.

The major forms of chromatography for the college physiology laboratory include thin-layer, paper, column, gas-liquid, and high-performance liquid chromatography. Descriptions of these procedures and their clinical applications can be found in a number of clinical method manuals.[2]

Gas and high-performance liquid chromatography offer the greatest sensitivity and quantitative ability, but the high initial investment usually makes these systems prohibitive unless they are already in place.

Thin-layer and paper chromatography are economical, and they can be performed with a minimum of equipment. Both methods can be used as qualitative or semiquantitative screening techniques to detect the presence of both endogenous and exogenous compounds.[3]

An example of a clinically significant screening test is the determination by thin-layer chromatography of abnormal levels of certain amino acids that are associated with genetic diseases affecting metabolism. The disorders phenylketonuria, alkaptonuria, and homocystinuria result in abnormal levels of phenylalanine, homogentisic acid, and methionine, respectively, in the urine and blood. The sample and standards are applied to a thin-layer plate coated with cellulose acetate, or a silica gel, or to a Whatman #4 chromatography paper, and run in a butanol/acetic acid/water solvent. For visualization and identification of amino acids, an indicator such as ninhydrin may be used. The color intensity for the appropriate amino acids can be compared to normal values.

Spectrophotometry

Exercise 29: Blood Analyze protein or lipid composition, or enzyme hydrolysis.

Exercise 39: Chemical and Physical Processes of Digestion Quantitative spectrophotometric analysis of enzyme hydrolysis.

Exercise 41: Urinalysis Analyze various substances present in urine.

Application

Spectrophotometry is a common procedure used in clinical and research settings for determining concentrations of substances in solution, based on the amount of radiant energy transmitted through or absorbed by a substance in solution. Spectrophotometric measurements include total protein, total lipid, cholesterol, lipoprotein, and hemoglobin.

Spectrophotometry can also be used as a quantitative measure of enzymatic hydrolysis using commercially available colorigenic substrates. Most determinations in spectrophotometry utilize wavelengths in visible or ultraviolet ranges. For a more detailed description of the theory of spectrophotometry and use of the equipment, refer to a biochemistry or clinical methods manual.

1. Due to the hazards associated with the laboratory use of human body fluids, it may be advisable to avoid using student-drawn blood samples for analysis. There are a wide variety of commercially available blood components, both normal and abnormal, as well as blood component standards.

2. A. J. Pesce and L. A. Kaplan. 1987. *Methods in Clinical Chemistry.* C.V. Mosby Co.; M. L. Bishop, J. L. Duben-Von Laufen, E. P. Fody. 2000. *Clinical Chemistry: Principles, Procedures, Correlations,* Fourth Edition. Lippincott Williams & Wilkins.

3. J. C. Touchstone and M. F. Dobbins. 1992. *The Practice of Thin-Layer Chromatography,* Third Edition. John Wiley and Sons.

Diagnostic kits (for specific diseases) include:

1. Bilirubin (liver disease)
2. Total cholesterol and HDL cholesterol (atherosclerosis)
3. Creatine kinase (striated muscle damage)
4. Hemoglobin (anemia)
5. Creatinine (kidney disease)

Electrophoresis

Exercise 29: Blood Analyze protein and lipid components of blood.
Exercise 45: Principles of Heredity DNA fingerprinting systems, comparison of adult and sickle cell hemoglobin.

Application

Electrophoretic techniques, which demonstrate the migration and separation of charged solutes in an electrical field, have many important applications in cell and molecular biology. The most commonly used techniques involve zone electrophoresis, in which migration occurs within a semisolid support medium. In a majority of these procedures, agarose, polyacrylamide, or sodium dodecyl sulfate gels are used as the support medium. Sample migration can be horizontal or vertical, depending on the type of apparatus. Directions for agarose gel separation of hemoglobin can be found in Exercise 45 of the laboratory manual.

An increasing number of supply companies are recognizing the importance of studies in molecular biology and their impact on the study of cell physiology and human disease. The companies are becoming involved with biotechnology education by offering lab systems that are designed to introduce the methods of molecular biology and biotechnology to students at the pre-college and college levels. These systems are often in kit form and facilitate hands-on experience with a variety of important procedures. Some of the experimental systems available are:

1. Molecular weight determination (proteins)
2. Separation and identification of serum proteins
3. Cardiac risk assessment—analysis of lipoproteins
4. DNA fingerprinting—restriction fragmentation patterns

Sources of Equipment and Reagents

Supplies for the biochemical techniques described in the above section can be obtained from the supply houses listed in Appendix A. The list is by no means complete but includes companies that are familiar to most educators. The Intelitool® products are best obtained directly from the company rather than through another vendor, as delivery times are much quicker.

The Language of Anatomy

If time is a problem, most of this exercise can be done as an out-of-class assignment.

 Time Allotment: 1/2 hour (in lab).

Laboratory Materials

Ordering information is based on a lab size of 24 students, working in groups of 4. A list of supply house addresses appears in Appendix A.

1–2 human torso models
2 human skeletons, one male
   and one female

3–4 preserved kidneys (sheep)
Scalpels

Gelatin-spaghetti molds
Post-it Notes

Advance Preparation

1. Set out human torso models and have articulated skeletons available.

2. Obtain three preserved kidneys (sheep kidneys work well). Cut one in transverse section, one in longitudinal section (usually a sagittal section), and leave one uncut. Label the kidneys and put them in a demonstration area. You may wish to add a fourth kidney to demonstrate a frontal section.

3. The day before the lab, prepare gelatin or Jell-O® using slightly less water than is called for and cook the spaghetti until it is al dente. Pour the gelatin into several small molds and drop several spaghetti strands into each mold. Refrigerate until lab time.

4. Set out gelatin-spaghetti molds and scalpel.

Comments and Pitfalls

1. Students will probably have the most trouble understanding *proximal* and *distal*, often confusing these terms with *superior* and *inferior*. They also find the terms *anterior/ventral* and *posterior/dorsal* confusing because these terms refer to the same directions in humans, but different directions in four-legged animals. Other than that there should be few problems.

Answers to Pre-Lab Quiz (p. 1)

1. false
2. axial
3. b, toward or at the body surface

4. b, sagittal
5. cranial, vertebral

Answers to Activity Questions

Activity 2: Practicing Using Correct Anatomical Terminology (p. 4)

1. The wrist is *proximal* to the hand.
2. The trachea (windpipe) is *anterior* or *ventral* to the spine.
3. The brain is *superior* or *cephalad* to the spinal cord.
4. The kidneys are *inferior* or *caudal* to the liver.
5. The nose is *medial* to the cheekbones.
6. The thumb is *lateral* to the ring finger.
7. The thorax is *superior* or *cephalad* to the abdomen.
8. The skin is *superficial* to the skeleton.

Activity 4: Identifying Organs in the Abdominopelvic Cavity (p. 8)

Name two organs found in the left upper quadrant: *stomach, spleen, large intestine*

Name two organs found in the right lower quadrant: *small intestine, large intestine, appendix*

What organ is divided into identical halves by the median plane? *urinary bladder*

Answers to Group Challenge (p. 10)

1. *nasal, mental, cervical, sternal, lumbar, coxal, femoral, crural, tarsal, plantar*
2. *brachial, antecubital, antebrachial, carpal, palmar, digital*
3. *umbilical, buccal, otic, axillary, acromial, pollex*
4. *hallux, plantar, calcaneal, sural, popliteal, femoral*
5. *transverse*
6. *hypogastric*
7. *appendicitis*

NAME _____

LAB TIME/DATE _____

The Language of Anatomy

Surface Anatomy

1. Match each of the numbered descriptions with the related term in the key, and record the key letter or term in front of the description.

Key: a. buccal   c. cephalic   e. patellar
      b. calcaneal   d. digital   f. scapular

a; buccal _____ 1. cheek   *e; patellar* _____ 4. anterior aspect of knee

d; digital _____ 2. fingers   *b; calcaneal* _____ 5. heel of foot

f; scapular _____ 3. shoulder blade region   *c; cephalic* _____ 6. head

2. Indicate the following body areas on the accompanying diagram by placing the correct key letter at the end of each line.

Key:

a. abdominal
b. antecubital
c. brachial
d. cervical
e. crural
f. femoral
g. fibular
h. gluteal
i. lumbar
j. occipital
k. oral
l. popliteal
m. pubic
n. sural
o. thoracic
p. umbilical

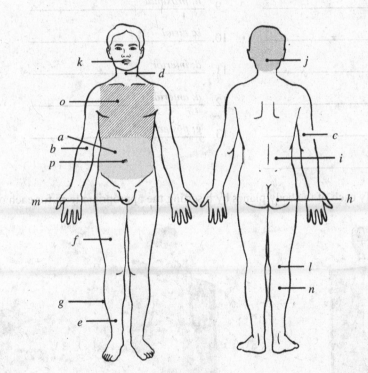

3. For each term in the key of question 2 above, determine which of the two major divisions it belongs to. Insert the appropriate key letters on the answer blanks.

b, c, e, f, g, l, n _____ 1. appendicular   *a, d, h, i, j, k, m, o, p* _____ 2. axial

Body Orientation, Direction, Planes, and Sections

4. Describe completely the standard human anatomical position. *Standing erect, feet together, head and toes pointed*

*forward, arms hanging at sides with palms forward*

5. Define *section*. <u>A cut along an imaginary plane through the body wall or organ</u>

6. Several incomplete statements appear below. Correctly complete each statement by choosing the appropriate anatomical term from the key. Record the key letters and/or terms on the corresponding numbered blanks below. Some terms are used more than once.

Key: a. anterior   d. inferior   g. posterior   j. superior
      b. distal   e. lateral   h. proximal   k. transverse
      c. frontal   f. medial   i. sagittal

In the anatomical position, the face and palms are on the <u>1</u> body surface; the buttocks and shoulder blades are on the <u>2</u> body surface; and the top of the head is the most <u>3</u> part of the body. The ears are <u>4</u> and <u>5</u> to the shoulders and <u>6</u> to the nose. The heart is <u>7</u> to the vertebral column (spine) and <u>8</u> to the lungs. The elbow is <u>9</u> to the fingers but <u>10</u> to the shoulder. The abdominopelvic cavity is <u>11</u> to the thoracic cavity and <u>12</u> to the spinal cavity. In humans, the dorsal surface can also be called the <u>13</u> surface; however, in quadruped animals, the dorsal surface is the <u>14</u> surface.

If an incision cuts the heart into right and left parts, the section is a <u>15</u> section; but if the heart is cut so that superior and inferior portions result, the section is a(n) <u>16</u> section. You are told to cut a dissection animal along two planes so that both kidneys are observable in each section. The two sections that can meet this requirement are the <u>17</u> and <u>18</u> sections. A section that demonstrates the continuity between the spinal and cranial cavities is a(n) <u>19</u> section.

1. <u>*a; anterior*</u>

2. <u>*g; posterior*</u>

3. <u>*j; superior*</u>

4. <u>*f; medial*</u>

5. <u>*j; superior*</u>

6. <u>*e; lateral*</u>

7. <u>*a; anterior*</u>

8. <u>*f; medial*</u>

9. <u>*h; proximal*</u>

10. <u>*b; distal*</u>

11. <u>*d; inferior*</u>

12. <u>*a; anterior*</u>

13. <u>*g; posterior*</u>

14. <u>*j; superior*</u>

15. <u>*i; sagittal*</u>

16. <u>*k; transverse*</u>

17. <u>*c; frontal*</u>

18. <u>*k; transverse*</u>

19. <u>*i; sagittal*</u>

7. Correctly identify each of the body planes by inserting the appropriate term for each on the answer line below the drawing.

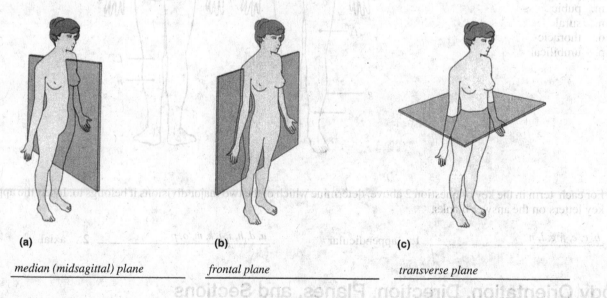

(a)   (b)   (c)

median (midsagittal) plane   *frontal plane*   *transverse plane*

8. Draw a kidney as it appears when sectioned in each of the three different planes.

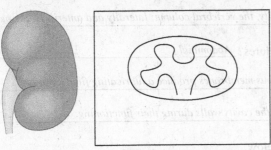

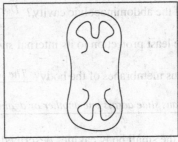

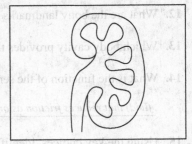

Transverse section   *Sagittal section*   *Frontal section*

9. Correctly identify each of the nine regions of the abdominopelvic cavity by inserting the appropriate term for each of the letters indicated in the drawing.

a. _epigastric region_

b. _right hypochondriac region_

c. _left hypochondriac region_

d. _umbilical region_

e. _right lumbar region_

f. _left lumbar region_

g. _hypogastric (pubic) region_

h. _right iliac (inguinal) region_

i. _left iliac (inguinal) region_

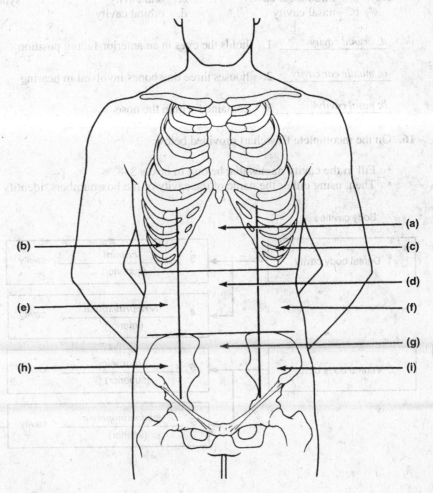

Body Cavities

10. Which body cavities would have to be opened for the following types of surgery or procedures? (Insert the letter of the key choice in the blank. More than one choice may apply.)

Key: a. abdominopelvic   c. dorsal   e. thoracic
         b. cranial   d. spinal   f. ventral

_e, f_ 1. surgery to remove a cancerous lung lobe   _a, f_ 4. appendectomy

_a, f_ 2. removal of the uterus, or womb   _a, f_ 5. stomach ulcer operation

_b, c_ 3. removal of a brain tumor   _d, c_ 6. delivery of preoperative "saddle" anesthesia

11. Name the muscle that subdivides the ventral body cavity. *Diaphragm*

12. What are the bony landmarks of the abdominopelvic cavity? *Dorsally, the vertebral column; laterally and anteriorly, the pelvis*

13. Which body cavity provides the least protection to its internal structures? *Abdominal*

14. What is the function of the serous membranes of the body? *The serous membranes produce a lubricating fluid (serous*

fluid) that reduces friction as organs slide across one another or against the cavity walls during their functioning.

15. Using the key choices, identify the small body cavities described below.

Key: a. middle ear cavity   c. oral cavity   e. synovial cavity
       b. nasal cavity   d. orbital cavity

d; orbital cavity   1. holds the eyes in an anterior-facing position   *c; oral cavity*   4. contains the tongue

a; middle ear cavity   2. houses three tiny bones involved in hearing   *e; synovial cavity*   5. surrounds a joint

b; nasal cavity   3. contained within the nose

16. On the incomplete flowchart provided below:

- Fill in the cavity names that belong in boxes 3–8.
- Then, using either the name of the cavity or the box numbers, identify the descriptions in the list that follows.

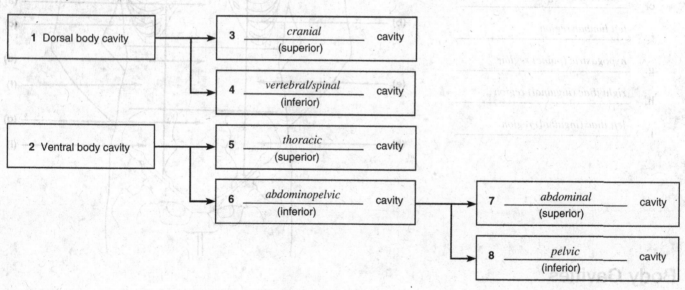

1 a. contained within the skull and vertebral column	*5* e. contains the heart
8 b. houses female reproductive organs	*6 or 7* f. contains the small intestine
1, 3, or 4 c. the most protective body cavity	*5* g. bounded by the ribs
2 d. its name means "belly"	*6 or 7* h. its walls are muscular

Organ Systems Overview

Time Allotment: 1 1/2 hours (rat dissection: 1 hour; if performing reproductive system dissection, 1/2 hour each for male and female; dissectible human torso model: 1/2 hour).

Multimedia Resources: See Appendix B for Guide to Multimedia Resource Distributors.

Homeostasis (FHS: 20 minutes, VHS, DVD, 3-year streaming webcast)
Homeostasis: The Body in Balance (HRM: 26 minutes, VHS, DVD)
Practice Anatomy Lab™ 3.0 (PAL) (PE: DVD, website)

Solutions:

Bleach Solution, 10%
Measure out 100 milliliters of household bleach. Add water to a final volume of 1 liter.

Laboratory Materials

Ordering information is based on a lab size of 24 students, working in groups of 4. A list of supply house addresses appears in Appendix A.

Dissectible human torso model or cadaver	6–12 blunt probes	6–12 dissecting trays
6–12 forceps	Disposable gloves, soap, and sponges	Lab disinfectant or 10% bleach solution
6–12 scissors	6–12 freshly killed or preserved rats	
	Twine or large dissecting pins	

Advance Preparation

1. Make arrangements for appropriate storage and disposal of dissection materials. Check with the Department of Health or the Department of Environmental Protection, or their counterparts, for state regulations.

2. Designate a disposal container for organic debris, set up a dishwashing area with hot soapy water and sponges, and provide lab disinfectant such as Wavicide-01 (Carolina) or bleach solution for washing down the lab benches.

3. Set out safety glasses and disposable gloves for dissection of freshly killed animals (to protect students from parasites) and for dissection of preserved animals.

4. Decide on the number of students in each dissecting group (a maximum of four is suggested, two is probably best). Each dissecting group should have a dissecting pan, dissecting pins, scissors, blunt probe, forceps, twine, and a preserved or freshly killed rat.

5. Preserved rats are more convenient to use unless small mammal facilities are available. If live rats are used, they may be killed a half-hour or so prior to the lab by administering an overdose of ether or chloroform. To do this, remove each rat from its cage and hold it firmly by the skin at the back of its neck. Put the rat in a container with cotton soaked in ether or chloroform. Seal the jar tightly and wait until the rat ceases to breathe.

6. Set out dissectible human torso models and a dissected human cadaver if available.

Comments and Pitfalls

1. Remind students that the rats are serving as model organisms for the human body. It is therefore important when working with rats to model the same types of behaviors we would use if working with a human cadaver. While excitement and enthusiasm are encouraged, students should be careful not to act in ways that might appear inappropriate or disrespectful of the specimens in the classroom.

2. Students may be overly enthusiastic when using the scalpel and cut away organs they are supposed to locate and identify. Therefore, use scissors to open the body. Have blunt probes available as the major dissecting tool.

3. Be sure the lab is well ventilated, and encourage students to take fresh air breaks if the preservative fumes are strong. If the dissection animal will be used only once, it can be rinsed to remove most of the excess preservative.

4. Organic debris may end up in the sinks, clogging the drains. Remind the students to dispose of all dissection materials in the designated container.

5. Inferior vena cava and aorta may be difficult to distinguish in uninjected specimens.

Answers to Pre-Lab Quiz (p. 15)

1. The cell
2. c, organ
3. nervous
4. urinary
5. diaphragm

Answers to Activity Questions

Activity 5: Examining the Human Torso Model (pp. 23–24)

2. From top to bottom, the organs pointed out on the torso model are: *brain, thyroid gland, trachea, lung, heart, diaphragm, liver, stomach, spleen, large intestine, greater omentum, small intestine*

3. Dorsal body cavity: *brain, spinal cord*

   Thoracic cavity: *aortic arch, bronchi, descending aorta (thoracic region), esophagus, heart, inferior vena cava, lungs, trachea*

   Abdominopelvic cavity: *adrenal gland, descending aorta (abdominal region), greater omentum, inferior vena cava, kidneys, large intestine, liver, mesentery, pancreas, rectum, small intestine, spleen, stomach, ureters, urinary bladder*

   Note: The diaphragm separates the thoracic cavity from the abdominopelvic cavity.

4. Digestive: *esophagus, liver, stomach, pancreas, small intestine, large intestine (including rectum)*

   Urinary: *kidneys, ureters, urinary bladder*

   Cardiovascular: *aortic arch, heart, descending aorta, inferior vena cava*

   Endocrine: *pancreas, adrenal gland, thyroid gland*

   Reproductive: *none*

   Respiratory: *lungs, bronchi, trachea*

   Lymphatic/Immunity: *spleen*

   Nervous: *brain, spinal cord*

Answers to Group Challenge (p. 24)

Some possible answers to the questions are listed below. Student answers may vary.

1. Which is the "odd organ"?		Why is it the odd one out?
Stomach (Teeth)	Small intestine Oral cavity	The teeth are an accessory structure of the digestive system whereas the oral cavity, stomach, and small intestine are part of the digestive tract.
2. Which is the "odd organ"?		Why is it the odd one out?
(Thyroid gland) Thymus	Spleen Lymph nodes	The thyroid gland is not an organ of the lymphatic system.
3. Which is the "odd organ"?		Why is it the odd one out?
Ovaries (Prostate gland)	Uterus Uterine tubes	The prostate gland is not a part of the female reproductive system.
4. Which is the "odd organ"?		Why is it the odd one out?
Stomach Small intestine	(Esophagus) Large intestine	The esophagus is in the thorax whereas the stomach, small intestine, and large intestine are in the abdominopelvic cavity.

Organ Systems Overview

1. Use the key below to indicate the body systems that perform the following functions for the body; note that some responses are used more than once. Then, circle the organ systems (in the key) that are present in all subdivisions of the ventral body cavity.

Key: a. cardiovascular   d. integumentary   g. nervous   j. skeletal
     b. digestive   e. lymphatic/immunity h. reproductive k. urinary
     c. endocrine   f. muscular   i. respiratory

k; urinary _____ 1. rids the body of nitrogen-containing wastes

c; endocrine _____ 2. is affected by removal of the thyroid gland

j; skeletal _____ 3. provides support and the levers on which the muscular system acts

a; cardiovascular _____ 4. includes the heart

h; reproductive _____ 5. has a menstrual cycle in females

d; integumentary _____ 6. protects underlying organs from drying out and from mechanical damage

e; lymphatic/immunity _____ 7. protects the body; destroys bacteria and tumor cells

b; digestive _____ 8. breaks down ingested food into its building blocks

i; respiratory _____ 9. removes carbon dioxide from the blood

a; cardiovascular _____ 10. delivers oxygen and nutrients to the tissues

f; muscular _____ 11. moves the limbs; facilitates facial expression

k; urinary _____ 12. conserves body water or eliminates excesses

c; endocrine _____, h; reproductive _____ 13. facilitate conception and childbearing

c; endocrine _____ 14. controls the body by means of chemical molecules called hormones

d; integumentary _____ 15. is damaged when you cut your finger or get a severe sunburn

2. Using the above key, choose the *organ system* to which each of the following sets of organs or body structures belongs.

e; lymphatic/immunity ___ 1. thymus, spleen, lymphatic vessels

j; skeletal ___ 2. bones, cartilages, tendons

c; endocrine ___ 3. pancreas, pituitary, adrenals

i; respiratory ___ 4. trachea, bronchi, lungs

d; integumentary ___ 5. epidermis, dermis, and cutaneous sense organs

h; reproductive ___ 6. testis, ductus deferens, urethra

b; digestive ___ 7. esophagus, large intestine, rectum

f; muscular ___ 8. muscles of the thigh, postural mutscles

3. Using the key, place the following organs in their proper body cavity. Some responses may be used more than once.

Key: a.   abdominopelvic   b. cranial   c. spinal   d. thoracic

a; abdominopelvic	1. stomach	_a; abdominopelvic_	4. liver	_d; thoracic_	7. heart
d; thoracic	2. esophagus	_c; spinal_	5. spinal cord	_d; thoracic_	8. trachea
a; abdominopelvic	3. large intestine	_a; abdominopelvic_	6. urinary bladder	_a; abdominopelvic_	9. rectum

4. Using the organs listed in question 3 above, record, by number, which would be found in the abdominopelvic regions listed below.

_3, 6, 9_	1. hypogastric region	_1, 3, 4_	4. epigastric region
_3_	2. right lumbar region	_3_	5. left iliac region
_3_	3. umbilical region	_1, 3_	6. left hypochondriac region

5. The levels of organization of a living body include _cell_ , _tissue_ , _organ_ , _organ system_ , and organism.

6. Define organ. _A body part (or structure) that is made up of two or more tissue types and performs a specific body function (e.g., the stomach, the kidney)_

7. Using the terms provided, correctly identify all of the body organs provided with leader lines in the drawings shown below. Then name the organ systems by entering the name of each on the answer blank below each drawing.

Key: blood vessels   heart   nerves   spinal cord   urethra
       brain   kidney   sensory receptor   ureter   urinary bladder

a. _nervous system_   b. _cardiovascular system_   c. _urinary system_

8. Why is it helpful to study the external and internal structures of the rat? _Many of the external and internal structures are similar to those in the human. Studying the rat can help you to understand your own structure._

The Microscope

If students have already had an introductory biology course in which the microscope has been introduced and used, there might be a temptation to skip this exercise. I have found that most students need the review, so I recommend spending this time early in the course to make sure they are all comfortable with the microscope, as it is used extensively throughout the laboratory manual.

 Time Allotment: 2 hours.

 Solutions:

Bleach Solution, 10%
Measure out 100 milliliters of household bleach. Add water to a final volume of 1 liter.

Methylene Blue Solution (Loeffler's)
Weigh out 0.5 grams methylene blue. Add 1 milliliter 1% potassium hydroxide solution, and 30 milliliters absolute ethanol to 100 milliliters distilled water. Warm the water to about 50°C, stir in methylene blue; filter.

Physiologic Saline (Mammalian, 0.9%)
Weigh out 9 grams of NaCl. Add distilled/deionized water to a final volume of 1 liter. Make fresh just prior to experiment.

Laboratory Materials

Ordering information is based on a lab size of 24 students, working in groups of 4. A list of supply house addresses appears in Appendix A.

- 24 compound microscopes, lens cleaning solution, lens paper, immersion oil
- 24 millimeter rulers
- 24 slides of the letter *e*
- 24 slides with millimeter grids

- 24 slides of crossed colored threads (threads should cross at a single junction)
- Filter paper or paper towels
- 1 box of microscope slides
- 1 box of coverslips
- 1 box of flat-tipped toothpicks

- 8–12 dropper bottles of physiologic saline
- 8–12 dropper bottles of methylene blue stain (dilute) or iodine
- 24 slides of cheek epithelial cells
- 10% bleach solution
- Autoclave bag, disposable

Advance Preparation

1. Provide each student with a compound microscope, millimeter ruler, bottle of immersion oil, lens paper, and millimeter grid slide. A supply of glass cleaner, such as Windex™, should be available for lens cleaning.

2. Have available slides of the letter *e* and slides of crossed colored threads. Some instructors prefer to have slides for an entire semester available in individual boxes, which can be handed out to students. Others prefer to keep the slides on trays to be distributed as needed.

3. Set up an area for wet mount supplies, including clean microscope slides and coverslips, flat-tipped toothpicks, *physiologic saline*, methylene blue stain or iodine, and filter paper, or set out prepared slides of cheek epithelial cells.

4. Set up a disposal area containing a 1 liter beaker of *10% bleach solution* and an autoclave bag. *Note:* Detailed instructions for treatment and disposal of materials used in labs involving human tissue and excretions are found in the preface of this Instructor's Guide.

5. If the microscopes are binocular rather than monocular, give additional instructions on focusing.

   a. After the parts of the microscope have been identified, turn on the light and adjust the interpupillary distance so that a single circle of light is visible through the eyepieces. This is difficult for some students, usually because they are moving back and forth and changing their eye position. Have each student record his or her own interpupillary distance for later use.

   b. For a microscope with an adjustable left eyepiece, focus the microscope as directed, using the right eye only.

   c. Focus using the left eyepiece with the right eye closed. Both eyepieces should now be focused on the specimen. (Reverse the directions if the right eyepiece is adjustable.)

6. The directions for perceiving depth (p. 33) are for microscopes with objective lenses that advance and retract during focusing. If the stage moves during focusing, the superior thread will come into focus first if these directions are followed. Alter instructions if necessary.

Comments and Pitfalls

1. Be sure to have the students check the orientation of the letter *e* on the slide before putting the slide on the microscope. If they forget to check, they will miss the point of the exercise.

2. Beware of common focusing problems: dirty lenses, inverted slide, objective lens not securely in place, and wrong lens in position (oil immersion instead of high-power).

3. It is difficult to use a millimeter ruler to measure the working distance of the high-power and oil immersion lenses on some microscopes. A best estimate is usually sufficient.

4. Many students have difficulty with the section on determining the size of the microscope field diameter. The direct measurement is usually no problem, although some students measure area rather than diameter, and some students will have both the letter *e* slide and the grid on the stage at the same time. Emphasize that direct measurement should be done using only one lens. Otherwise, measuring discrepancies cause confusion. The problem is often with the math involved. It is probably worthwhile to stop the class and work through the use of the formula (p. 32) when you see that most students are at this point in the exercise.

5. Clarify what is meant by "detail observed" in the chart on p. 31.

6. Students may forget safety precautions when preparing the wet mount. Emphasize the importance of following directions for safe disposal of toothpicks and proper cleanup of glassware.

7. Many students forget to adjust the iris diaphragm and may end up using the light at its highest intensity, which is hard on the bulb. Remind students that the iris diaphragm should be adjusted so that the field is just filled with light when observed with the ocular lens removed. In practice, it may be necessary to adjust the iris diaphragm for best contrast, although some resolution may be lost.

Answers to Pre-Lab Quiz (p. 27)

1. d, stage
2. b, The slide should be almost in focus when changing to higher magnifications.
3. 350×
4. c, with special lens paper and cleaner
5. false

Answers to Activity Questions

Activity 2: Viewing Objects Through the Microscope (pp. 29–31)

5. Answers will vary depending on the lenses used. Working distance decreases as lens power increases. The *e* appears upside down and backward.

6. The image moves toward you. The image moves to the right.

7. and 8. Grains begin to appear and are very visible with the high-power lens.

   The image is much larger.

   The entire *e* is visible with the low-power lens, but less than 1/4 of the letter is probably visible with the high-power lens.

   The field is smaller.

   The object must be centered so that it falls into the field of the higher-power lens.

   The light to the field is reduced as the iris diaphragm is closed.

   The light intensity often must be increased when changing to a higher magnification, as the lens has a smaller diameter and therefore lets in less light. In practice, if the microscope does not have a variable light intensity adjustment, the iris diaphragm should be adjusted to obtain the best contrast.

9. Grains are very visible. Yes.

   The working distance is less than that of the high-power lens.

   It is desirable to begin focusing with a low-power lens because the field is larger, making it easier to find the specimen on the slide, and the working distance is larger, reducing the chance of hitting the slide with the lens.

Activity 3: Estimating the Diameter of the Microscope Field (pp. 32–33)

3. Answers depend on the field diameter of lenses used. For lenses with field diameters of 1.8 millimeters, 0.45 millimeter, and 0.18 millimeter, respectively, the estimated lengths are about 1.2 millimeters, 0.14 millimeter, and 0.18 millimeter.

Activity 4: Perceiving Depth (p. 33)

2. When the stage descends, the first clearly focused thread is the bottom thread; the last clearly focused thread is the top one.

   Answers depend on the order of the threads on the particular slides used.

Activity 5: Preparing and Observing a Wet Mount (pp. 33–34)

8. Most of the cells are separated from each other rather than in a continuous sheet.

10. A cheek epithelial cell is about 80–100 micrometers (μm) (0.08–0.1 millimeter) in diameter.

   They are more similar to those in Figure 3.5 and easier to measure because they are in a continuous sheet.

NAME _____

LAB TIME/DATE _____

The Microscope

Care and Structure of the Compound Microscope

1. Label all indicated parts of the microscope.

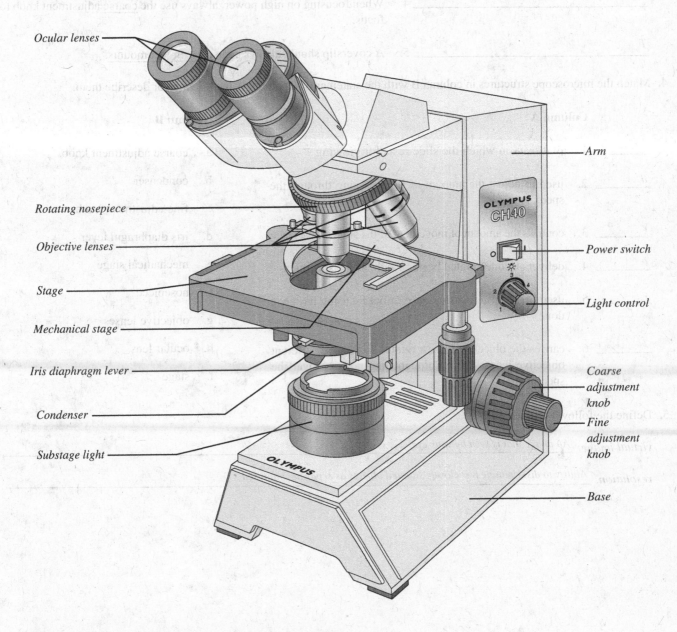

Ocular lenses

Rotating nosepiece

Objective lenses

Stage

Mechanical stage

Iris diaphragm lever

Condenser

Substage light

Arm

Power switch

Light control

Coarse adjustment knob

Fine adjustment knob

Base

OLYMPUS CH40

OLYMPUS

2. Explain the proper technique for transporting the microscope.

Carry with two hands—one supporting the base, the other holding the arm.

3. The following statements are true or false. If true, write *T* on the answer blank. If false, correct the statement by writing on the blank the proper word or phrase to replace the one that is underlined.

with grit-free lens paper _____ 1. The microscope lens may be cleaned <u>with any soft tissue</u>.

low-power or scanning _____ 2. The microscope should be stored with the <u>oil immersion</u> lens in position over the stage.

_T_ _____ 3. When beginning to focus, use the <u>lowest power</u> lens.

fine _____ 4. When focusing on high power, always use the <u>coarse</u> adjustment knob to focus.

_T_ _____ 5. A coverslip should always be used <u>with wet mounts</u>.

4. Match the microscope structures in column B with the statements in column A that identify or describe them.

Column A	Column B
_i_ 1. platform on which the slide rests for viewing	a. coarse adjustment knob
_d_ 2. used to adjust the amount of light passing through the specimen	b. condenser
	c. fine adjustment knob
_e_ 3. controls the amount of movement of the slide on the stage	d. iris diaphragm lever
_b_ 4. delivers a concentrated beam of light to the specimen	e. mechanical stage
	f. nosepiece
_c_ 5. used for precise focusing once initial focusing has been done	g. objective lenses
	h. ocular lens
_f_ 6. carries the objective lenses; rotates so that the different objective lenses can be brought into position over the specimen	i. stage

5. Define the following terms.

virtual image: _An image that is seen by your eye_ _____

resolution: _Ability to discriminate two closely situated objects as separate, not fused_ _____

Viewing Objects Through the Microscope

6. Complete, or respond to, the following statements:

working distance   1. The distance from the bottom of the objective lens to the surface of the slide is called the _____.

to the left   2. Assume there is an object on the left side of the field that you want to bring to the center (that is, toward the apparent right). In what direction would you move your slide? _____

field diameter   3. The area of the slide seen when looking through the microscope is the _____.

_95_   4. If a microscope has a 10× ocular lens and the total magnification at a particular time is 950×, the objective lens in use at that time is _____×.

increases contrast   5. Why should the light be dimmed when looking at living (nearly transparent) cells?

parfocal   6. If, after focusing in low power, only the fine adjustment need be used to focus the specimen at the higher powers, the microscope is said to be _____.

_0.75_   7. If, when using a 10× ocular and a 15× objective, the field diameter is 1.5 mm, the approximate field size with a 30× objective is _____ mm.

_0.4_   8. If the diameter of the high-power field is 1.2 mm, an object that occupies approximately a third of that field has an estimated diameter of _____ mm.

7. You have been asked to prepare a slide with the letter _k_ on it (as shown below). In the circle below, draw the k as seen in the low-power field.

8. Calculate the magnification of fields 1 and 3, and the field diameter of 2. (_Hint:_ Use your ruler.) Note that the numbers for the field diameters below are too large to represent the typical compound microscope lens system, but the relationships depicted are accurate.

     5 mm   _2.5_ mm   0.5 mm

1.   _50_ ×   2.   100×   3.   _500_ ×

9. Say you are observing an object in the low-power field. When you switch to high power, it is no longer in your field of view.

Why might this occur? _The field decreases proportionately as magnification increases. Therefore, unless the object is centered at low power, it might be outside the higher-power field._

What should be done initially to prevent this from happening? _Center the object that you wish to view._

10. Do the following factors increase or decrease as one moves to higher magnifications with the microscope?

resolution: _increases (to a point)_   amount of light needed: _increases_

working distance: _decreases_   depth of field: _decreases_

11. A student has the high-power lens in position and appears to be intently observing the specimen. The instructor, noting a working distance of about 1 cm, knows the student isn't actually seeing the specimen.

How so? *The working distance for the high-power lens is closer to 1 mm.*

12. Describe the proper procedure for preparing a wet mount.

Place the specimen on the slide with a medicine dropper or place a drop of water or saline on the slide. Mix specimen into

drop using a toothpick. If staining, add a drop of stain and mix with a toothpick. Hold a coverslip with forceps so that the

coverslip touches one side of the specimen drop, and then **slowly** *and* **carefully** *lower the angled coverslip onto the specimen.*

13. Indicate the probable cause of the following situations during use of a microscope.

a. Only half of the field is illuminated: *The lens is not correctly rotated into place.*

b. The field visible does not change as the mechanical stage is moved: *The slide is not correctly positioned in the clamp*

on the mechanical stage and does not move when the mechanical stage moves.

The Cell: Anatomy and Division

The Anatomy of the Composite Cell section can be given as an out-of-class assignment to save time. This might be necessary if audiovisual material is used.

 Time Allotment: 2 hours.

 Multimedia Resources: See Appendix B for Guide to Multimedia Resource Distributors.

Inside the Living Cell (WNS: 50 minutes, DVD)
An Introduction to the Living Cell (CBS: 30 minutes, DVD)
A Journey Through the Cell (FHS: DVD)
    Part One: *Cells: An Introduction* (20 minutes)
    Part Two: *Cell Functions: A Closer Look* (20 minutes)
Mitosis and Meiosis (DE: 23 minutes, VHS, DVD)
Practice Anatomy Lab™ 3.0 (PAL) (PE: DVD, website)

Laboratory Materials

Ordering information is based on a lab size of 24 students, working in groups of 4. A list of supply house addresses appears in Appendix A.

3-D model of composite cell or chart
    of cell anatomy
24 slides of simple squamous epithelium
24 slides of teased smooth muscle
24 slides of human blood cell smear

24 slides of sperm
24 slides of whitefish blastulae
24 compound microscopes, lens paper,
    lens cleaning solution, immersion
    oil

3-D models of mitotic stages
Video or animation of mitosis
Chenille sticks (pipe cleaners), two
    different colors, cut into 3-inch
    pieces

Advance Preparation

1. Set out slides (one per student) of simple squamous epithelium, teased smooth muscle, human blood cell smear, sperm, and whitefish blastulae. Students will also need lens paper, lens cleaning solution, immersion oil, and compound microscopes.

2. Set out a model or a lab chart of a composite cell, and models of mitotic stages.

3. Obtain the chenille sticks (pipe cleaners) in two different colors, and cut each into 3-inch pieces. Set out 8 pieces per group, 4 of each color.

Comments and Pitfalls

1. Observing differences and similarities in cell structure often gives students trouble, as many of them have never seen any cells other than epithelial cells. Slides or pictures of these cell types might help.

Answers to Pre-Lab Quiz (p. 39)

1. The structural and functional unit of all living things
2. a, chromatin
3. d, selective permeability
4. ribosomes
5. c, mitochondria
6. interphase
7. false
8. Four
9. b, interphase
10. false

Answers to Activity Questions

Activity 5: Observing Various Cell Structures (pp. 43–44)

4. Simple squamous epithelial cells are relatively large and irregularly ("fried-egg") shaped. Smooth muscle cells are also relatively large, but are long and spindle shaped. Red blood cells and sperm are both examples of small cells. Red blood cells appear round, while sperm cells are streamlined with long flagella.

Cell shape is often directly related to function. Epithelial cells fit tightly together and cover large areas. Elongated muscle cells are capable of shortening during contraction. The red blood cells are small enough to fit through capillaries, and are actually biconcave in shape, which makes them flexible and increases surface area (not obvious to the students at this point). Sperm cells' streamlined shape and flagella are directly related to efficient locomotion.

The sperm cells have visible projections (flagella), which are necessary for sperm motility.

The function of sperm is to travel through the female reproductive system to reach the ovum in the uterine tubes. This requires motility, provided by the flagella.

None of the cells lacks a plasma membrane.

Mature red blood cells have no nucleus.

Nucleoli will probably be clearly visible in the epithelial cells, and possibly visible in the other nuclei.

No. Identifiable organelles are not visible in most of these cells. Filaments may be visible in the smooth muscle preparations. The details of organelle structure are usually below the limit of resolution of the light microscope. Unless special stains are used, there is no way to see or distinguish the organelles at this level.

Activity 7: "Chenille Stick" Mitosis (pp. 45–48)

2. The centromere
3. The mitotic spindle
4. Kinetochores

   The nuclear envelope
5. The metaphase plate
6. Pulling apart of the sister chromatids.

   Each sister chromatid is now a chromosome.
7. The events of telophase cause the chromosomes and cell structures to revert to their interphase appearance: the chromosomes uncoil, a nuclear envelope forms around each chromatin mass, nucleoli appear in the nucleus, and the spindle breaks down and disappears.

NAME _____

LAB TIME/DATE _____

The Cell: Anatomy and Division

Anatomy of the Composite Cell

1. Define the following terms:

    organelle: *A highly organized intracellular structure that performs a specific (metabolic) function for the cell*

    cell: *The basic structural and functional unit of living organisms*

2. Although cells have differences that reflect their specific functions in the body, what functions do they have in common?

    Ability to metabolize, to reproduce, to grow (increase in mass), to respond to a stimulus, and to move

3. Identify the following cell structures:

    plasma membrane   1. external boundary of cell; regulates flow of materials into and out of the cell; site of cell signaling

    lysosome   2. contains digestive enzymes of many varieties; "suicide sac" of the cell

    mitochondria   3. scattered throughout the cell; major site of ATP synthesis

    microvilli   4. slender extensions of the plasma membrane that increase its surface area

    inclusions   5. stored glycogen granules, crystals, pigments present in some cell types

    Golgi apparatus   6. membranous system consisting of flattened sacs and vesicles; packages proteins for export

    nucleus   7. control center of the cell; necessary for cell division and cell life

    centrioles   8. two rod-shaped bodies near the nucleus; associated with the formation of the mitotic spindle

    nucleolus   9. dense nuclear body; packaging site for ribosomes

    microfilaments   10. contractile elements of the cytoskeleton

    rough ER   11. membranous tubules covered with ribosomes; involved in intracellular transport of proteins

    ribosomes   12. attached to membrane systems or scattered in the cytoplasm; site of protein synthesis

    chromatin or chromatin threads   13. threadlike structures in the nucleus; contain genetic material (DNA)

    peroxisome   14. site of free radical detoxification

4. In the following diagram, label all parts provided with a leader line.

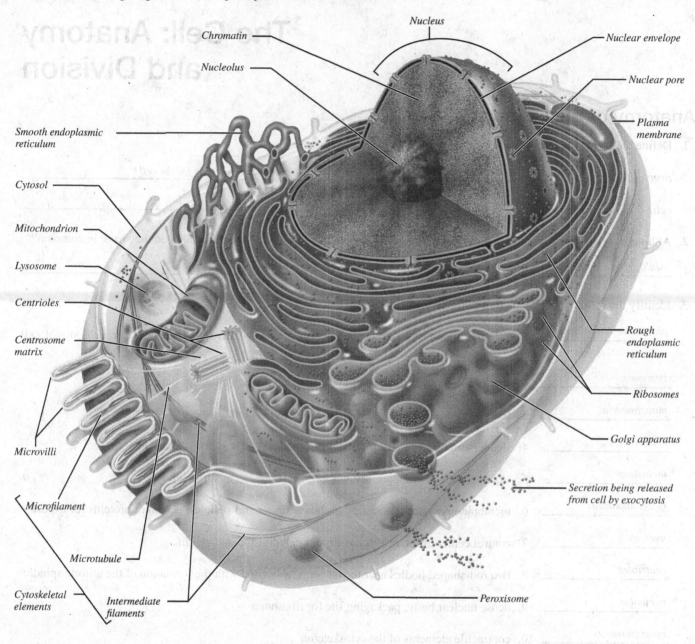

Nucleus

Chromatin

Nucleolus

Nuclear envelope

Nuclear pore

Plasma membrane

Smooth endoplasmic reticulum

Cytosol

Mitochondrion

Lysosome

Centrioles

Centrosome matrix

Rough endoplasmic reticulum

Ribosomes

Golgi apparatus

Microvilli

Microfilament

Secretion being released from cell by exocytosis

Microtubule

Cytoskeletal elements

Intermediate filaments

Peroxisome

Differences and Similarities in Cell Structure

5. For each of the following cell types, list (a) *one* important structural characteristic observed in the laboratory, and (b) the function that the structure complements or ensures.

squamous epithelium   a.   *cells fit closely together like floor tiles* _____

                       b.   *often a lining or covering tissue* _____

sperm   a.   *has a tail or flagellum* _____

                       b.   *allows sperm to propel itself to an egg* _____

smooth muscle a.   *cells have an elongated shape*

red blood cells b.   *a long axis allows a greater degree of shortening*

                 a.   *anucleate (no nucleus); disc shaped*

                 b.   *more "room" to carry hemoglobin or oxygen; large surface area*

6. What is the consequence of the red blood cell being anucleate (without a nucleus)? *Has limited life span and does not*

reproduce; the nucleus is gone, therefore the cell cannot manufacture new proteins; etc.

Did it ever have a nucleus? (Use an appropriate reference.) *Yes*   If so, when? *Before its release into the bloodstream*

7. Of the four cells observed microscopically (squamous epithelial cells, red blood cells, smooth muscle cells, and sperm), which has the smallest diameter? *Sperm*   Which is longest? *Smooth muscle or sperm (variable)*

Cell Division: Mitosis and Cytokinesis

8. Identify the three phases of mitosis in the following photomicrographs.

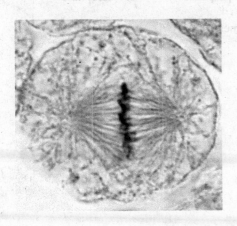 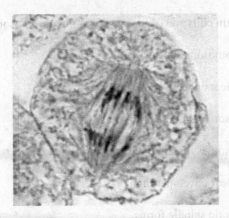 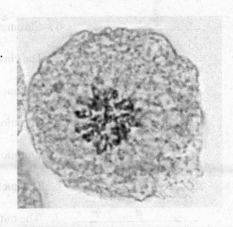

a. *metaphase*   b. *anaphase*   c. *prophase*

9. What is the function of mitotic cell division? *Provides cells for body growth and for repair of damaged tissue; or,*

provides additional cells with the same genetic makeup

10. Draw the phases of mitosis for a cell that contains four chromosomes as its diploid or 2*n* number.

11. Complete or respond to the following statements:

   Division of the _1_ is referred to as mitosis. Cytokinesis is division of the _2_. The major structural difference between chromatin and chromosomes is that the latter are _3_. Chromosomes attach to the spindle fibers by undivided structures called _4_. If a cell undergoes mitosis but not cytokinesis, the product is _5_. The structure that acts as a scaffolding for chromosomal attachment and movement is called the _6_. _7_ is the period of cell life when the cell is not involved in division. Three cell populations in the body that do not routinely undergo cell division are _8_, _9_, and _10_.

1. *nucleus*
2. *cytoplasm*
3. *coiled/condensed/shortened*
4. *centromeres*
5. *a binucleate cell or multinucleated cell*
6. *mitotic spindle*
7. *interphase*
8. *neurons*
9. *skeletal muscle cells*
10. *cardiac muscle cells*

12. Using the key, categorize each of the events described below according to the phase in which it occurs. Some terms may be used more than once.

Key: a. anaphase   b. interphase   c. metaphase   d. prophase   e. telophase

_____*d*_____ 1. Chromatin coils and condenses, forming chromosomes.

_____*a*_____ 2. The chromosomes are V shaped.

_____*e*_____ 3. The nuclear envelope re-forms.

_____*e*_____ 4. Chromosomes stop moving toward the poles.

_____*c*_____ 5. Chromosomes line up in the center of the cell.

_____*d*_____ 6. The nuclear envelope fragments.

_____*d*_____ 7. The mitotic spindle forms.

_____*b*_____ 8. DNA replication occurs.

_____*b*_____ 9. Centrioles replicate.

_____*d*_____ 10. Chromosomes first appear to be duplex structures.

_____*e*_____ 11. Cleavage furrow forms.

_____*a*_____ and _____*c*_____ 12. The nuclear envelope is completely absent.

13. What is the physical advantage of the chromatin's coiling and condensing to form short chromosomes at the onset of mitosis?

   Short, compact bodies are mechanically much easier to manipulate during mitosis than are long, thin chromatin threads.

The Cell: Transport Mechanisms and Cell Permeability

This exercise has many parts to it. If students have had an introductory cell biology course, much of it should be review.

Time Allotment:

Observing Diffusion of Dye Through Agar Gel—setup: 5 minutes; observation:
    60 minutes
Observing Diffusion of Dye Through Water—setup: 5 minutes; observation at end of lab session:
    10 minutes
Observing Diffusion and Osmosis Through Nonliving Membranes—setup: 15–30 minutes; diffusion:
    60 minutes; observation: 20 minutes
Investigating Diffusion and Osmosis Through Living Membranes: 25 minutes
        Experiment 1—setup: 10 minutes; observation: 60 minutes
        Experiment 2—15 minutes
Observing the Process of Filtration—15 minutes
Observations for diffusion and osmosis through living membranes, osmometer, and filtration can be done while waiting for the results of the other experiments.

Multimedia Resources: See Appendix B for Guide to Multimedia Resource Distributors.

PhysioEx™ 9.1: Exercise 1 (PE: CD-ROM, website)
An Introduction to the Living Cell (CBS: 30 minutes, DVD)
Mitosis and Meiosis (DE: 23 minutes, VHS, DVD)
The Outer Envelope (WNS: 13 minutes, DVD)
The Plasma Membrane and Cellular Transport (CVB: CD-ROM)

Solutions:

Agar Gel, 1.5%
Weigh out 15 grams of dried agar. Slowly add 1 liter of distilled water while heating. Bring slowly to a boil, stirring constantly until the agar dissolves. For immediate use, allow the agar to cool to about 45°C. Pour into petri dishes to solidify. Refrigerate in an inverted position. If the plates are to be kept for a longer time (more than one day), autoclave the agar solution in the flask, pour into sterile petri plates, allow the agar to solidify, invert the plates, and store in a refrigerator.

Benedict's Solution

• 173.0 grams sodium citrate
• 100.0 grams sodium carbonate, anhydrous
• 17.3 grams cupric sulfate (pure crystalline)

Add the citrate and carbonate salts to 700–800 milliliters distilled water and heat to dissolve. Add the cupric sulfate to 100 milliliters distilled water and heat to dissolve. Cool the solutions and then combine. Add distilled water to make 1 liter of solution. Benedict's solution is available for purchase from biology supply companies such as Carolina, WARD'S, or Fisher.

Bleach Solution, 10%
Measure out 100 milliliters of bleach and add water to a final volume of 1 liter.

Glucose, 40%

For each 100 milliliters of solution, weigh out 40 grams of glucose and bring to 100 milliliters with distilled water. It may be necessary to heat the mixture to get the glucose into solution. Refrigerate when not in use.

Methylene Blue Solution, 0.1 M

Weigh out 3.2 grams of methylene blue powder and bring to 100 milliliters with distilled water.

Physiologic Saline (Mammalian, 0.9%)

Weigh out 9 grams of NaCl. Add distilled water to a final volume of 1 liter. Make fresh immediately prior to experiment.

Potassium Permanganate Solution, 0.1 M (1.6%)

Weigh out 1.6 grams of potassium permanganate crystals and bring to 100 milliliters with distilled water.

Silver Nitrate (2.9% or 3%)

Weigh out 2.9 grams (for 2.9%) or 3 grams (for 3%) of silver nitrate. **Use caution; this is an oxidizing substance**. Add distilled water to make 100 milliliters of solution. Store in light-resistant bottles. Make fresh for each use.

Sodium Chloride (NaCl), 5%

Weigh out 5 grams NaCl. Add distilled water to a final volume of 100 milliliters.

Sodium Chloride (NaCl), 10%

For each 100 milliliters of solution, weigh out 10 grams of NaCl and bring to 100 milliliters with distilled water. It may be necessary to heat the mixture to get the NaCl into solution.

Sucrose, 30%

For each 100 milliliters of solution, weigh out 30 grams of sucrose and bring to 100 milliliters with distilled water. It may be necessary to heat the mixture to get the sucrose into solution. Refrigerate when not in use.

Sucrose, 40% (with Congo Red Dye)

For each 100 milliliters of solution, weigh out 40 grams of sucrose and bring to 100 milliliters with distilled water. Add 0.5 grams of Congo red dye. It may be necessary to heat the solution to get the sucrose into solution. Refrigerate when not in use.

Uncooked Starch Solution

Add 20 grams of corn starch to 100 milliliters of distilled water and gently stir to form a milky solution. After 15 minutes, stir again. Stir before making filtration solution. Refrigerate when not in use.

Laboratory Materials

Ordering information is based on a lab size of 24 students, working in groups of 4. A list of supply house addresses appears in Appendix A.

24 compound microscopes, lens paper, lens cleaning solution, immersion oil
1 box of microscope slides
1 box of coverslips
6 hot plates and large beakers for hot water bath
6 forceps
6 petri plates with 1.5% agar gel
6 dropper bottles of 3.5% methylene blue solution

6 dropper bottles of 1.6% potassium permanganate solution
1000-milliliter graduated cylinder
6 15-milliliter graduated cylinders
Large beaker
Thistle tube osmometer
Molasses
6 millimeter rulers
25 dialysis sacs (or small Hefty® sandwich bags)
12 small funnels

6 dropper bottles of silver nitrate
6 dropper bottles of Benedict's solution
24 test tubes
6 test tube holders
6 test tube racks
18 wax marking pencils
6 25-milliliter graduated cylinders
24 250-milliliter beakers
40% glucose solution
10% NaCl solution

40% sucrose solution with Congo red dye

6 rolls of fine twine or 48 dialysis tubing clamps

6 laboratory balances

Animal blood (if used)

6 dropper bottles of distilled water

6 dropper bottles of physiologic saline (mammalian, 0.9%)

6 dropper bottles of 5% NaCl solution

Container of 10% bleach solution

6 wash bottles of 10% bleach

12 medicine droppers

Autoclave bag, disposable

Disposable gloves

7 ring stands, rings, and clamps

Filter paper

Paper towels

Millimeter-ruled graph paper

Videotape of phagocytosis (if available)

VHS or DVD player

Solution of uncooked starch, powdered charcoal, and copper sulfate ($CuSO_4$) crystals

Potassium permanganate crystals

10-milliliter graduated cylinder

100-milliliter beaker

12 400-milliliter beakers

12 deshelled eggs

6 200-milliliter bottles of 30% sucrose solution

6 dropper bottles of Lugol's Iodine (IKI) solution

48 weight boats

Distilled water

Advance Preparation

Note: This lab has many components. Either clearly designate supply areas for each part of the lab, or provide each lab group with its own set of supplies at the outset. The supplies for each part of the exercise are listed separately in case sections of the exercise are omitted. Some equipment is common to several parts of the lab.

1. Set out slides and coverslips. Have compound microscopes available.

2. *Observing Diffusion of Dye Through Agar Gel.* Set out 0.1 *M* or 3.5% methylene blue solution (Carolina) and 0.1 *M* or 1.6% potassium permanganate solution (Carolina), 1.5% agar plates (12 milliliters of 1.5% agar per plate, one per group), medicine droppers, and millimeter rulers.

3. *Observing Diffusion of Dye Through Water (Demonstration).* On the morning of the laboratory session, place some crystals of potassium permanganate in the bottom of a 1000-milliliter graduated cylinder. Slowly and carefully fill the cylinder to the 1000-milliliter mark with water. Record the time at which the demonstration is set up. Set out millimeter rulers.

4. *Investigating Diffusion and Osmosis Through Nonliving Membranes.* For each group, set out four dialysis sacs (WARD'S) or 10-centimeter lengths of dialysis tubing (Carolina), five 250-milliliter beakers, a wax marking pencil, 750 milliliters of distilled water, 20 milliliters of *10% NaCl solution*, 20 milliliters of *40% sucrose–Congo red dye solution*, 150 milliliters of *40% glucose solution*, dropper bottles of *Benedict's solution* (Carolina, or see above), *silver nitrate*, four test tubes, a test tube rack, test tube holder, small graduated cylinder, a small funnel, hot plate, and balance. Dialysis sacs can be prepared from cut sections of dialysis tubing. Soak dialysis tubing in a beaker of water for about 15 minutes. Once dialysis tubing has been soaked, open it by rubbing it between the thumb and forefinger until the tubing material separates. Tie the ends with fine twine or close with dialysis tubing closures (Carolina).

5. *Observing Osmometer Results (Demonstration).* At the beginning of the laboratory session, set up an osmometer using a thistle tube and molasses. Fill the expanded end of the thistle tube with molasses and cover it securely with a differentially permeable membrane. Clamp the thistle tube to a stand and put the broad end into a beaker of distilled water. Mark the level of the molasses in the tube and record the time that the osmometer is set up. Set out millimeter rulers.

6. *Investigating Diffusion and Osmosis Through Living Membranes*

Experiment 1: Deshell eggs 48 to 72 hours before the day of the lab. To deshell eggs: Immerse eggs in vinegar. After 24 hours, gently rub eggs under running water to remove shell. If there is any shell remaining, immerse in fresh vinegar. Repeat rubbing under water and immersion in fresh vinegar until all shell has been removed. Give each group two deshelled eggs, two 400-ml beakers, 200 ml distilled water, 200 ml 30% sucrose solution, wax markers, paper towels, weight boat, and laboratory balance.

Experiment 2: Give each group 6 microscope slides and coverslips, dropper bottles of distilled water, filter paper, plastic gloves, physiologic saline, 5% NaCl, a vial of animal blood, and medicine droppers (one per student). Set out a basin of 10% bleach, a wash bottle of 10% bleach, and a disposable autoclave bag.

7. *Observing the Process of Filtration.* Give each group a ring stand with ring clamp and ring attached, a funnel, a piece of filter paper, a beaker, a 10-ml graduated cylinder, 100 ml filtration solution, and a dropper bottle of Lugol's iodine. Prepare the filtration solution by mixing 100 ml uncooked starch solution, 10 grams copper sulfate, and 10 grams powdered charcoal.

Comments and Pitfalls

1. Caution students to keep careful track of time during the diffusion experiments. Lab timers might help. Suggestions for variables include different concentrations of solutions.

2. Dialysis sacs may leak. Check to see that they are tightly sealed.

3. You may substitute Clinitest™ tablets for Benedict's solution.

4. Silver nitrate will stain and possibly damage clothing. Warn students to be careful.

5. Note that the *40% glucose solution* used in sac 1 of the osmosis experiment is not isoosmotic to the *10% NaCl solution* in sac 3, so caution students about the types of conclusions they may draw from this experiment. Also, sometimes no glucose will be present in the beaker at the end of the hour. You may need to extend the time for this part of the experiment.

6. Emphasize the importance of labeling test tubes and slides.

7. Red blood cells in physiologic saline may begin to crenate as the slide begins to dry out. Encourage students to make their observations quickly. If there is still trouble with crenation, use a slightly hypotonic saline solution.

8. Caution students to be careful when pouring starch solution into filter paper so that the solution does not overflow or cause the filter paper to collapse.

Answers to Pre-Lab Quiz (p. 53)

1. diffusion

2. b, it contains more nonpenetrating solute particles than the interior of the cell

3. d, vesicular transport

4. phagocytosis

5. active

Answers to Activity Questions

Activity 1: Observing Diffusion of Dye Through Agar Gel (pp. 55–56)

6. Potassium permanganate (MW 158) diffused more rapidly than methylene blue (MW 320). The smaller the molecular weight, the faster the rate of diffusion. The dye molecules moved because they possess kinetic energy.

Activity 2: Observing Diffusion of Dye Through Water (p. 56)

4. Potassium permanganate diffuses more rapidly through the water. Although the agar gel is largely water, it does contain more solid particles, which hinder free diffusion.

Activity 3: Investigating Diffusion and Osmosis Through Nonliving Membranes (pp. 56–58)

5. After 1 hour, sac 1 (originally containing 40% glucose) should have gained weight.

   Water is moving into the sac by osmosis.

   Glucose is still present in the sac, and a small amount of glucose may also be present in the beaker.

   If the Benedict's test is positive, glucose was able to pass through the dialysis membrane.

6. There should be no net weight change in sac 2.

   Since the concentrations of glucose and water are the same on both sides of the membrane, there is no net movement of water or glucose.

7. Sac 3 will increase in weight, perhaps only by a small amount.

There has been a net movement of water into the sac and the weight of the water was not completely offset by the movement of the NaCl out of the sac.

The solution in beaker 3 reacts with silver nitrate, indicating the presence of chloride in the beaker.

Net dialysis of NaCl occurred.

8. There should be an increase in weight in sac 4.

The water color did not turn pink; the dye was not able to diffuse out of the sac.

The Benedict's test for sugar was negative. Sucrose did not diffuse from the sac to the beaker.

The dye and sucrose are too large to diffuse through the pores in the membrane or their rate of diffusion is too slow given the allowed time.

9. Net osmosis occurred in situations 1, 3, and 4.

Net simple diffusion occurred in situations 1, 3, and 4.

Water molecules are very small, and move quickly down a concentration gradient. Na^+ and Cl^- in solution behave like slightly larger molecules, but are smaller than glucose molecules, which move slowly, if at all, through the dialysis tubing. (See item 5 in Comments and Pitfalls.) *Note:* Students may be able to conclude only that Na^+ and Cl^- in solution and water molecules are small, and glucose, sucrose, and Congo red dye molecules are larger, or that Na^+ and Cl^- in solution and water and glucose molecules are smaller than sucrose molecules.

The dialysis sac is often compared to the plasma membrane of the cell.

Activity 4: Observing Osmometer Results (p. 58)

Net osmosis, movement of water into the molasses, occurred as shown by the increased distance that the column of water moved.

Activity 5: Investigating Diffusion and Osmosis Through Living Membranes— Experiment 1 (pp. 58–59)

Conclusions: The egg placed in the distilled water gained weight because the egg is hypertonic to the distilled water. The egg placed in 30% sucrose solution lost weight because the egg (14% solution) is hypotonic to the 30% sucrose solution. Water moves from an area of higher water concentration into an area of lower water concentration.

Activity 5: Investigating Diffusion and Osmosis Through Living Membranes— Experiment 2 (pp. 59–60)

3. The cells begin to shrink and develop a multipointed star shape.

4. When distilled water is added, the cells should begin to revert to their normal shape. Eventually they begin to look very bloated, and finally begin to disappear as their membranes burst open.

Activity 6: Observing the Process of Filtration (pp. 60–61)

3. Passed: starch, copper sulfate, water

Retained: powdered charcoal

The filter paper represents a cell membrane.

The filtration rate was greatest during the first 10-second counting period because the hydrostatic pressure was greater during that period.

The characteristic of the three solutes that determines whether or not they passed through the filter paper is their size in relation to the size of the pores in the filter paper.

Answers to Group Challenge (p. 62)

Some possible answers to the questions are listed below. Student answers may vary.

Membrane transport processes	Similarities	Differences
Simple diffusion Osmosis	Both are passive processes. Both require a differentially permeable membrane. In both cases, the substances move down their concentration gradients.	During simple diffusion, solutes are moving. During osmosis, water is moving.
Simple diffusion Facilitated diffusion	Both are passive processes. Both require a differentially permeable membrane.	In simple diffusion, substances move directly through the plasma membrane. In facilitated diffusion, the substance moves on a carrier or through a channel.
Active transport Facilitated diffusion	Both processes require a membrane-bound protein.	Active transport requires ATP, and solutes move against (up) their concentration gradient. Facilitated diffusion is passive, and solutes down their concentration gradient.
Filtration Osmosis	Both are passive processes. Both involve the movement of water.	The driving force for filtration is hydrostatic pressure. The driving force for osmosis is a concentration gradient.
Pinocytosis Receptor-mediated endocytosis	Both are types of endocytosis where molecules are moving into the cell. Both are active processes.	Pinocytosis is nonspecific and doesn't require receptors. Receptor-mediated endocytosis is specific and requires receptors.

NAME _____

LAB TIME/DATE _____

The Cell: Transport Mechanisms and Permeability

Choose all answers that apply to questions 1 and 2, and place their letters on the response blanks to the right.

1. Molecular motion _a, d_ _____.

    a.   reflects the kinetic energy of molecules   c.   is ordered and predictable

    b.   reflects the potential energy of molecules   d.   is random and erratic

2. Speed of molecular movement _b, c, e_ _____.

    a.   is higher in larger molecules   d.   decreases with increasing temperature

    b.   is lower in larger molecules   e.   reflects kinetic energy

    c.   increases with increasing temperature

3. Summarize below the results of Activity 3, Investigating Diffusion and Osmosis Through Nonliving Membranes. List and explain your observations relative to tests used to identify diffusing substances, and the changes in sac weight you observed.

    Sac 1 containing 40% glucose, suspended in distilled water

    Glucose diffused from the sac into the water; using the Benedict's test indicated the presence of the glucose that passed membrane.

    Water moved into the sac by osmosis; sac gained weight.

    Sac 2 containing 40% glucose, suspended in 40% glucose

    There was no net diffusion of glucose or osmosis because the water concentration on both sides of the membrane was the same.

    Net movement occurs only when there is a concentration gradient.

    Sac 3 containing 10% NaCl, suspended in distilled water

    NaCl diffused from the sac into the water; silver nitrate added to the water showed the presence of Cl⁻. Osmosis caused

    water to enter the sac because the solution in the sac was hypertonic to the distilled water in the beaker.

    Sac 4 containing 40% sucrose and Congo red dye, suspended in distilled water

    The Congo red dye did not diffuse from the sac into the water; the water in the beaker did not turn red. The sucrose did

    not diffuse from the sac; upon boiling, some of the sucrose bonds are hydrolyzed, releasing glucose and fructose. Using

    Benedict's test then indicates the presence of glucose if sucrose passed through the membrane; the Benedict's test was

    negative. Water moved into the sac by osmosis; the sac gained weight.

4. What single characteristic of the selectively permeable membranes *used in the laboratory* determines the substances that

can pass through them? *Size of pores*

In addition to this characteristic, what other factors influence the passage of substances through living membranes?

Solubility in the lipid portion of the membrane and/or presence of membrane "carriers" for the substance(s)

5. A semipermeable sac filled with a solution containing 4% NaCl, 9% glucose, and 10% albumin is suspended in a solution with the following composition: 10% NaCl, 10% glucose, and 40% albumin. Assume that the sac is permeable to all substances except albumin. State whether each of the following will (a) move into the sac, (b) move out of the sac, or (c) not move.

glucose: *a; moves into sac*   albumin: *c; does not move*

water: *b; moves out of sac*   NaCl: *a; moves into sac*

6. Summarize the results of Activity 5, Experiment 1 (Investigating Diffusion and Osmosis Through Living Membranes—the egg), below. List and explain your observations.

Egg 1 in distilled water: *The egg gained weight because the concentration of the egg, 14%, is hypertonic to the water.*

Water moves by osmosis from an area of higher water concentration into an area of lower water concentration.

Egg 2 in 30% sucrose: *The egg lost weight because the concentration of the egg, 14%, is hypotonic to the 30% sucrose*

solution. Water moves by osmosis from an area of higher water concentration into an area of lower water concentration.

7. The diagrams below represent three microscope fields containing red blood cells. Arrows show the direction of net osmosis.

Which field contains a hypertonic solution? *c*   The cells in this field are said to be *crenated*   . Which

field contains an isotonic bathing solution? *b*   Which field contains a hypotonic solution? *a*   What is happening

to the cells in this field? *Hemolysis; they are bursting as excessive water entry occurs.*

(a)   (b)   (c)

Why This Matters

8. Many classroom protocols for extracting DNA from cheek cells instruct the student to swish a sports drink in their mouths as they gently scrape the inside of their cheek with their teeth. Why do you think it would be better to use a sports drink than plain water? (*Hint:* You want the DNA from the cheek cells to end up in the test tube, not in your mouth.)

A sports drink is used because it is isotonic with respect to the cheek cells. Plain water would be hypotonic, possibly resulting in the

cells lysing and releasing the DNA into your mouth, not in the tube.

9. Drinking too much plain water in a short period of time can result in water intoxication. As a result blood plasma will become hypotonic. What effect do you think this would have on cells, and why?

This can result in a condition known as hyponatremia where the level of sodium in the blood is low. This will result in blood and

tissue cells swelling, which can lead to seizures, coma, and death.

10. Assume you are conducting the experiment illustrated in the next figure. Both hydrochloric acid (HCl) with a molecular weight of about 36.5 and ammonium hydroxide (NH_4OH) with a molecular weight of 35 are volatile and easily enter the gaseous state. When they meet, the following reaction will occur:

$$HCl + NH_4OH \rightarrow H_2O + NH_4Cl$$

Ammonium chloride (NH_4Cl) will be deposited on the glass tubing as a smoky precipitate where the two gases meet. Predict which gas will diffuse more quickly and indicate to which end of the tube the smoky precipitate will be closer.

a. The faster-diffusing gas is _NH_4OH_.

b. The precipitate forms closer to the _HCl_ end.

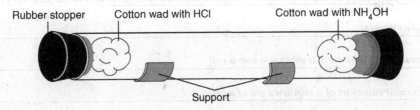

Rubber stopper   Cotton wad with HCl   Cotton wad with NH_4OH

Support

11. What determines whether a transport process is active or passive? *Whether or not the cell must provide ATP for the*

process; if so, the process is active.

12. Characterize membrane transport as fully as possible by choosing all the phrases that apply and inserting their letters on the answer blanks.

Passive processes: _a, c, e, f (sometimes)_   Active processes: _b, d, f (sometimes)_

a. account for the movement of fats and respiratory gases through the plasma membrane

b. explain solute pumping, phagocytosis, and pinocytosis

c. include osmosis, simple diffusion, and filtration

d. may occur against concentration and/or electrical gradients

e. use hydrostatic pressure or molecular energy as the driving force

f. move ions, amino acids, and some sugars across the plasma membrane

13. For the osmometer demonstration (Activity 4), explain why the level of the water column rose during the laboratory session.

The thistle tube was immersed in a dialysis sac which, in turn, was immersed in water. Because water will move down its

concentration gradient if it is able, water diffused from the beaker into the sac, where its concentration was much lower. As a result,

the fluid column (molasses and entering water) rose in the thistle tube.

14. Define the following terms.

selective permeability: _The property of a plasma membrane to allow some substances to pass while excluding others_

diffusion: _Movement of molecules from a region of their higher concentration to a region of their lower concentration_

simple diffusion: _The unassisted diffusion of solutes across a selectively permeable membrane_

facilitated diffusion: _The passive transport of molecules across a membrane with the assistance of either a protein carrier or a water-filled protein channel. The molecules move down their concentration gradients._

osmosis: _The diffusion of water across a selectively permeable membrane. Water moves down its concentration gradient._

filtration: _A passive process in which water and solutes are forced through a membrane by hydrostatic pressure_

vesicular transport: _The transport of fluids containing large particles and macromolecules across a cell membrane inside of a membranous sac called a vesicle. Vesicular transport requires energy, usually in the form of ATP; it is an active transport process._

endocytosis: _The vesicular transport of a substance into a cell_

exocytosis: _The vesicular transport of a substance out of a cell_

6

Classification of Tissues

 Time Allotment: 2 hours.

 Multimedia Resources: See Appendix B for Guide to Multimedia Resource Distributors.

Eroschenko's Interactive Histology (DE: CD-ROM)
Practice Anatomy Lab™ 3.0 (PAL) (PE: DVD, website)

Laboratory Materials

Ordering information is based on a lab size of 24 students, working in groups of 4. A list of supply house addresses appears in Appendix A.

24 compound microscopes, lens paper, lens cleaning solution, immersion oil
24 slides of simple squamous, simple cuboidal, simple columnar, stratified squamous (nonkeratinized), stratified cuboidal, stratified columnar, pseudostratified ciliated columnar, and transitional epithelium

24 slides of mesenchyme; adipose, areolar, reticular, and dense connective tissue, regular (tendon) and irregular (dermis); hyaline cartilage, elastic cartilage, fibrocartilage; bone (cross section); and blood smear
24 slides of skeletal, cardiac, and smooth muscle (longitudinal sections)

24 slides of nervous tissue (spinal cord smear)
6 envelopes containing color images of epithelial tissues
6 envelopes containing color images of connective tissues, nervous tissue, and muscle tissues
6 envelopes containing a color image of a section of the trachea

Advance Preparation

1. Set out prepared slides of simple squamous, simple cuboidal, simple columnar, stratified squamous (nonkeratinized), stratified cuboidal, stratified columnar, pseudostratified ciliated columnar, and transitional epithelium.

2. Set out prepared slides of mesenchyme; adipose tissue, areolar connective tissue, reticular connective tissue, dense connective tissue regular (tendon), and irregular (dermis) varieties; hyaline cartilage, elastic cartilage, and fibrocartilage; bone (cross section); and blood (smear).

3. Set out prepared slides of skeletal, cardiac, and smooth muscle (longitudinal sections).

4. Set out prepared slides of spinal cord smear.

5. Set out lens paper and lens cleaning solution. Have compound microscopes available.

6. For Group Challenge 1, obtain 6 medium brown envelopes. Using old histology atlases or lab manuals, cut out several color images of each of the epithelial tissues. Place various examples of the tissues in each of the 6 envelopes. You need not include all of the tissues in each envelope. Distribute 1 envelope to each group after they have studied the epithelial tissues.

7. For Group Challenge 2, obtain 6 medium brown envelopes. Using old histology atlases or lab manuals, cut out several color images of each of the connective tissues, nervous tissue, and each of the muscle tissues. Place various examples of the tissues in each of the 6 envelopes. You need not include all of the tissues in each envelope. Distribute 1 envelope to each group after they have studied the connective tissues, nervous

tissue, and the muscle tissues. For the second part of this Group Challenge, obtain 6 more medium brown envelopes. Using old histology atlases or lab manuals, cut out a color image of a section of the trachea. As you proceed away from the luminal side of the tissue, you should see ciliated pseudostratifed columnar epithelium, areolar connective tissue of the lamina propria, epithelial tissue of the submucosal glands, and hyaline cartilage. Give this envelope to each group at the end of the study of tissues.

Comments and Pitfalls

1. Slides of the lung are suggested for simple squamous epithelium, and slides of the kidney are suggested for simple cuboidal epithelium. An analogy using a quarter or pavement stone will help students visualize the three-dimensional shape of a squamous cell.

2. The dense fibrous regular connective tissue slide is sometimes labeled white fibrous tissue.

3. Students may have trouble locating the appropriate tissue on slides with multiple tissue types. Encourage them to consult lab manual Figures 6.3–6.7, available histology texts, and each other for help.

4. A television camera with a microscope adapter and monitor is very useful in this lab. By watching the monitor, students can observe the instructor locating the correct area of tissue on the slide (see item 3 in Comments and Pitfalls). It also makes it easier to answer student questions and share particularly good slides with the class.

5. Use the final envelope containing a section of the tracheal wall to help students understand how tissues are organized to form an organ. Encourage them as they look at this complicated image; tell them to start at the luminal surface and look at each tissue carefully.

Answers to Pre-Lab Quiz (p. 67)

1. d, tissues
2. 4
3. true
4. c, squamous
5. c, mesenchyme

6. c, neurons
7. true
8. neurons
9. 3
10. c, smooth muscle

Answers to Group Challenge 1 (p. 74)

Magnified appearance	Tissue type	Locations in the body
• Apical surface has dome-shaped cells (flattened cells may also be mixed in). • Multiple layers of cells are present.	*Transitional epithelium*	*Urinary bladder, ureters, and part of the urethra*
• Cells are mostly columnar. • Not all cells reach the apical surface. • Nuclei are located at different levels. • Cilia are located at the apical surface.	*Pseudostratified (ciliated) columnar epithelium*	*Trachea and most of the upper respiratory tract*
• Apical surface has flattened cells with very little cytoplasm. • Cells are not layered.	*Simple squamous epithelium*	*Alveoli (air sacs of the lungs), blood vessels, lymphatic vessels, lining of the heart, lining of the ventral body cavity*
• Apical surface has square cells with a round nucleus. • Cells are not layered.	*Simple cuboidal epithelium*	*Kidney tubules, ducts of small glands, surface of the ovary*

Answers to Activity Questions

Activity 2: Examining Connective Tissue Under the Microscope (p. 76)

All connective tissues consist of cells located within a matrix. Blood is no exception, but its cells float freely in a liquid matrix. The matrix ground substance is the straw-colored fluid called plasma. Its proteins are soluble, rather than fibrous, and include albumin, globulins, and fibrinogen.

Answers to Group Challenge 2 (p. 86)

Magnified appearance	Tissue type	Locations in the body
• Large, round cells are densely packed. • Nucleus is pushed to one side.	*Adipose tissue*	*Under the skin, around kidneys and eyeballs, within the abdomen, in breasts*
• Lacunae (small cavities within the tissue) are present. • Lacunae are not arranged in a concentric circle. • No visible fibers are in the matrix.	*Hyaline cartilage*	*Embryonic skeleton, the ends of long bones, costal cartilage (ribs), nose, trachea, larynx*
• Fibers and cells are loosely packed with visible space between fibers. • Fibers overlap but do not form a network.	*Areolar connective tissue*	*Key type of connective tissue located beneath epithelia*
• Extracellular fibers run parallel to each other. • Nuclei of fibroblasts are visible.	*Dense regular connective tissue*	*Tendons and ligaments*
• Lacunae are sparsely distributed. • Lacunae are not arranged in a concentric circle. • Fibers are visible and fairly organized.	*Fibrocartilage*	*Intervertebral discs, pubic symphysis, discs of the knee joint*
• Tapered cells with darkly stained nucleus centrally located are seen. • No striations are present. • Cells are layered to form a sheet.	*Smooth muscle*	*The walls of hollow organs*

Classification of Tissues

Tissue Structure and Function—General Review

1. Define tissue. *A group of cells similar to one another in structure that perform a common or related function*

2. Use the key choices to identify the major tissue types described below.

Key: a.   connective tissue   b.   epithelium   c.   muscle   d.   nervous tissue

b; epithelium _____ 1. lines body cavities and covers the body's external surface

c; muscle _____ 2. pumps blood, flushes urine out of the body, allows one to swing a bat

d; nervous , *c; muscle* _____ 3. transmits electrical signals

a; connective _____ 4. anchors, packages, and supports body organs

b; epithelium _____ 5. cells may absorb, secrete, and filter

d; nervous _____ 6. most involved in regulating and controlling body functions

c; muscle _____ 7. major function is to contract

b; epithelium _____ 8. synthesizes hormones

a; connective _____ 9. includes abundant nonliving extracellular matrix

a; connective _____ 10. most widespread tissue in the body

d; nervous _____ 11. forms nerves and the brain

Epithelial Tissue

3. Describe five general characteristics of epithelial tissue. *(1) The cells fit closely together, forming sheetlike membranes.*

(2) Little intercellular material between the cells. (3) Avascular. (4) Membrane has a free edge. (5) Generally has a high

regenerative capacity.

4. How are epithelial tissues classified? *Number of layers and cell shape*

Why This Matters

5. Which type of epithelium is removed with a buccal swab? *Stratified squamous epithelium (nonkeratinized) is found in the oral cavity.*

6. Explain why a buccal swab procedure shouldn't cause bleeding. *Epithelial tissues are avascular. They contain no blood vessels. They receive their nutrients from the underlying connective tissue.*

7. List five major functions of epithelium in the body, and give examples of cells or organs that provide each function.

Function 1: *protection*   Example: *stratified squamous cells*

Function 2: *absorption*   Example: *cells lining digestive tract*

Function 3: *filtration secretion and excretion*   Example: *kidney tubule cells*

Function 4: *secretion*   Example: *glandular cells or kidney cells*

Function 5: *sensory reception*   Example: *skin*

8. How does the function of stratified epithelia differ from the function of simple epithelia? *Stratified epithelia have more layers for protection. Simple epithelia allow materials to move across them and are less protective.*

9. Where is ciliated epithelium found? *Lining of the trachea and upper respiratory tract and of the female reproductive tracts (uterine tubes)*

What role does it play? *In the respiratory tract, it acts to sweep mucus superiorly away from the lungs. In the reproductive tracts, it acts to propel ova along the tract.*

10. Transitional epithelium is actually stratified squamous epithelium with special characteristics.

How does it differ structurally from other stratified squamous epithelia? *When stretched, its top layers are squamous, but when not stretched, its top layers are pillow shaped.*

How does the structural difference support its function? *The surface cells have the ability to slide over one another, increasing the internal volume of the organ (e.g., bladder) as it fills and maintaining an intact lining whether stretched or contracted.*

11. How do the endocrine and exocrine glands differ in structure and function? *Endocrine glands are ductless glands. They produce hormones, which are liberated into the extracellular fluid to enter the blood. Exocrine glands maintain their ducts and manufacture secretions of various types (perspiration, oil, digestive enzymes, etc.), which are ducted to the body (or membrane) surface.*

12. Respond to the following with the key choices. Some choices are used more than once.

Key: a. simple squamous   c. simple columnar   e. stratified squamous
      b. simple cuboidal   d. pseudostratified ciliated columnar   f. transitional

e; stratified squamous   1. lining of the esophagus

c; simple columnar   2. lining of the stomach

a; simple squamous   3. alveolar sacs of lungs

b; simple cuboidal   4. tubules of the kidney

d; pseudostratified ciliated columnar   5. lining of the trachea

f; transitional   6. lining of bladder; peculiar cells that have the ability to slide over each other

a; simple squamous   7. forms the thin serous membranes; a single layer of flattened cells

Connective Tissue

13. What are three general characteristics of connective tissues? *Common origin of connective tissue from mesenchyme, varied*

degrees of vascularity, and a large amount of extracellular matrix that varies with tissue type

14. What functions are performed by connective tissue? *Protection, support, and the binding together of other body tissues.*

Transportation of substances within the body is another function.

15. How are the functions of connective tissue reflected in its structure? *There is a wide variety in the structures of connective tissue.*

This is reflected in the wide variety of functions they perform. Also, the large amount of nonliving matrix seen provides the strength

needed to protect the body and carry out the normal functions of the body.

16. Using the key, choose the best response to identify the connective tissues described below. Some responses are used more than once.

Key: a. adipose connective tissue   d. dense regular connective tissue   g. fibrocartilage
      b. areolar connective tissue   e. elastic cartilage   h. hyaline cartilage
      c. dense irregular connective tissue   f. elastic connective tissue   i. osseous tissue

d; dense regular   1. attaches bones to bones and muscles to bones

a; adipose   2. insulates against heat loss

c; dense irregular, *b; areolar*   3. the dermis of the skin

g; fibrocartilage   4. makes up the intervertebral discs

b; areolar   5. composes basement membranes; a soft packaging tissue with a jellylike matrix

h; hyaline cartilage   6. forms the larynx, the costal cartilages of the ribs, and the embryonic skeleton

e; elastic cartilage _____ 7. provides a flexible framework for the external ear

i; osseous _____ 8. matrix hard owing to calcium salts; provides levers for muscles to act on

f; elastic _____ 9. walls of large arteries

17. Why do adipose cells remind people of a signet ring (a ring with a single jewel)? _They contain a large fat-filled vacuole_

occupying most of the cell volume. The nucleus is pushed to the periphery, giving the cell a "signet ring" appearance.

Nervous Tissue

18. What two physiological characteristics are highly developed in neurons (nerve cells)? _Irritability and conductivity._

19. In what ways are neurons similar to other cells? _They contain a nucleus and the usual organelles._

How are they structurally different? _Their cytoplasm is drawn out into long processes._

20. Describe how the unique structure of a neuron relates to its function in the body.

Neurons conduct impulses over relatively long distances in the body. This is facilitated by their long cytoplasmic extensions.

Muscle Tissue

21. The three types of muscle tissue exhibit similarities as well as differences. Check the appropriate space in the chart to indicate which muscle types exhibit each characteristic.

Characteristic	Skeletal	Cardiac	Smooth
Voluntarily controlled	✓		
Involuntarily controlled		✓	✓
Striated	✓	✓	
Has a single nucleus in each cell		✓	✓
Has several nuclei per cell	✓		
Found attached to bones	✓		
Allows you to direct your eyeballs	✓		
Found in the walls of the stomach, uterus, and arteries			✓
Contains spindle-shaped cells			✓
Contains branching cylindrical cells		✓	
Contains long, nonbranching cylindrical cells	✓		
Has intercalated discs		✓	
Concerned with locomotion of the body as a whole	✓		
Changes the internal volume of an organ as it contracts		✓	✓
Tissue of the heart		✓	

For Review

22. Label the tissue types illustrated here and on the next page, and identify all structures provided with leaders.

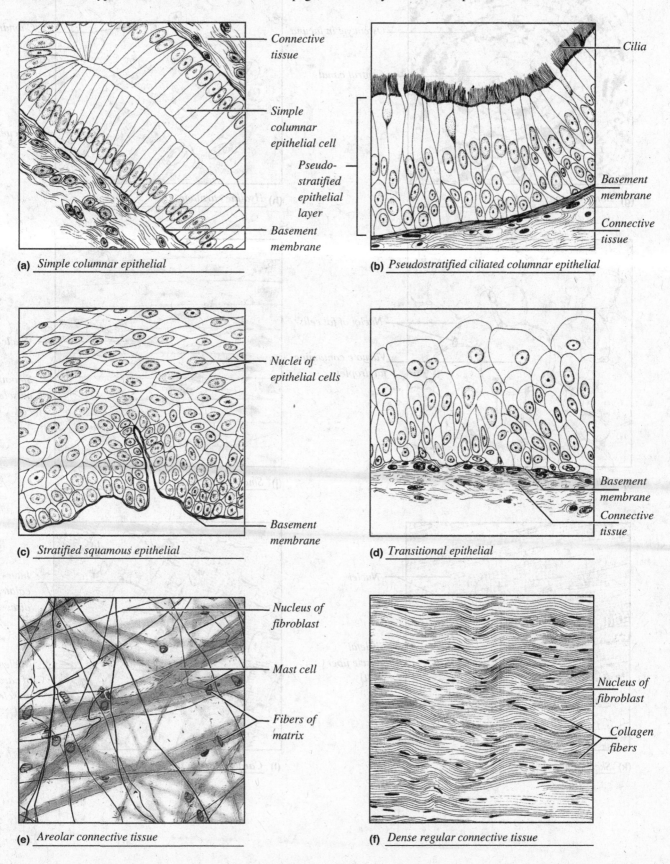

Connective tissue

Simple columnar epithelial cell

Pseudo-stratified epithelial layer

Basement membrane

(a) Simple columnar epithelial

Cilia

Basement membrane

Connective tissue

(b) Pseudostratified ciliated columnar epithelial

Nuclei of epithelial cells

Basement membrane

(c) Stratified squamous epithelial

Basement membrane

Connective tissue

(d) Transitional epithelial

Nucleus of fibroblast

Mast cell

Fibers of matrix

(e) Areolar connective tissue

Nucleus of fibroblast

Collagen fibers

(f) Dense regular connective tissue

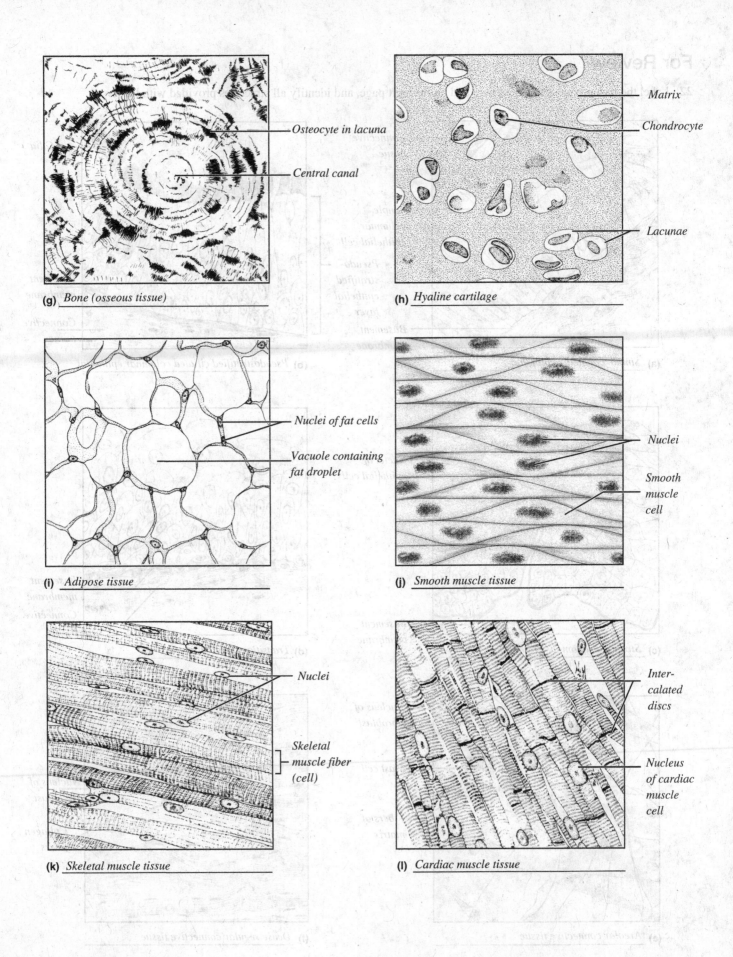

(g) Bone (osseous tissue)

Osteocyte in lacuna

Central canal

(h) Hyaline cartilage

Matrix

Chondrocyte

Lacunae

(i) Adipose tissue

Nuclei of fat cells

Vacuole containing fat droplet

(j) Smooth muscle tissue

Nuclei

Smooth muscle cell

(k) Skeletal muscle tissue

Nuclei

Skeletal muscle fiber (cell)

(l) Cardiac muscle tissue

Inter-calated discs

Nucleus of cardiac muscle cell

The Integumentary System

 Time Allotment: 1 1/2 hours.

 Multimedia Resources: See Appendix B for Guide to Multimedia Resource Distributors.

Practice Anatomy Lab™ 3.0 (PAL) (PE: DVD, website)
The Senses: Skin Deep (FHS: 26 minutes, DVD, 3-year streaming webcast)
Skin (FHS: 20 minutes, DVD, 3-year streaming webcast)
The Skin (NIMCO: 28 minutes, DVD)

 Solutions:

Lugol's Iodine (IKI)

• 20 grams potassium iodide

• 4 grams iodine crystals

Dissolve potassium iodide in 1 liter distilled water. Add the iodine crystals and stir to dissolve. Store in dark bottles.

Laboratory Materials

Ordering information is based on a lab size of 24 students, working in groups of 4. A list of supply house addresses appears in Appendix A.

24 compound microscopes, lens paper, lens cleaning solution	Adhesive tape	Disposable gloves
Model of the skin	24 pairs of scissors	Porelon fingerprint pad or portable inking foils
24 slides of human scalp	24 Betadine® swabs or 24 cotton swabs and 6 dropper bottles of Lugol's iodine	Ink cleaning towelettes
24 slides of skin of palm or sole		Index cards (4 × 6)
1 sheet of 20# bond paper	Data collection sheets	24 magnifying glasses
Ruler		

Advance Preparation

1. Set out models of the skin, prepared slides of human scalp with hair follicles and skin of palm or sole, lens paper, and lens cleaning solution. Have compound microscopes available.

2. Terminology for layers of the epidermis differs from text to text. Decide on the terminology to be used, and inform the students at the onset of the laboratory session if there is a discrepancy between the laboratory manual and the text.

3. Set out 20# bond paper ruled in 1-centimeter squares, scissors, Betadine swabs, or *Lugol's iodine* (Carolina, or see above), cotton swabs, and adhesive tape.

4. Prepare a data collection sheet for "palm" and "forearm" sweat gland data.

5. Set out 4 × 6 index cards, Porelon fingerprint pad or portable inking foils, ink cleaner towelettes, and magnifying glasses (all available from Sirchie®-Fingerprint & Forensic Supplies, 1-800-356-7311 or www.sirchie.com).

Comments and Pitfalls

1. Students may have difficulty finding the arrector pili muscles and sweat glands. Some students will confuse the fibers of the dermis (dense irregular connective tissue) with smooth muscle.

Answers to Pre-Lab Quiz (p. 93)

1. d, site of vitamin A synthesis
2. epidermis, dermis
3. d, stratum corneum
4. five
5. b, Carotene
6. c, melanocytes
7. true
8. d, shaft
9. sebaceous
10. Apocrine

Answers to Activity Questions

Activity 3: Comparing Hairy and Relatively Hair-Free Skin Microscopically (pp. 98–99)

1. The stratified squamous epithelium of the skin consists of several cell layers, the outermost of which contains keratinized or dead cells. Hair follicles are also present.

   Both types of epithelia are protective, but the skin epithelium also protects against water loss to the external environment, UV damage, and chemical damage in addition to protecting against mechanical damage and bacterial invasion.

2. The thickness of the skin can be attributed to the presence of a fifth epithelial layer, the stratum lucidum, and a thicker stratum corneum and dermis. Thick skin lacks hair follicles, arrector pili muscles, and sebaceous glands that are present on thin skin of the scalp.

Activity 4: Differentiating Sebaceous and Sweat Glands Microscopically (p. 100)

Eccrine sweat glands have long, straight, or undulating ducts with twisted coils at their base. In contrast, sebaceous glands have short ducts leading from a fan-shaped base. Sebaceous glands are usually associated with hair follicles.

Activity 5: Plotting the Distribution of Sweat Glands (pp. 100–101)

6. In most students, the palm has a greater density of sweat glands when compared to the forearm.

Activity 6: Taking and Identifying Inked Fingerprints (pp. 101–102)

7. Sometimes it was easy to classify the prints; at other times it was difficult.

   This has to do with the clarity of the prints taken and the fact that more information on fingerprints is necessary to make accurate identifications.

   The same individual would probably affect the fingerprinting process in the same way each time.

NAME _____

LAB TIME/DATE _____

The Integumentary System

Basic Structure of the Skin

1. Complete the following statements by writing the appropriate word or phrase on the correspondingly numbered blank:

The two basic tissues of which the skin is composed are dense irregular connective tissue, which makes up the dermis, and _1_, which forms the epidermis. The tough water-repellent protein found in the epidermal cells is called _2_. The pigments melanin and _3_ contribute to skin color. A localized concentration of melanin is referred to as a(n) _4_.

1. _stratified squamous epithelium_

2. _keratin_

3. _carotene_

4. _freckle_

2. Four protective functions of the skin are

a. _Prevents desiccation_

b. _Prevents bacterial invasion_

c. _Protects against thermal damage_

d. _Protects against UV radiation_

3. Using the key choices, choose all responses that apply to the following descriptions. Some terms are used more than once.

Key: a. stratum basale   d. stratum lucidum   g. reticular layer
b. stratum corneum   e. stratum spinosum   h. epidermis as a whole
c. stratum granulosum   f. papillary layer   i. dermis as a whole

d; stratum lucidum   1. layer of translucent cells in thick skin containing dead keratinocytes

b; stratum corneum, _d; stratum lucidum_   2. two layers containing dead cells

f; papillary layer   3. dermal layer responsible for fingerprints

i; dermis (or f, g)   4. vascular region of the skin (as a whole)

h; epidermis   5. major skin area as a whole that produces derivatives (nails and hair)

a; stratum basale   6. epidermal layer exhibiting the most rapid cell division

b; stratum corneum   7. layer including scalelike dead cells, full of keratin, that constantly slough off

e; stratum spinosum   8. layer filled with intermediate filaments

i; dermis (or g)   9. major skin area as a whole that has abundant elastic and collagenic fibers

a; stratum basale   10. location of melanocytes and tactile (Merkel) cells

e; stratum spinosum   11. area where weblike pre-keratin filaments first appear

f; papillary layer   12. layer of areolar connective tissue

4. Label the skin structures and areas indicated in the accompanying diagram of thin skin. Then, complete the statements that follow.

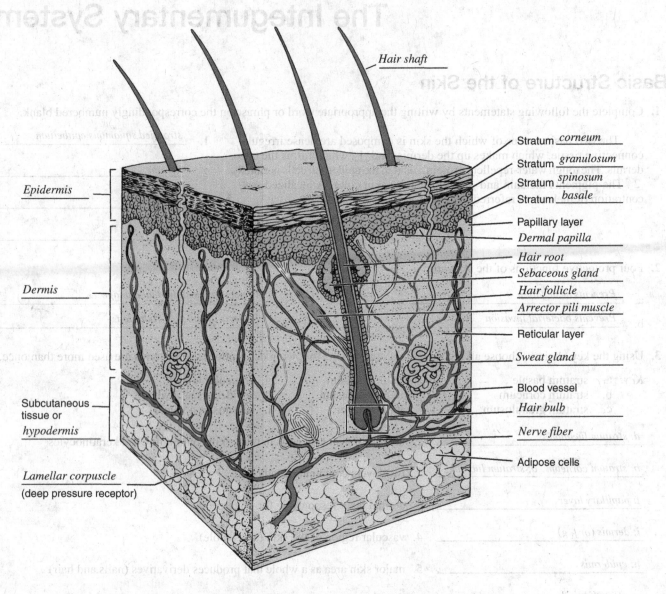

Hair shaft

Stratum _corneum_
Stratum _granulosum_
Stratum _spinosum_
Stratum _basale_
Papillary layer
Dermal papilla
Hair root
Sebaceous gland
Hair follicle
Arrector pili muscle
Reticular layer
Sweat gland
Blood vessel
Hair bulb
Nerve fiber
Adipose cells

Epidermis

Dermis

Subcutaneous tissue or hypodermis

Lamellar corpuscle
(deep pressure receptor)

a. _Lamellar_ _____ granules contain glycolipids that prevent water loss from the skin.

b. Fibers in the dermis are produced by _fibroblasts_ _____.

c. Glands that respond to rising androgen levels are the _sebaceous (and apocrine sweat)_ glands.

d. Phagocytic cells that occupy the epidermis are called _dendritic or Langerhans cells_ _____.

e. A unique touch receptor formed from a stratum basale cell and a nerve fiber is a _tactile or Merkel disc_ _____.

f. What layer is present in thick skin but not in thin skin? _Stratum lucidum_ _____

g. What anchoring junctions hold the cells of the stratum spinosum tightly together? _Desmosomes_ _____

5. What substance is manufactured in the skin and plays a role in calcium absorption elsewhere in the body?

Vitamin D

6. List the sensory receptors found in the dermis of the skin. *Free nerve endings (for pain, temperature), tactile corpuscles*

(for touch in hairless skin), lamellar corpuscles (for pressure)

7. A nurse tells a doctor that a patient is cyanotic. Define cyanosis. *A blue cast to the skin*

What does its presence imply? *Inadequate oxygenation of the blood*

8. What is a bedsore (decubitus ulcer)? *Localized area of tissue necrosis and death*

Why does it occur? *Pressure areas (points of increased pressure over bony areas) restrict the blood supply to the area.*

Accessory Organs of the Skin

9. Match the key choices with the appropriate descriptions. Some terms are used more than once.

Key: a. arrector pili
       b. cutaneous receptors
       c. hair

d. hair follicle
e. nail
f. sebaceous glands

g. sweat gland—apocrine
h. sweat gland—eccrine

f; sebaceous gland _____ 1. produces an accumulation of oily material that is known as a blackhead

a; arrector pili _____ 2. tiny muscles, attached to hair follicles, that pull the hair upright during fright or cold

h; sweat gland—eccrine _____ 3. sweat gland with a role in temperature control

d; hair follicle _____ 4. sheath formed of both epithelial and connective tissues

g; sweat gland—apocrine _____ 5. less numerous type of sweat-producing gland; found mainly in the pubic and axillary regions

c; hair , *d; hair follicle* , *f; sebaceous gland* _____ 6. found everywhere on the body except the palms of hands and soles of feet (three responses from key)

c; hair, *e; nail* _____ 7. primarily dead/keratinized cells (two responses from key)

b; cutaneous receptors _____ 8. specialized nerve endings that respond to temperature, touch, etc.

f; sebaceous gland _____ 9. secretes a lubricant for hair and skin

e; nail _____ 10. "sports" a lunule and a cuticle

10. Describe two integumentary system mechanisms that help regulate body temperature. *(1) When capillary blood flow to*

the skin is enhanced (by nervous system controls), heat radiates from the skin surface; restriction of blood flow conserves body heat.

(2) Activity of sweat glands (i.e., when perspiration evaporates from the skin surface, heat is lost).

11. Several structures or skin regions are listed below. Identify each by matching its letter with the appropriate area on the figure.

a. adipose cells

b. dermis

c. epidermis

d. hair follicle

e. hair shaft

f. sloughing stratum corneum cells

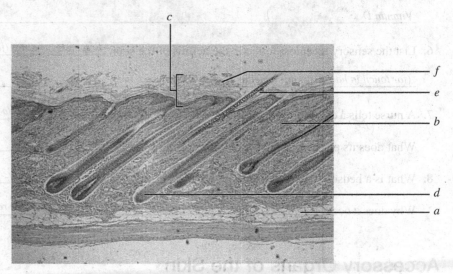

Plotting the Distribution of Sweat Glands

12. With what substance in the bond paper does the iodine painted on the skin react? *The starch*

13. Based on class data, which skin area—the forearm or palm of hand—has more sweat glands? *Palm*

Was this an expected result? *Yes* Explain. *For most people, hands sweat more than the forearm.*

Which other body areas would, if tested, prove to have a high density of sweat glands? *Face, axillae*

14. What organ system controls the activity of the eccrine sweat glands? *Nervous system (sympathetic division)*

Dermography: Fingerprinting

15. Why can fingerprints be used to identify individuals?

Everyone's fingerprints are genetically distinct.

16. Name the three common fingerprint patterns.

loops, *arches*, and *whorls*

Overview of the Skeleton: Classification and Structure of Bones and Cartilages

Time Allotment: 45 minutes.

Multimedia Resources: See Appendix B for Guide to Multimedia Resource

Distributors. See Exercise 6 for histology listings.

Practice Anatomy Lab™ 3.0 (PAL) (DVD, website)

Skeletal System: The Infrastructure (FHS: 25 minutes, DVD, 3-year streaming webcast)

Solutions:

Hydrochloric Acid (HCl), 10%

Add 36 milliliters of concentrated HCl to 200 milliliters of distilled water. Add water to a final volume of 360 milliliters.

Laboratory Materials

Ordering information is based on a lab size of 24 students, working in groups of 4. A list of supply house addresses appears in Appendix A.

Articulated skeleton
Numbered disarticulated bones
  showing four types
24 compound microscopes, lens paper,
  lens cleaning solution
Long bone sawed longitudinally

Long bone soaked in 10% HCl or
  vinegar
Long bone baked at 250°F
24 slides of ground bone (cross
  section)
Disposable gloves

3-D models of microscopic structure
  of compact bone
24 slides of developing long bone
  undergoing endochondral
  ossification

Advance Preparation

1. If you have a local source, arrange to have a long bone sawed longitudinally. Keep refrigerated or frozen until used. Preserved, sawed long bones can be used instead. Provide disposable gloves at the demonstration area.

2. Bake some long bones (chicken or turkey bones work well) at 250°F for 2 hours or until they are brittle and snap or crumble easily. Prepare these the day before lab observations are to take place.

3. Soak some long bones in *10% hydrochloric acid* or vinegar until flexible. Overnight soaking is usually sufficient for the hydrochloric acid; vinegar will take longer. Prepare well in advance.

4. Prepare numbered samples of long, short, flat, and irregular bones. These can be set out at a station in the lab where students can work on identification.

5. Put out prepared slides of ground bone (cross section) and developing long bone undergoing endochondral ossification. Also set out lens paper and lens cleaning solution, and have compound microscopes available.

6. Set out models of the microscopic structure of bone.

Comments and Pitfalls

1. Students may initially have some trouble classifying bones by shape; other than that, this lab should cause no problems.
2. Emphasize that all long bones have a long axis, but some long bones are much shorter than others! Long bones include most of the bones of the upper and lower limbs (humerus, radius, ulna, femur, tibia, fibula, metacarpals, metatarsals, phalanges). Short bones include the carpals and the tarsals. Flat bones are thin and include the bones of the roof of the cranial cavity, sternum, scapula, and ribs. Irregular bones include some skull bones, the vertebrae, and possibly bones of the pelvic girdle. Bones included in each of these categories vary from author to author.

Answers to Pre-Lab Quiz (p. 107)

1. b, production of melanin
2. axial
3. b, fibrocartilage
4. Compact
5. a, flat
6. c, long
7. diaphysis
8. a, osteon
9. false
10. false

Answers to Activity Questions

Activity 2: Examining the Effects of Heat and Hydrochloric Acid on Bones (p. 113)

The heated bone is very brittle and responds to gentle pressure by breaking.

The acid-treated bone is very flexible.

The acid appears to remove the calcium salts from the bone.

Heating dries out the organic matrix.

The acid-treated bone most closely resembles the bones of a child with rickets.

Overview of the Skeleton: Classification and Structure of Bones and Cartilages

Cartilages of the Skeleton

1. Using the key choices, identify each type of cartilage described (in terms of its body location or function) below.

   Key: a. elastic   b. fibrocartilage   c. hyaline

a; elastic	1. supports the external ear	
b; fibrocartilage	2. between the vertebrae	
c; hyaline	3. forms the walls of the voice box (larynx)	
a; elastic	4. the epiglottis	
c; hyaline	5. articular cartilages	

b; fibrocartilage	6. meniscus in a knee joint
c; hyaline	7. connects the ribs to the sternum
b; fibrocartilage	8. most effective at resisting compression
a; elastic	9. most springy and flexible
c; hyaline	10. most abundant

Classification of Bones

2. The four major anatomical classifications of bones are long, short, flat, and irregular. Which category has the least amount of spongy bone relative to its total volume? *Long* _____

3. Place the name of each labeled bone in Figure 8.1, p. 108, into the appropriate column of the chart here.

Long	Short	Flat	Irregular
humerus, radius, ulna, phalanges, metacarpals, femur, tibia, metatarsals, fibula	*carpals, tarsals, patella, calcaneus*	*skull or cranium, sternum, scapula, ribs, clavicle*	*vertebra, ilium, ischium, pubis, bones of pelvic girdle*

Bone Markings

4. Match the terms in column B with the appropriate description in column A.

Column A		Column B
m; spine	1. sharp, slender process*	a. condyle
o; tubercle	2. small rounded projection*	b. crest
b; crest	3. narrow ridge of bone*	c. epicondyle
p; tuberosity	4. large rounded projection*	d. facet
h; head	5. structure supported on neck†	e. fissure
k; ramus	6. armlike projection†	f. foramen
a; condyle	7. rounded, articular projection†	g. fossa
e; fissure	8. narrow opening‡	h. head
i; meatus	9. canal-like structure	i. meatus
f; foramen	10. round or oval opening through a bone‡	j. process
g; fossa	11. shallow depression	k. ramus
l; sinus	12. air-filled cavityy	l. sinus
n; trochanter	13. large, irregularly shaped projection*	m. spine
c; epicondyle	14. raised area on or above a condyle*	n. trochanter
j; process	15. projection or prominence	o. tubercle
d; facet	16. smooth, nearly flat articular surface†	p. tuberosity

*a site of muscle and ligament attachment
†takes part in joint formation
‡a passageway for nerves or blood vessels

Gross Anatomy of the Typical Long Bone

5. Match the key terms with the descriptions.

Key:
a. articular cartilage
b. diaphysis
c. endosteum
d. epiphyseal line
e. epiphysis
f. medullary cavity
g. periosteum
h. red marrow

_e_ 1. end portion of long bone

_a_ 2. helps reduce friction at joints

_h_ 3. site of blood cell formation

_c_, _g_ 4. major submembranous sites of osteogenic cells (two responses from key)

_b_ 5. scientific term for bone shaft

_f_ 6. contains yellow marrow in adult bones

_d_ 7. growth plate remnant

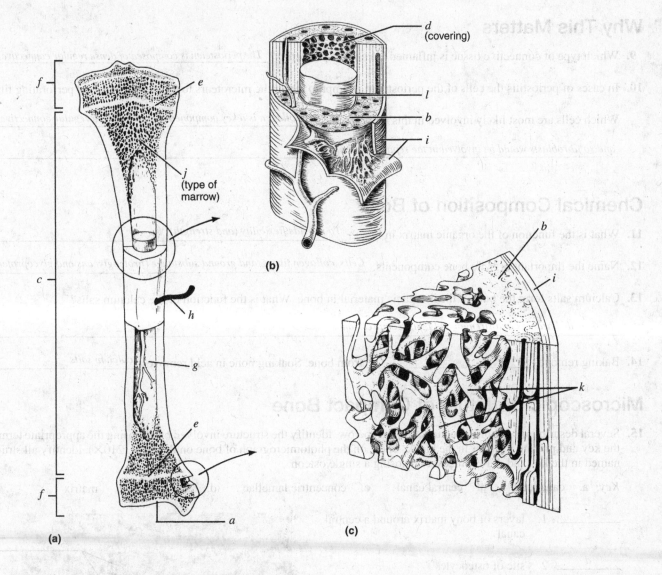

d
(covering)

l

b

i

f

e

j
(type of
marrow)

c

h

g

e

f

a

(a)

(b)

b

i

k

(c)

6. Use the key terms to identify the structures marked by leader lines and braces in the diagrams. Some terms are used more than once.

a. articular cartilage   e. epiphyseal line   i. periosteum
b. compact bone   f. epiphysis   j. red marrow
c. diaphysis   g. medullary cavity   k. trabeculae of spongy bone
d. endosteum   h. nutrient artery   l. yellow marrow

7. What differences between compact and spongy bone can be seen with the unaided eye? _Compact bone appears homogeneous;_

spongy bone has obvious spaces.

8. What is the function of the periosteum? _Protects the bone and is the structure from which blood vessels and nerves enter bone;_

provides an attachment site for tendons and ligaments and supplies osteoblasts for new bone

Why This Matters

9. Which type of connective tissue is inflamed in cases of periostitis? _The periosteum is composed of dense regular connective tissue._

10. In cases of periostitis the cells of the periosteum attempt to repair the microtears to the periosteum and perforating fibers.

    Which cells are most likely involved in this repair process? _Collagen is a key component found in dense regular connective tissue_

    and so fibroblasts would be involved in the repair process.

Chemical Composition of Bone

11. What is the function of the organic matrix in bone? _To provide flexibility (and strength)_

12. Name the important organic bone components. _Cells, collagen fibers, and ground substance (proteoglycans and glycoproteins)_

13. Calcium salts form the bulk of the inorganic material in bone. What is the function of the calcium salts?

    To provide hardness and strength and resist compression

14. Baking removes _water_ from bone. Soaking bone in acid removes _calcium salts_ .

Microscopic Structure of Compact Bone

15. Several descriptions of bone structure are given below. Identify the structure involved by choosing the appropriate term from the key and placing its letter in the blank. Then, on the photomicrograph of bone on the right (210×), identify all structures named in the key and draw a bracket enclosing a single osteon.

    Key: a. canaliculi   b. central canal   c. concentric lamellae   d. lacunae   e. matrix

    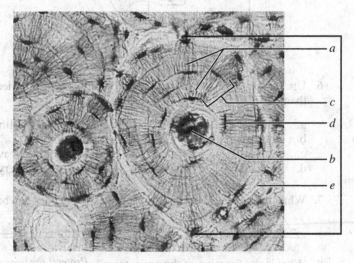

    ____c____ 1. layers of bony matrix around a central canal

    ____d____ 2. site of osteocytes

    ____b____ 3. longitudinal canal carrying blood vessels, lymphatics, and nerves

    ____a____ 4. tiny canals connecting osteocytes of an osteon

    ____e____ 5. inorganic salts deposited in organic ground substance

Ossification: Bone Formation and Growth in Length

16. Compare and contrast events occurring on the epiphyseal and diaphyseal faces of the epiphyseal plate.

    Epiphyseal face: _Cartilage cells are resting and relatively inactive. Right below this, the cartilage cells are rapidly reproducing._

    Diaphyseal face: _Chondrocytes are dying, the matrix is calcifying, and the cartilage is being replaced by bone._

The Axial Skeleton

Time Allotment: 2¹/₂ hours.

Multimedia Resources: See Appendix B for Guide to Multimedia Resource Distributors.

Interactive Functional Anatomy, 2nd Edition (ET: DVD)
Practice Anatomy Lab™ 3.0 (PAL) (BC: CD-ROM, website)

Laboratory Materials

Ordering information is based on a lab size of 24 students, working in groups of 4. A list of supply house addresses appears in Appendix A.

Articulated vertebral column	X rays of individuals with kyphosis,	Isolated cervical, thoracic, and lumbar
Beauchene skull	scoliosis, and lordosis	vertebrae, sacrum, and coccyx
6–12 intact skulls	(if available)	6–12 disarticulated skeletons
2 articulated skeletons (one male, one	X-ray viewing box	Isolated fetal skull
female)	Removable intervertebral discs	

Advance Preparation

1. Set out one intact skull per group. A group of 3–4 students is ideal.
2. Set out labeled samples of disarticulated vertebrae, an articulated spinal column, a disarticulated skull, and a Beauchene skull.
3. Have articulated skeletons available. There should be a minimum of two, one male and one female.
4. Display X rays of individuals with scoliosis, kyphosis, and lordosis, if available. Students are often willing to bring in X rays for the class to use if none are available.
5. Set out blunt probes, pipe cleaners, or unsharpened pencils with erasers for the students to use while studying the bones. Caution them against marking the bones with pencils or markers.
6. Set out an isolated fetal skull in a demonstration area, unless enough are available for each group. If you don't already know it, figure out the approximate age of the fetus, since someone is sure to ask. Developmental charts are usually available in developmental anatomy texts.

Comments and Pitfalls

1. Point out sutures; remind students to look for sutures surrounding each bone.
2. Suggest that students identify all bones of the skull before identifying bone features.
3. Students may have some trouble with the numerous foramina of the skull. You may wish to have them locate all of the foramina at this time, but hold them responsible for identifying a smaller number.
4. The ethmoid bone may cause some problems, especially if the skulls are old and the conchae have begun to crumble. The disarticulated and Beauchene skulls will come in handy here.

5. "Saddle block" anesthesia is similar to epidural anesthesia.

6. There is the occasional student who asks whether males have one less rib than females. A trip to the articulated skeletons provides the answer: no.

Answers to Pre-Lab Quiz (p. 121)

1. a, thoracic cage
2. a, cranium
3. 14
4. mandible
5. body

6. a, cervical
7. d, thoracic
8. c, sternum
9. false
10. d, all of the above

Answers to Group Challenge (p. 131)

Some possible answers to the questions are listed below. Student answers may vary.

1. Which is the "odd bone"?	Why is it the odd one out?
Zygomatic bone (Vomer) Maxilla Nasal bone	*The vomer is a single bone. It cannot be palpated.*
2. Which is the "odd bone"?	Why is it the odd one out?
Parietal bone (Sphenoid bone) Frontal bone Occipital bone	*The sphenoid bone is not a flat bone, nor is it curved.*
3. Which is the "odd bone"?	Why is it the odd one out?
Lacrimal bone (Nasal bone) Zygomatic bone Maxilla	*The nasal bone is not a part of the bony orbit.*

Answers to Activity Questions

Activity 3: Examining Spinal Curvatures (p. 134)

2. When the fibrous disc is properly positioned, the spinal cord and peripheral nerves are not impaired in any way.

   If the disc is removed, the intervertebral foramina are reduced in size, and might pinch the nerves exiting at that level.

   Slipped discs often put pressure on spinal nerves, causing pain and/or loss of feeling.

Activity 6: Examining a Fetal Skull (p. 140)

1. Yes, the fetal and adult skulls have the same bones, although the fetal frontal bone is bipartite as opposed to the single frontal bone seen in the adult skull.

   The fetal face is foreshortened and overshadowed by the cranium; the maxillae and mandible are very tiny.

   In the adult skull the cranium is proportionately smaller and the facial skeleton proportionately larger.

NAME _____

LAB TIME/DATE _____

The Axial Skeleton

The Skull

1. First, match the bone names in column B with the descriptions in column A (the items in column B may be used more than once). Then, circle the bones in column B that are cranial bones.

Column A

b; frontal	1.	forehead bone
o; zygomatic	2.	cheekbone
f; mandible	3.	lower jaw
h; nasal	4.	bridge of nose
j; palatine	5.	posterior bones of the hard palate
k; parietal	6.	much of the lateral and superior cranium
i; occipital	7.	most posterior part of cranium
l; sphenoid	8.	single, irregular, bat-shaped bone forming part of the cranial base
e; lacrimal	9.	tiny bones bearing tear ducts
g; maxilla	10.	anterior part of hard palate
a; ethmoid	11.	superior and middle nasal conchae form from its projections
m; temporal	12.	site of mastoid process
l; sphenoid	13.	site of sella turcica
a; ethmoid	14.	site of cribriform plate
f; mandible	15.	site of mental foramen
m; temporal	16.	site of styloid process
a; ethmoid , b; frontal , g; maxilla , l; sphenoid	17.	four bones containing paranasal sinuses
i; occipital	18.	condyles here articulate with the atlas
i; occipital	19.	foramen magnum contained here
c; hyoid	20.	small U-shaped bone in neck, where many tongue muscles attach
m; temporal	21.	organ of hearing found here
n; vomer , a; ethmoid	22.	two bones that form the nasal septum
a; ethmoid	23.	bears an upward protrusion, the "rooster's comb," or crista galli
f; mandible , g; maxilla	24.	contain sockets bearing teeth
d; inferior nasal concha	25.	forms the most inferior turbinate

Column B

a. ethmoid

b. frontal

c. hyoid

d. inferior nasal concha

e. lacrimal

f. mandible

g. maxilla

h. nasal

i. occipital

j. palatine

k. parietal

l. sphenoid

m. temporal

n. vomer

o. zygomatic

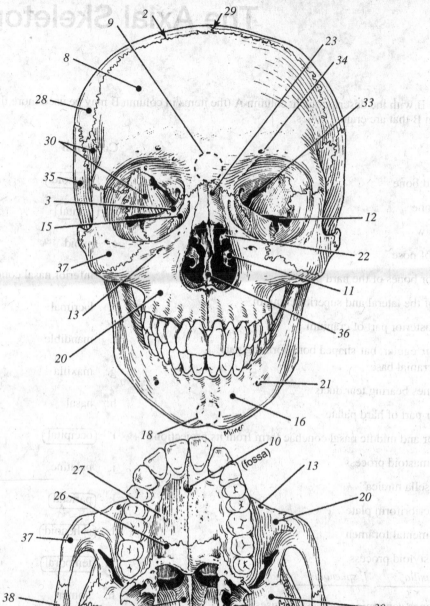

2. Using choices from the numbered key to the right, identify all bones (——→), sutures (——➤), and bone markings (___) provided with various leader lines in the two diagrams below. Some responses from the key will be used more than once.

Key:

1. carotid canal
2. coronal suture
3. ethmoid bone
4. external occipital protuberance
5. foramen lacerum
6. foramen magnum
7. foramen ovale
8. frontal bone
9. glabella
10. incisive fossa
11. inferior nasal concha
12. inferior orbital fissure
13. infraorbital foramen
14. jugular foramen
15. lacrimal bone
16. mandible
17. mandibular fossa
18. mandibular symphysis
19. mastoid process
20. maxilla
21. mental foramen
22. middle nasal concha of ethmoid
23. nasal bone
24. occipital bone
25. occipital condyle
26. palatine bone
27. palatine process of maxilla
28. parietal bone
29. sagittal suture
30. sphenoid bone
31. styloid process
32. stylomastoid foramen
33. superior orbital fissure
34. supraorbital foramen
35. temporal bone
36. vomer
37. zygomatic bone
38. zygomatic process of temporal bone

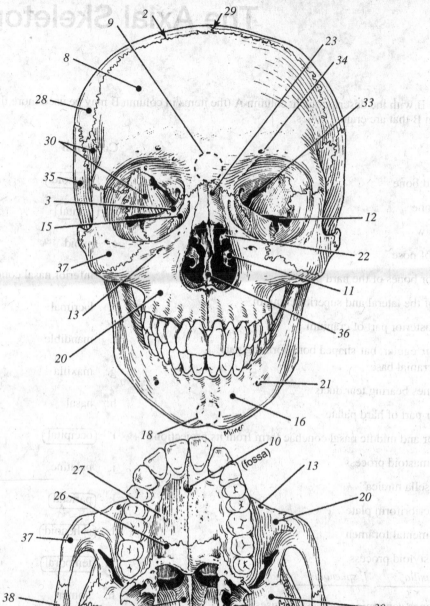

3. Define *suture*. _Fibrous joint between skull bones_

4. With one exception, the skull bones are joined by sutures. Name the exception. _Joint(s) between the mandible and_

   temporal bones

5. What bones are connected by the lambdoid suture?

   Occipital and parietal

   What bones are connected by the squamous suture?

   Temporal and parietal

6. Name the eight bones of the cranium. (Remember to include left and right.)

   frontal _occipital_ _right parietal_ _left parietal_

   sphenoid _ethmoid_ _right temporal_ _left temporal_

7. Give two possible functions of the sinuses. _(1) Lighten the skull, (2) resonance chambers for speech_

8. What is the orbit? _Bony socket for the eye_

   What bones contribute to the formation of the orbit? _Ethmoid, lacrimal, frontal, sphenoid, zygomatic, maxillary, palatine_

9. Why can the sphenoid bone be called the keystone of the cranium? _It articulates with all of the other cranial bones._

The Vertebral Column

10. The distinguishing characteristics of the vertebrae composing the vertebral column are noted below. Correctly identify each described structure by choosing a response from the key.

    Key: a. atlas   d. coccyx   f. sacrum
         b. axis   e. lumbar vertebra g. thoracic vertebra
         c. cervical vertebra—typical

    c; cervical 1. vertebra type containing foramina in the transverse processes, through which the vertebral arteries ascend to reach the brain

    b; axis 2. dens here provides a pivot for rotation of the first cervical vertebra (C_1)

    g; thoracic 3. transverse processes faceted for articulation with ribs; spinous process pointing sharply downward

    f; sacrum 4. composite bone; articulates with the hip bone laterally

    e; lumbar 5. massive vertebra; weight-sustaining

    d; coccyx 6. "tail bone"; vestigial fused vertebrae

    a; atlas 7. supports the head; allows a rocking motion in conjunction with the occipital condyles

11. Using the key, correctly identify the vertebral parts/areas described below. (More than one choice may apply in some cases.) Also use the key letters to correctly identify the vertebral areas in the diagram.

Key: a. body   d. pedicle   g. transverse process
      b. intervertebral foramina   e. spinous process   h. vertebral arch
      c. lamina   f. superior articular facet   i. vertebral foramen

_____*i*_____ 1. cavity enclosing the nerve cord

_____*a*_____ 2. weight-bearing portion of the vertebra

_____*e*___, __*g*___ 3. provide levers against which muscles pull

_____*a*___, __*g*___ 4. provide an articulation point for the ribs

_____*b*_____ 5. openings providing for exit of spinal nerves

_____*a*___, __*h*___ 6. structures that form an enclosure for the spinal cord

_____*c*_, _*d*_, _*e*_ 7. structures that form the vertebral arch

12. Describe how a spinal nerve exits from the vertebral column. *Via the intervertebral foramina found between the pedicles of*

adjacent vertebrae

13. Name two factors/structures that permit flexibility of the vertebral column.

Intervertebral discs   and *curvatures*

14. What kind of tissue makes up the intervertebral discs? *Fibrocartilage*

15. What is a herniated disc? *A ruptured disc in which a portion of the disc protrudes outward*

What problems might it cause? *It might compress a nerve, leading to pain and possibly paralysis.*

16. Which two spinal curvatures are obvious at birth? *Thoracic* and *sacral*

Under what conditions do the secondary curvatures develop? *The cervical curvature develops when the baby begins to raise its*

head independently. The lumbar curvature forms when the baby begins to walk (assumes upright posture).

17. On this illustration of an articulated vertebral column, identify each curvature indicated and label it as a primary or a secondary curvature. Also identify the structures provided with leader lines, using the letters of the terms listed in the key below.

Key: a.   atlas

        b.   axis

        c.   intervertebral disc

        d.   sacrum

        e.   two thoracic vertebrae

        f.   two lumbar vertebrae

        g.   vertebra prominens

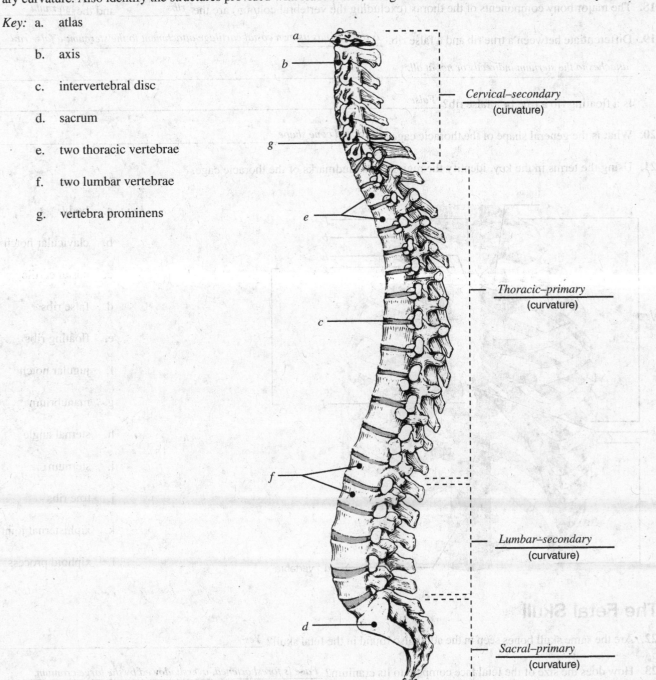

Cervical–secondary
(curvature)

Thoracic–primary
(curvature)

Lumbar–secondary
(curvature)

Sacral–primary
(curvature)

The Thoracic Cage

18. The major bony components of the thorax (excluding the vertebral column) are the _ribs_ and the _sternum_.

19. Differentiate between a true rib and a false rib. _A true rib has its own costal cartilage attachment to the sternum; a false rib_

    attaches to the sternum indirectly or not at all.

    Is a floating rib a true or a false rib? _False_

20. What is the general shape of the thoracic cage? _Inverted cone shape_

21. Using the terms in the key, identify the regions and landmarks of the thoracic cage.

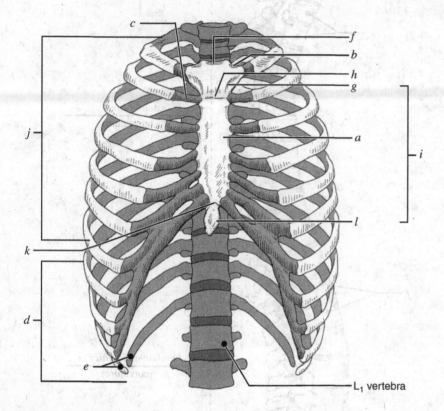

L₁ vertebra

Key:
a. body
b. clavicular notch
c. costal cartilage
d. false ribs
e. floating ribs
f. jugular notch
g. manubrium
h. sternal angle
i. sternum
j. true ribs
k. xiphisternal joint
l. xiphoid process

The Fetal Skull

22. Are the same skull bones seen in the adult also found in the fetal skull? _Yes_

23. How does the size of the fetal face compare to its cranium? _Face is foreshortened, overshadowed by the large cranium._

    Maxillae and mandible are very tiny

    How does this compare to the adult skull? _In the adult the cranium is proportionately smaller and the facial bones are_

    proportionately larger and more prominent.

24. What are the outward conical projections on some of the fetal cranial bones? _These are ossification (growth) centers._

25. What is a fontanelle? _A fibrous membrane connecting fetal skull bones_

What is its fate? _Progressively ossified; replaced by a suture_

What is the function of the fontanelles in the fetal skull? _They allow the fetal skull to be compressed slightly during birth_

passage; allow for fetal (and infant) brain growth.

26. Using the terms listed, identify each of the fontanelles shown on the fetal skull below.

Key:

a. anterior fontanelle

b. mastoid fontanelle

c. posterior fontanelle

d. sphenoidal fontanelle

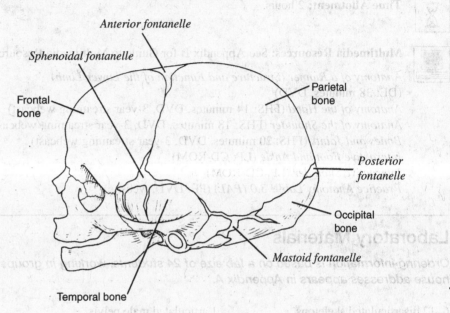

The Appendicular Skeleton

 Time Allotment: 2 hours.

 Multimedia Resources: See Appendix B for Guide to Multimedia Resource Distributors.

Anatomy of a Runner (Structure and Function of the Lower Limb)
(DE: 38 minutes, DVD)
Anatomy of the Hand (FHS: 14 minutes, DVD, 3-year streaming webcast)
Anatomy of the Shoulder (FHS: 18 minutes, DVD, 3-year streaming webcast)
Bones and Joints (FHS: 20 minutes, DVD, 3-year streaming webcast)
Interactive Foot and Ankle (LP: CD-ROM)
Interactive Shoulder (LP: CD-ROM)
Practice Anatomy Lab™ 3.0 (PAL) (PE: DVD, website)

Laboratory Materials

Ordering information is based on a lab size of 24 students, working in groups of 4. A list of supply house addresses appears in Appendix A.

6–12 disarticulated skeletons
2 articulated skeletons (one male, one female)

1 articulated male pelvis
1 articulated female pelvis

X rays of bones of the appendicular skeleton

Advance Preparation

1. Have articulated skeletons (male and female) available.
2. Set out disarticulated skeletons. One per group of 3–4 students is ideal.
3. Set out male and female articulated pelves in a demonstration area.
4. Set out blunt probes, pipe cleaners, or unsharpened pencils with erasers for use during bone identification.
5. Set out X rays of bones of the appendicular skeleton.

Comments and Pitfalls

1. Students may have trouble distinguishing between right and left samples of bones. Remind them to review the bone markings before checking the disarticulated skeleton.
2. Stress the importance of bony landmarks for muscle location and identification.

Answers to Pre-Lab Quiz (p. 149)

1. appendicular
2. pectoral
3. scapulae
4. b, humerus
5. metacarpals
6. Female
7. a, femur
8. patella
9. true
10. 26

NAME _____

LAB TIME/DATE _____

The Appendicular Skeleton

Bones of the Pectoral Girdle and Upper Limb

1. Match the bone names or markings in column B with the descriptions in column A. The items in column B may be used more than once.

	Column A		Column B
g; deltoid tuberosity	1. raised area on lateral surface of humerus to which deltoid muscle attaches	a.	acromion
i; humerus	2. arm bone	b.	capitulum
d; clavicle, *p; scapula*	3. bones of the shoulder girdle	c.	carpals
o; radius, *r; ulna*	4. forearm bones	d.	clavicle
a; acromion	5. scapular feature to which the clavicle connects	e.	coracoid process
p; scapula	6. shoulder girdle bone that does not articulate with the axial skeleton	f.	coronoid fossa
d; clavicle	7. shoulder girdle bone that acts as a brace and articulates with the axial skeleton	g.	deltoid tuberosity
h; glenoid cavity	8. depression in the scapula that articulates with the humerus	h.	glenoid cavity
		i.	humerus
e; coracoid process	9. process above the glenoid cavity that permits muscle attachment	j.	medial epicondyle
l; olecranon fossa	10. posterior depression on the distal humerus	k.	metacarpals
q; trochlea	11. distal condyle of the humerus that articulates with the ulna	l.	olecranon fossa
r; ulna	12. medial bone of forearm in anatomical position	m.	phalanges
b; capitulum	13. rounded knob on the humerus; adjoins the radius	n.	radial notch
f; coronoid fossa	14. anterior depression, superior to the trochlea, that receives part of the ulna when the forearm is flexed	o.	radius
n; radial notch	15. surface on the ulna that articulates with the head of the radius	p.	scapula
c; carpals	16. wrist bones	q.	trochlea
m; phalanges	17. finger bones	r.	ulna
k; metacarpals	18. heads of these bones form the knuckles		
j; medial epicondyle	19. small bump often called the "funny bone"		

2. How is the arm held clear of the top of the thoracic cage?

The clavicle acts as a strut to hold the glenoid cavity of the scapula (therefore the arm) laterally away from the narrowest dimension of

the rib cage.

3. What is the total number of phalanges in the hand? _14_

4. What is the total number of carpals in the wrist? _8_

Name the carpals (medial to lateral) in the proximal row. _Pisiform, triquetrum, lunate, scaphoid_

In the distal row, they are (medial to lateral) _hamate, capitate, trapezoid, trapezium_

5. Using items from the list at the right, identify the anatomical landmarks and regions of the scapula.

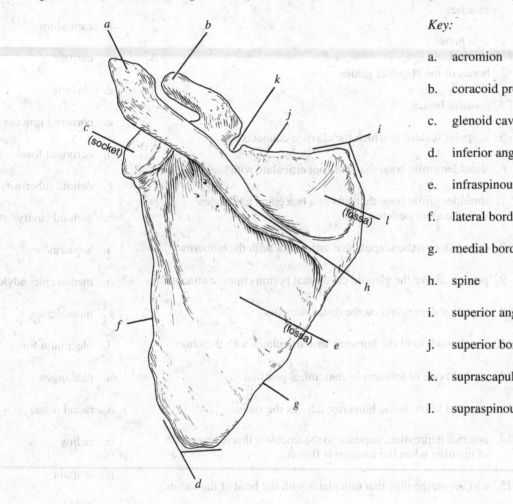

Key:

a. acromion

b. coracoid process

c. glenoid cavity

d. inferior angle

e. infraspinous fossa

f. lateral border

g. medial border

h. spine

i. superior angle

j. superior border

k. suprascapular notch

l. supraspinous fossa

6. Match the terms in the key with the appropriate leader lines on the drawings of the humerus and the radius and ulna. Also decide whether the bones shown are right or left bones and whether the view shown is an anterior or a posterior view.

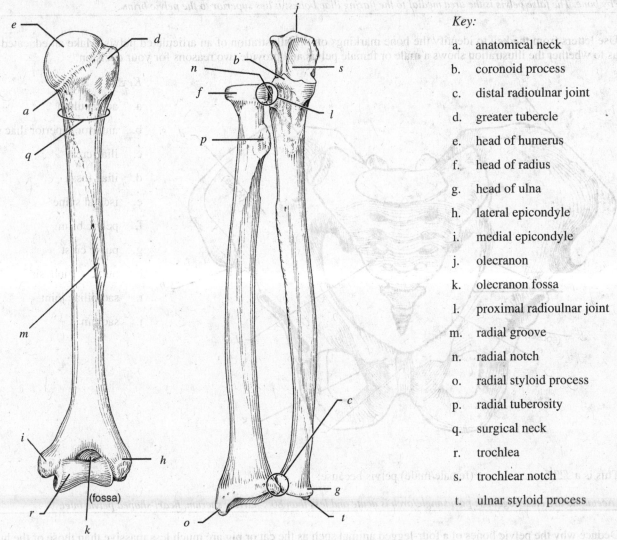

Key:

a. anatomical neck

b. coronoid process

c. distal radioulnar joint

d. greater tubercle

e. head of humerus

f. head of radius

g. head of ulna

h. lateral epicondyle

i. medial epicondyle

j. olecranon

k. olecranon fossa

l. proximal radioulnar joint

m. radial groove

n. radial notch

o. radial styloid process

p. radial tuberosity

q. surgical neck

r. trochlea

s. trochlear notch

t. ulnar styloid process

Circle the correct term for each pair in parentheses:

The humerus is a (right/left) bone in (an anterior/a posterior) view. The radius and ulna are (right/left) bones in (an anterior/a posterior) view.

Bones of the Pelvic Girdle and Lower Limb

7. Compare the pectoral and pelvic girdles by choosing appropriate descriptive terms from the key.

Key: a. flexibility most important   d. insecure axial and limb attachments
      b. massive   e. secure axial and limb attachments
      c. lightweight   f. weight-bearing most important

Pectoral: ___*a*___, ___*c*___, ___*d*___   Pelvic: ___*b*___, ___*e*___, ___*f*___

8. What organs are protected, at least in part, by the pelvic girdle? *Uterus (female), urinary bladder, small intestine, rectum*

9. Distinguish between the true pelvis and the false pelvis. *The true pelvis is the region inferior to the pelvic brim, which is encircled by bone. The false pelvis is the area medial to the flaring iliac bones; it lies superior to the pelvic brim.*

10. Use letters from the key to identify the bone markings on this illustration of an articulated pelvis. Make an educated guess as to whether the illustration shows a male or female pelvis and provide two reasons for your decision.

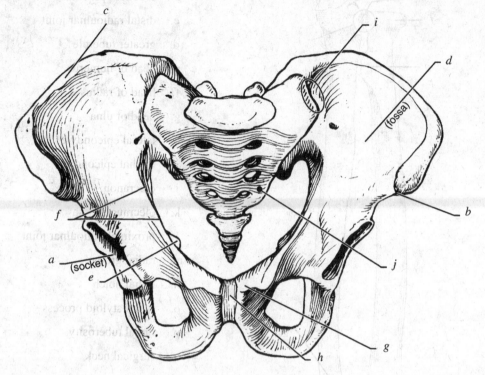

Key:

a. acetabulum
b. anterior superior iliac spine
c. iliac crest
d. iliac fossa
e. ischial spine
f. pelvic brim
g. pubic crest
h. pubic symphysis
i. sacroiliac joint
j. sacrum

This is a __male_____ (female/male) pelvis because:

Acetabula are close together; pubic angle/arch is acute and less than 80°; narrow sacrum, heart-shaped pelvic inlet.

11. Deduce why the pelvic bones of a four-legged animal such as the cat or pig are much less massive than those of the human. *The pelvic girdle does not have to carry the entire weight of the trunk in the quadruped animal.*

12. A person instinctively curls over his abdominal area in times of danger. Why? *Abdominal area organs receive the least protection from the skeletal system.*

13. For what anatomical reason do many women appear to be slightly knock-kneed? *The pelvis is broader and the acetabula and ilia are more laterally positioned. Thus, the femur runs downward to the knee more obliquely than in the male.*

How might this anatomical arrangement contribute to knee injuries in female athletes? *The more oblique angle in females causes greater forces on the anterior cruciate ligament (ACL) during knee rotation, and the smaller female intercondylar notch can pinch the ACL during twisting or hyperextended movements. Both events can cause a tear or rupture of the ACL.*

14. What structural changes result in *fallen* arches? *A weakening of the tendons and ligaments supporting the arches of the foot*

15. Match the bone names and markings in column B with the descriptions in column A. The items in column B may be used more than once.

Column A

i; ilium , k; ischium , s; pubis 1. fuse to form the hip bone

j; ischial tuberosity 2. rough projection that supports body weight when sitting

r; pubic symphysis 3. point where the hip bones join anteriorly

h; iliac crest 4. superiormost margin of the hip bone

a; acetabulum 5. deep socket in the hip bone that receives the head of the thigh bone

t; sacroiliac joint 6. joint between axial skeleton and pelvic girdle

c; femur 7. longest, strongest bone in body

d; fibula 8. thin lateral leg bone

g; greater sciatic notch 9. permits passage of the sciatic nerve

m; lesser sciatic notch 10. notch located inferior to the ischial spine

x; tibial tuberosity 11. point where the patellar ligament attaches

q; patella 12. kneecap

w; tibia 13. shinbone

n; medial malleolus 14. medial ankle projection

l; lateral malleolus 15. lateral ankle projection

b; calcaneus 16. largest tarsal bone

v; tarsals 17. ankle bones

o; metatarsals 18. bones forming the instep of the foot

p; obturator foramen 19. opening in hip bone formed by the pubic and ischial rami

e; gluteal tuberosity , _f; greater and lesser trochanters_

20. sites of muscle attachment on the proximal femur

u; talus 21. tarsal bone that "sits" on the calcaneus

w; tibia 22. weight-bearing bone of the leg

u; talus 23. tarsal bone that articulates with the tibia

Column B

a. acetabulum

b. calcaneus

c. femur

d. fibula

e. gluteal tuberosity

f. greater and lesser trochanters

g. greater sciatic notch

h. iliac crest

i. ilium

j. ischial tuberosity

k. ischium

l. lateral malleolus

m. lesser sciatic notch

n. medial malleolus

o. metatarsals

p. obturator foramen

q. patella

r. pubic symphysis

s. pubis

t. sacroiliac joint

u. talus

v. tarsals

w. tibia

x. tibial tuberosity

16. Match the terms in the key with the appropriate leader lines on the drawings of the femur and the tibia and fibula. Also decide if these bones are right or left bones and whether the view shown is an anterior or a posterior view. Some items may be used more than once.

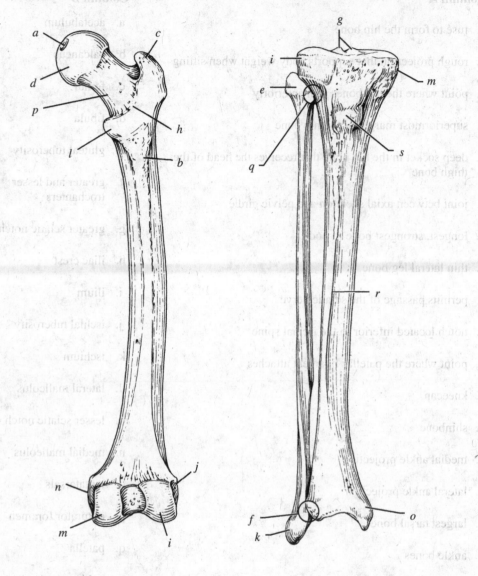

Key:

a. fovea capitis

b. gluteal tuberosity

c. greater trochanter

d. head of femur

e. head of fibula

f. inferior tibiofibular joint

g. intercondylar eminence

h. intertrochanteric crest

i. lateral condyle

j. lateral epicondyle

k. lateral malleolus

l. lesser trochanter

m. medial condyle

n. medial epicondyle

o. medial malleolus

p. neck of femur

q. proximal tibiofibular joint

r. tibial anterior border

s. tibial tuberosity

Circle the correct term for each pair in parentheses:

The femur is a (right/left) bone in (an anterior/a posterior) view. The tibia and fibula are (right/left) bones in (an anterior/a posterior) view.

Summary of Skeleton

17. Identify all indicated bones (or groups of bones) in the diagram of the articulated skeleton (p. 72).

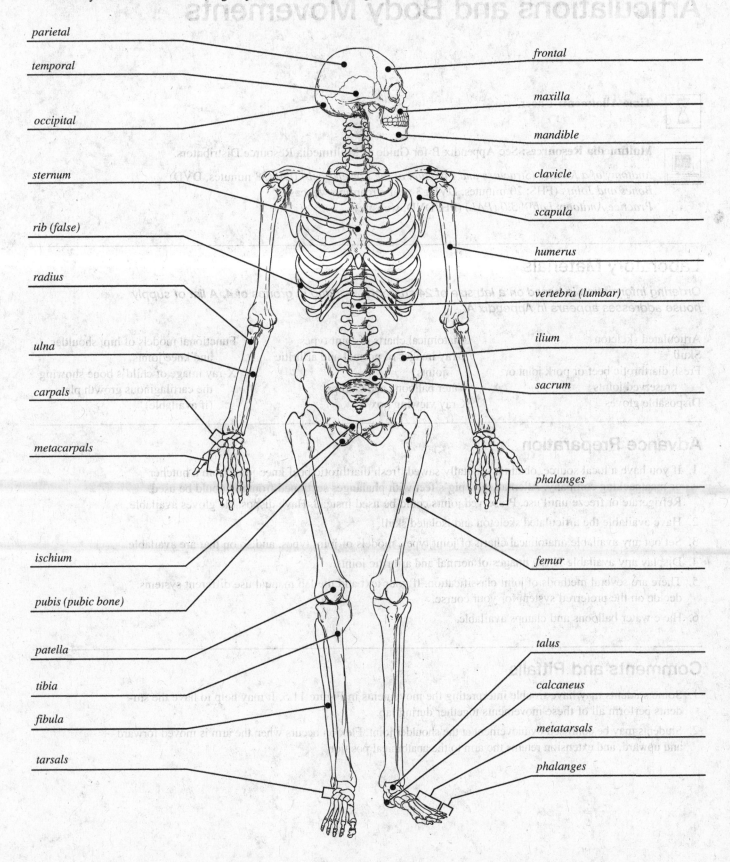

parietal

temporal

occipital

sternum

rib (false)

radius

ulna

carpals

metacarpals

ischium

pubis (pubic bone)

patella

tibia

fibula

tarsals

frontal

maxilla

mandible

clavicle

scapula

humerus

vertebra (lumbar)

ilium

sacrum

phalanges

femur

talus

calcaneus

metatarsals

phalanges

Articulations and Body Movements

Time Allotment: 1 hour.

Multimedia Resources: See Appendix B for Guide to Multimedia Resource Distributors.

Anatomy of a Runner (Structure and Function of the Lower Limb) (DE: 38 minutes, DVD)
Bones and Joints (FHS: 20 minutes, DVD, 3-year streaming webcast)
Practice Anatomy Lab™ 3.0 (PAL) (PE: DVD, website)

Laboratory Materials

Ordering information is based on a lab size of 24 students, working in groups of 4. A list of supply house addresses appears in Appendix A.

Articulated skeleton	Anatomical charts of joint types	Functional models of hip, shoulder,
Skull	X-ray images of normal and arthritic	and knee joints
Fresh diarthrotic beef or pork joint or	joints	X-ray image of child's bone showing
preserved joints	Water balloons and clamps	the cartilaginous growth plate
Disposable gloves	X-ray viewing box	(if available)

Advance Preparation

1. If you have a local source, obtain a sagittally sawed, fresh diarthrotic beef knee joint from a butcher or meatpacking company. Alternatively, pig's feet with phalanges sectioned frontally could be used. Refrigerate or freeze until use. Preserved joints could be used instead. Have disposable gloves available.

2. Have available the articulated skeleton and isolated skull.

3. Set out any available anatomical charts of joint types, models of joint types, and so on that are available.

4. Display any available X-ray images of normal and arthritic joints.

5. There are several methods of joint classification. If your text and the lab manual use different systems, decide on the preferred system for your course.

6. Have water balloons and clamps available.

Comments and Pitfalls

1. Some students may have trouble interpreting the movements in Figure 11.5. It may help to have the students perform all of these movements together during lab.

2. Students may be confused by movement at the shoulder joint. Flexion occurs when the arm is moved forward and upward, and extension returns the arm to the anatomical position.

Answers to Pre-Lab Quiz (p. 171)

1. Holds bones together; allows the rigid skeleton some flexibility so that gross body movements can occur

2. c, amount of movement allowed by the joint

3. synovial

4. fibrous

5. true

6. insertion

7. a, ball-and-socket

8. a, abduction

9. rotation

10. false

Answers to Activity Questions

Activity 4: Demonstrating the Importance of Friction-Reducing Structures (p. 174)

4. The fluid-filled sac greatly reduces the friction between the two surfaces. The water balloon represents a synovial cavity, bursae, or tendon sheaths. The fists represent two articulating bones on opposite sides of a synovial cavity. They may also represent muscles, tendons, or ligaments in the case of bursae and tendon sheaths.

Answers to Group Challenge (p. 184)

1. Name of joint (any one)	Movement allowed
elbow (hinge)	flexion and extension
proximal and distal radioulnar (pivot)	rotation
atlas and dens of axis (pivot)	rotation
interphalangeal/finger (hinge)	flexion and extension
ankle (hinge)	dorsiflexion and plantar flexion
interphalangeal/toe (hinge)	flexion and extension
temporomandibular (modified hinge)	elevation and depression

2. Name of joint (any one)	Movement allowed	Movement allowed
carpometacarpal of digit 1 (saddle)	flexion, extension	abduction, adduction
metacarpophalangeal/knuckles (condylar)	flexion, extension	abduction, adduction
atlanto-occipital (condylar)	flexion, extension	lateral flexion, circumduction
wrist (condylar)	flexion, extension	abduction, adduction
tibiofemoral/knee (modified hinge)	flexion, extension	some rotation
metatarsophalangeal (condylar)	flexion, extension	abduction, adduction

3. Name of joint (any two)	Movement allowed	Movement allowed	Movement allowed
shoulder (ball-and-socket)	flexion, extension	abduction, adduction	rotation, circumduction
hip (ball-and-socket)	flexion, extension	abduction, adduction	rotation, circumduction
sternoclavicular (shallow saddle)	moves in all axes		

Articulations and Body Movements

Fibrous, Cartilaginous, and Synovial Joints

1. Use key responses to identify the joint types described below.

   Key: a. cartilaginous   b. fibrous   c. synovial

   b; fibrous _____ 1. fibers connecting the tibia and fibula

   a; cartilaginous _____ 2. includes joints between the vertebral bodies and the pubic symphysis

   a; cartilaginous _____ 3. found in the epiphyseal plate

   b; fibrous _____ 4. sutures are memorable examples

   a; cartilaginous _____ 5. characterized by cartilage connecting the bony portions

   c; synovial _____ 6. all characterized by a fibrous articular capsule lined with a synovial membrane surrounding a joint cavity

   c; synovial _____ 7. all are freely movable or diarthrotic

   b; fibrous _____ 8. bone regions united by dense regular connective tissue

   c; synovial _____ 9. include the hip, knee, and elbow joints

2. Describe the tissue type and function of the following structures in relation to a synovial joint and label the structures indicated by leader lines in the diagram. Use an appropriate reference if needed.

   ligament: *Dense regular connective tissue; attaches bones together; reinforces joints*

   tendon: *Dense regular connective tissue attaching muscle to bone; reinforces the joint capsule as it spans a joint*

   articular cartilage: *Hyaline cartilage; reduces friction where bones articulate*

   synovial membrane: *Loose connective tissue; produces synovial fluid which decreases friction within the joint capsule*

   bursa: *Fluid-filled synovial sac which cushions the tendon where it crosses the bone*

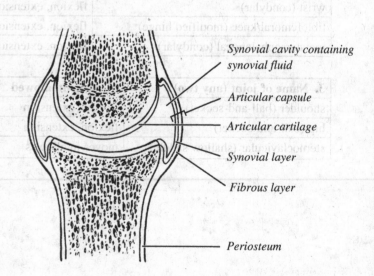

Synovial cavity containing synovial fluid

Articular capsule

Articular cartilage

Synovial layer

Fibrous layer

Periosteum

3. Match the synovial joint categories in column B with their descriptions in column A.

Column A

d; pivot _____ 1. joint between the axis and atlas

a; ball-and-socket _____ 2. hip joint

e; plane _____ 3. intervertebral joints (between articular processes)

b; condylar _____ 4. joint between forearm bones and wrist

c; hinge _____ 5. elbow

c; hinge _____ 6. interphalangeal joints

e; plane _____ 7. intercarpal joints

c; hinge _____ 8. joint between talus and tibia/fibula

b; condylar _____ 9. joint between skull and vertebral column

c; hinge _____ 10. joint between jaw and skull

b; condylar _____ 11. joints between proximal phalanges and metacarpal bones

a; ball-and-socket _____ 12. a multiaxial joint

b; condylar, *f; saddle* __ 13. biaxial joints

c; hinge, *d; pivot* _____ 14. uniaxial joints

Column B

a. ball-and-socket

b. condylar

c. hinge

d. pivot

e. plane

f. saddle

4. Indicate the number of planes in which each joint can move.

one _____ uniaxial joints *two* _____ biaxial joints *three or more* _____ multiaxial joints

5. What characteristics do all joints have in common? *All consist of bony regions held together by fibrous or cartilaginous connective*

tissue, or by a joint capsule. _____

Selected Synovial Joints

6. Which joint, the hip or the knee, is more stable? *Hip* _____

Name two important factors that contribute to the stability of the hip joint.

Deep socket for femur _____ and *strongly reinforced articular capsule* _____

Name two important factors that contribute to the stability of the knee.

The menisci _____ and *ligaments and tendons crossing joint* _____

7. The diagram shows a frontal section of the hip joint. Identify its major structural elements by using the key letters.

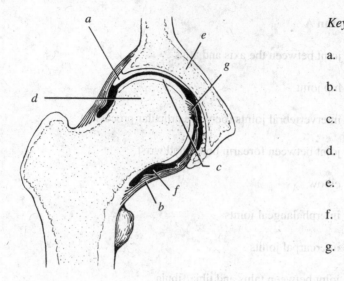

Key:

a. acetabular labrum

b. articular capsule

c. articular cartilage

d. head of the femur

e. hip bone

f. joint cavity

g. ligament of the head of the femur

8. The shoulder joint is built for mobility. List four factors that contribute to the large range of motion at the shoulder:

1. *The large head of the humerus moves easily against the shallow glenoid cavity of the scapula.*

2. *The glenoid labrum only slightly deepens the glenoid cavity.*

3. *The articular capsule is thin and loose.*

4. *There are few ligaments that strengthen the joint.*

9. In which direction does the shoulder usually dislocate? *The humerus usually dislocates in the forward and downward direction.*

Movements Allowed by Synovial Joints

10. Which letter of the adjacent diagram marks the origin

of the muscle? ___*A*___ Which letter marks the

insertion? ___*B*___

Insert the words *origin* and *insertion* into the following sentence:

During muscle contraction, the ___*insertion*___ moves

toward the ___*origin*___ .

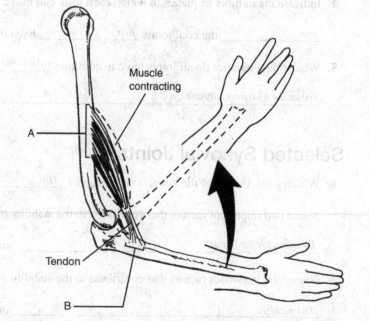

Muscle contracting

A

Tendon

B

11. Complete the descriptions below the diagrams by inserting the type of movement in each answer blank.

 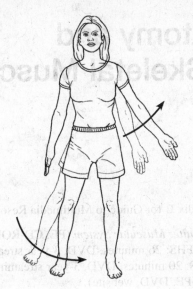 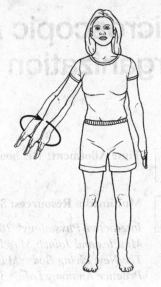

(a) _flexion_ **at the elbow**

(b) _extension_ **at the knee**

(c) _abduction_ **of the upper limb**

(d) _adduction_ **of the lower limb**

(e) _circumduction_ **of the upper limb**

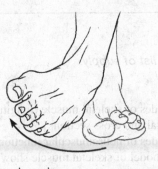 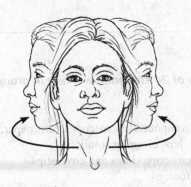 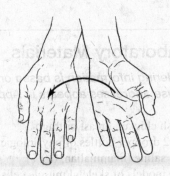

(f) _inversion_ **of the foot**

(g) _rotation_ **of the head**

(h) _pronation_ **of the forearm**

Joint Disorders

12. What structural joint changes are common to the elderly? _Degenerative changes (adhesions and bone spurs) begin to "sprout up"_

in diarthrotic joints; intervertebral discs begin to degenerate. These changes lead to increased joint stiffness and pain.

13. Define the following terms.

sprain: _Ligaments reinforcing a joint are damaged by excessive stretching, or torn away from the bony attachment._

dislocation: _Bones are forced out of their normal positions in a joint cavity._

14. What types of tissue damage might you expect to find in a dislocated joint?

Torn or stressed ligaments and inflammation. The joint capsule and ligaments may remain stretched.

Microscopic Anatomy and Organization of Skeletal Muscle

Time Allotment: 1 1/2 hours.

Multimedia Resources: See Appendix B for Guide to Multimedia Resource Distributors.

Interactive Physiology® 10-System Suite: Muscular System (PE: CD-ROM, website)
Muscles and Joints: Muscle Power (FHS: 26 minutes, DVD, 3-year streaming webcast)
The New Living Body: Muscles (FHS: 20 minutes, DVD, 3-year streaming webcast)
Practice Anatomy Lab™ 3.0 (PAL) (PE: DVD, website)

Solutions:

Saline Solution, 0.9%
Weigh out 0.9 gram of NaCl. Add distilled water to a final volume of 100 milliliters.

Laboratory Materials

Ordering information is based on a lab size of 24 students, working in groups of 4. A list of supply house addresses appears in Appendix A.

Fresh chicken breast or thigh
6–12 dropper bottles of physiologic
saline (mammalian, 0.9%)
3-D models of skeletal muscle cells
(if available)

24 compound microscopes, lens paper,
lens cleaning solution
Microscope slides and coverslips
24 forceps
48 dissecting needles

24 slides of skeletal muscle (longitudinal and cross sections)
24 slides of neuromuscular junctions
3-D model of skeletal muscle showing
neuromuscular junction
(if available)

Advance Preparation

1. Purchase chicken breasts or thighs from the meat market (one per lab). Refrigerate until used. Cut or tear the meat into small strips just before the lab. Provide gloves.

2. Set out forceps, dissecting needles, *0.9% saline solution* in dropper bottles, and microscope slides and coverslips for each student. Designate an organic matter disposal area.

3. Set out prepared slides of skeletal muscle (longitudinal and cross sections), and slides showing neuromuscular (myoneural) junctions. (Because the latter slides are expensive, a demonstration microscope is an alternative to providing a slide for each student.) Set out lens paper and lens cleaning solution. Have compound microscopes available.

4. Set out any available models of skeletal muscle cells and neuromuscular junctions.

Comments and Pitfalls

1. Students may have difficulty observing the muscle banding pattern. This is usually because the light intensity is set too high and the iris diaphragm is not closed down.

2. Emphasize the importance of understanding the organization and terminology of muscle structure. The organization and terminology of the nerves are very similar.

Answers to Pre-Lab Quiz (p. 189)

1. c, it is one of the major components of hollow organs
2. fibers
3. true
4. actin, myosin
5. c, endomysium

6. b, a tendon
7. neuromuscular junction
8. true
9. sarcomere
10. false

Answers to Activity Questions

Activity 1: Examining Skeletal Muscle Cell Anatomy (p. 192)

4. The banding pattern and limits of the cells are much clearer on the prepared slides.

Microscopic Anatomy and Organization of Skeletal Muscle

Skeletal Muscle Cells and Their Organization into Muscles

1. Use the items in the key to correctly identify the structures described below.

Key:

g; perimysium	1. connective tissue covering a bundle of muscle fibers	a. endomysium
c; fascicle	2. bundle of muscle fibers	b. epimysium
i; sarcomere	3. contractile unit of muscle	c. fascicle
d; muscle fiber	4. a muscle cell	d. muscle fiber
a; endomysium	5. thin areolar connective tissue surrounding each muscle fiber	e. myofibril
h; sarcolemma	6. plasma membrane of the muscle fiber	f. myofilament
e; myofibril	7. a long organelle with a banded appearance found within muscle cells	g. perimysium
f; myofilament	8. actin- or myosin-containing structure	h. sarcolemma
k; tendon	9. cord of collagen fibers that attaches a muscle to a bone	i. sarcomere
		j. sarcoplasm
		k. tendon

2. List three reasons why the connective tissue wrappings of skeletal muscle are important.

   The connective tissue wrappings (a) bundle the muscle fibers together, increasing coordination of their activity; (b) add strength to the muscle; and (c) provide a route for entry and exit of blood vessels and nerves to the muscle fibers.

3. Why are there more indirect—that is, tendinous—muscle attachments to bone than there are direct attachments?

   They conserve space (less bulky than fleshy muscle attachments) and are more durable than muscle tissue where bony prominences must be spanned.

4. How does an aponeurosis differ from a tendon structurally? *An aponeurosis is a sheet of white fibrous connective tissue; a tendon is a band or cord of the same tissue.*

   How is an aponeurosis functionally similar to a tendon? *Both serve to attach muscles to bones or to other muscles.*

5. The diagram illustrates a small portion of several myofibrils. Using letters from the key, correctly identify each structure indicated by a leader line or a bracket.

Key: a. A band
      b. actin filament
      c. I band

      d. myosin filament
      e. T tubule
      f. terminal cistern

      g. triad
      h. sarcomere
      i. Z disc

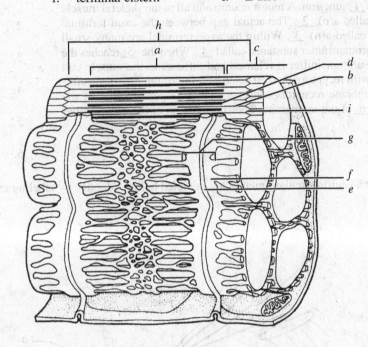

6. On the following figure, label a blood vessel, endomysium, epimysium, a fascicle, a muscle cell, perimysium, and the tendon.

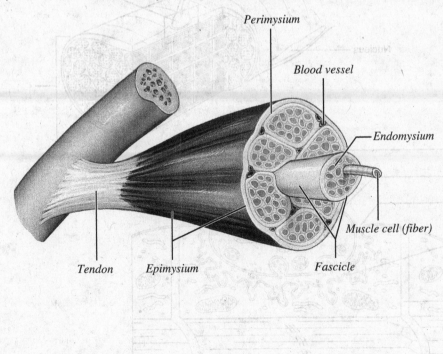

The Neuromuscular Junction

7. Complete the following statements:

The junction between a motor neuron's axon terminal and the muscle cell membrane is called a(n) _1_ junction. A motor neuron and all of the skeletal muscle fibers it stimulates is called a(n) _2_. The actual gap between the axon terminal and the muscle fiber is called a(n) _3_. Within the axon terminal are many small vesicles containing a neurotransmitter substance called _4_. When the _5_ reaches the ends of the axon, the neurotransmitter is released and diffuses to the muscle cell membrane to combine with receptors there. The combining of the neurotransmitter with the muscle membrane receptors causes a change in permeability of the membrane resulting in _6_ of the membrane. Then contraction of the muscle fiber occurs.

1. *neuromuscular*

2. *motor unit*

3. *synaptic cleft*

4. *acetylcholine*

5. *action potential (nerve impulse)*

6. *depolarization*

8. The events that occur at a neuromuscular junction are depicted below. Identify by labeling every structure provided with a leader line.

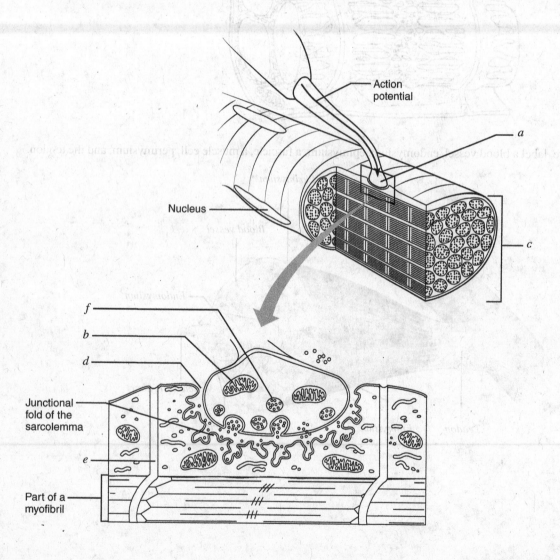

Key:

a. axon terminal

b. mitochondrion

c. muscle fiber

d. synaptic cleft

e. T tubule

f. vesicle containing ACh

Why This Matters

9. Botulinum toxin binds to receptors present at the axon terminal in order to enter the neuron. What vesicular transport process do you think is involved in the toxin entering the neuron? *Receptor-mediated endocytosis would most likely be involved.*

10. Explain how botulinum toxin alters the normal sequence of events at the neuromuscular junction to result in paralysis. Be sure to include the vesicular transport process that is inhibited.

    Botulinum toxin inhibits the release of exocytosis of the vesicles filled with the neurotransmitter, acetylcholine. Without acetylcholine

    to bind to the receptors on the sarcolemma, the muscle fiber is not stimulated to contract and therefore is paralyzed.

13
EXERCISE

Gross Anatomy of the Muscular System

Time Allotment: 2–3 hours in lab plus time outside of lab.

Multimedia Resources: See Appendix B for Guide to Multimedia Resource Distributors.

Anatomy of a Runner (Structure and Function of the Lower Limb) (DE: 38 minutes, DVD)
Human Musculature Videotape (PE: 23 minutes, DVD. *See Lab Manual Preface for more details.*)
Major Skeletal Muscles and Their Actions (DE: 19 minutes, VHS, DVD)
The New Living Body: Muscles (FHS: 20 minutes, DVD, 3-year streaming webcast)
Practice Anatomy Lab™ 3.0 (PAL) (PE: DVD, website)

Laboratory Materials

Ordering information is based on a lab size of 24 students, working in groups of 4. A list of supply house addresses appears in Appendix A.

Prosected human cadaver (if available)

Human torso models and/or anatomical charts of muscles
Disposable gloves

6–12 tubes of body (or face) paint
6–12 1-inch-wide art brushes

Advance Preparation

1. Set out models of the human torso and upper and lower limbs. It helps to have the muscles labeled on some of the models. Have model keys available.

2. Set out anatomical charts of human musculature.

3. If possible, have a prosected human cadaver available. Be prepared to inform students as to which muscles should be identified.

4. Set out functional knee and hip models available from biology supply companies.

Comments and Pitfalls

1. Identification of the intercostal and abdominal oblique muscles will be much easier if students carefully observe muscle fiber direction.

Answers to Pre-Lab Quiz (p. 199)

1. a, agonist
2. Direction of muscle fibers, relative size of muscles, location of muscle, number of origins, location of origin and insertion, shape of muscle, action of muscle
3. true
4. c, trunk
5. a, lower limb

6. a, biceps brachii
7. b, rectus abdominis
8. gastrocnemius
9. c, gluteus maximus
10. false

86

Answers to Group Challenge (p. 224)

Origin	Insertion	Muscle	Primary action
Zygomatic arch and maxilla	Angle and ramus of the mandible	*Masseter*	*Prime mover of jaw closure*
Anterior surface of ribs 3–5	Coracoid process of the scapula	*Pectoralis minor*	*With ribs fixed, draws scapula forward and inferiorly*
Inferior border of rib above	Superior border of rib below	*External intercostals*	*Pulls ribs toward each other to elevate the rib cage*
Distal portion of anterior humerus	Coronoid process of the ulna	*Brachialis*	*A major flexor of the forearm*
Anterior inferior iliac spine and superior margin of acetabulum	Tibial tuberosity and patella	*Rectus femoris*	*Extends the leg and flexes the thigh at the hip*
By two heads from medial and lateral condyles of femur	Calcaneus via calcaneal tendon	*Gastrocnemius*	*Plantar flexes the foot when the knee is extended*

Gross Anatomy of the Muscular System

Classification of Skeletal Muscles

1. Several criteria were given for the naming of muscles. Match the criteria (column B) to the muscle names (column A). Note that more than one criterion apply in most cases. The number in parentheses indicates the number of criteria that apply.

Column A		Column B	
_e, g_	1. gluteus maximus (2)	a.	action of the muscle
_a, g_	2. adductor magnus (2)	b.	shape of the muscle
_d, e_	3. biceps femoris (2)	c.	location of the origin and/or insertion of the muscle
_e, f_	4. transversus abdominis (2)	d.	number of origins
_a, c, e_	5. extensor carpi ulnaris (3)	e.	location of the muscle relative to a bone or body region
_b_	6. trapezius	f.	direction in which the muscle fibers run relative to some imaginary line
_e, f_	7. rectus femoris (2)	g.	relative size of the muscle
_e, f_	8. external oblique (2)		

2. Match the key terms to the muscles and movements described below.

Key: a. prime mover (agonist)   b. antagonist   c. synergist   d. fixator

a; prime mover 1. term for the biceps brachii during forearm flexion

c; synergist 2. term that describes the relation of brachioradialis to biceps brachii during forearm flexion

b; antagonist 3. term for the triceps brachii during forearm flexion

b; antagonist 4. term for the iliopsoas during thigh extension

a; prime mover 5. term for the gluteus maximus during thigh extension when walking up stairs

d; fixator 6. term for the rotator cuff muscles and deltoid when the forearm is flexed and the hand grabs a tabletop to lift the table

Muscles of the Head and Neck

3. Using choices from the key at the right, correctly identify muscles provided with leader lines on the diagram.

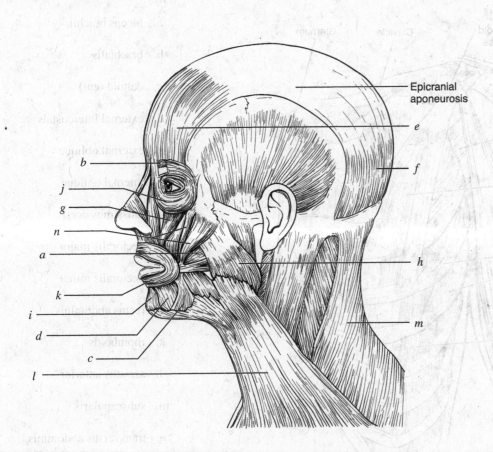

Key:

a. buccinator

b. corrugator supercilii

c. depressor anguli oris

d. depressor labii inferioris

e. epicranius (frontal belly)

f. epicranius (occipital belly)

g. levator labii superioris

h. masseter

i. mentalis

j. orbicularis oculi

k. orbicularis oris

l. platysma

m. trapezius

n. zygomaticus major and minor

4. Using the key provided in question 3, identify the muscles described next.

_n___ 1. used in smiling

_a___ 2. used to suck in your cheeks

_j___ 3. used in blinking and squinting

_c___ 4. used to pout (pulls the corners of the mouth downward)

_e___ 5. raises your eyebrows for a questioning expression

_b___ 6. used to form the vertical frown crease on the forehead

_k___ 7. your kissing muscle

_h___ 8. prime mover of jaw closure

_l___ 9. tenses skin of the neck during shaving

Muscles of the Trunk

5. Correctly identify both intact and transected (cut) muscles depicted in the diagram, using the key given at the right. (Not all terms will be used in this identification.)

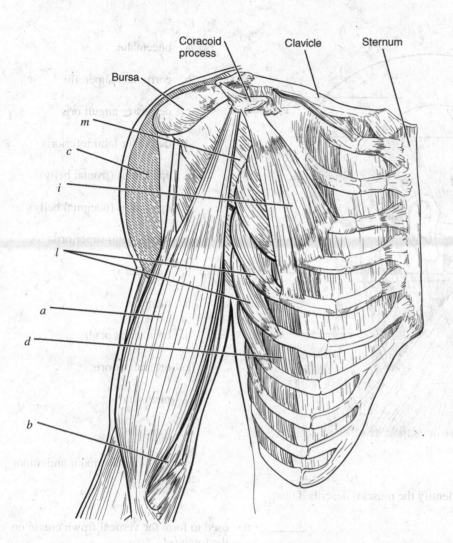

Key:

a. biceps brachii

b. brachialis

c. deltoid (cut)

d. external intercostals

e. external oblique

f. internal oblique

g. latissimus dorsi

h. pectoralis major

i. pectoralis minor

j. rectus abdominis

k. rhomboids

l. serratus anterior

m. subscapularis

n. transversus abdominis

o. trapezius

6. Using the key provided in question 5 above, identify the major muscles described below.

_j___ 1. a major flexor of the vertebral column

_g___ 2. prime mover for arm extension

_h___ 3. prime mover for arm flexion

_e, f, n, (j)_ 4. assume major responsibility for forming the abdominal girdle (three pairs of muscles)

_c___ 5. prime mover of arm abduction

_g, h_ 6. important in arm adduction; antagonists of the arm abductor (two muscles)

_l___ 7. moves the scapula forward and rotates scapula upward

_d___ 8. small, inspiratory muscles between the ribs; elevate the rib cage

_o___ 9. extends the head

_k___ 10. pull the scapulae medially

Muscles of the Upper Limb

7. Using terms from the key on the right, correctly identify all muscles provided with leader lines in the diagram. (Not all the listed terms are used in this exercise.)

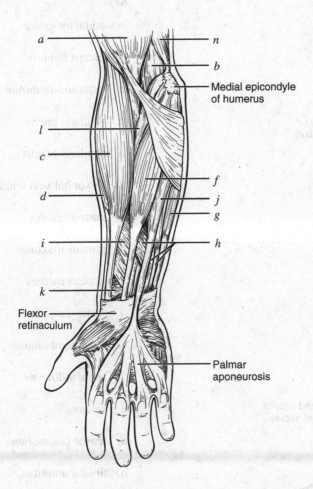

Key:

a. biceps brachii

b. brachialis

c. brachioradialis

d. extensor carpi radialis longus

e. extensor digitorum

f. flexor carpi radialis

g. flexor carpi ulnaris

h. flexor digitorum superficialis

i. flexor pollicis longus

j. palmaris longus

k. pronator quadratus

l. pronator teres

m. supinator

n. triceps brachii

8. Use the key provided in question 7 to identify the muscles described below.

<u>a</u>   1. flexes and supinates the forearm

<u>m</u>   2. synergist for supination of forearm

<u>b, c</u>   3. forearm flexors; no role in supination (two muscles)

<u>n</u>   4. forearm extensor

<u>f</u>   5. power flexor and abductor of the hand

<u>h</u>   6. flexes hand and middle phalanges

<u>k, l</u>   7. pronate the forearm (two muscles)

<u>i</u>   8. flexes the thumb

<u>d</u>   9. extends and abducts the hand

<u>e</u>   10. extends the hand and digits

<u>j</u>   11. flat muscle that is a weak hand flexor; tenses skin of the palm

Muscles of the Lower Limb

9. Using the terms from the key on the right, correctly identify all muscles provided with leader lines in the diagram below. (Not all listed terms are used in this exercise.)

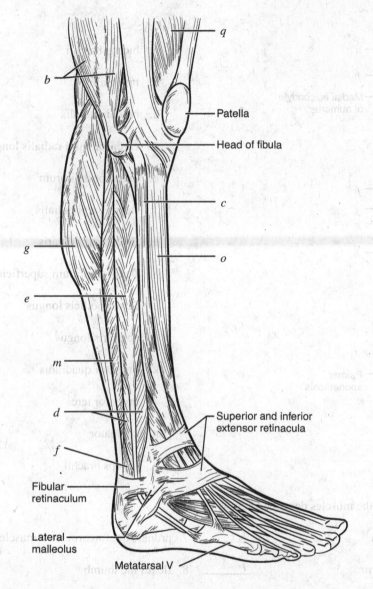

q
b
Patella
Head of fibula
c
g
o
e
m
d
f
Superior and inferior extensor retinacula
Fibular retinaculum
Lateral malleolus
Metatarsal V

Key:

a. adductor group

b. biceps femoris

c. extensor digitorum longus

d. fibularis brevis

e. fibularis longus

f. flexor hallucis longus

g. gastrocnemius

h. gluteus maximus

i. gluteus medius

j. rectus femoris

k. semimembranosus

l. semitendinosus

m. soleus

n. tensor fasciae latae

o. tibialis anterior

p. tibialis posterior

q. vastus lateralis

10. Use the key terms in question 9 to respond to the descriptions below.

_f_ 1. flexes the great toe and inverts the foot

_d, e_ 2. lateral compartment muscles that plantar flex and evert the foot (two muscles)

_i, n_ 3. abduct the thigh to take the "at ease" stance (two muscles)

_h_ 4. used to extend the thigh when climbing stairs

_g, m_ 5. posterior compartment muscles that plantar flex the foot (two muscles)

_p_ 6. prime mover of inversion of the foot

_o_ 7. prime mover of dorsiflexion of the foot

_a_ 8. adduct the thigh, as when standing at attention

_c_ 9. extends the toes

_b, k, l_ 10. extend thigh and flex leg (three muscles)

_j_ 11. extends leg and flexes thigh

General Review: Muscle Recognition

11. Identify each lettered muscle in the diagram of the human anterior superficial musculature by matching its letter with one of the following muscle names:

jj	1. adductor longus
g	2. biceps brachii
i	3. brachioradialis
e	4. deltoid
s	5. extensor digitorum longus
ee	6. external oblique
r	7. fibularis longus
j	8. flexor carpi radialis
l	9. flexor carpi ulnaris
u	10. frontal belly of epicranius
ll	11. gastrocnemius
kk	12. gracilis
m	13. iliopsoas
cc	14. intercostals
ff	15. internal oblique
b	16. masseter
v	17. orbicularis oculi
x	18. orbicularis oris
k	19. palmaris longus
n	20. pectineus
aa	21. pectoralis major
c	22. platysma
h	23. pronator teres
dd	24. rectus abdominis
o	25. rectus femoris
ii	26. sartorius
bb	27. serratus anterior
mm	28. soleus
z	29. sternocleidomastoid
y	30. sternohyoid
a	31. temporalis

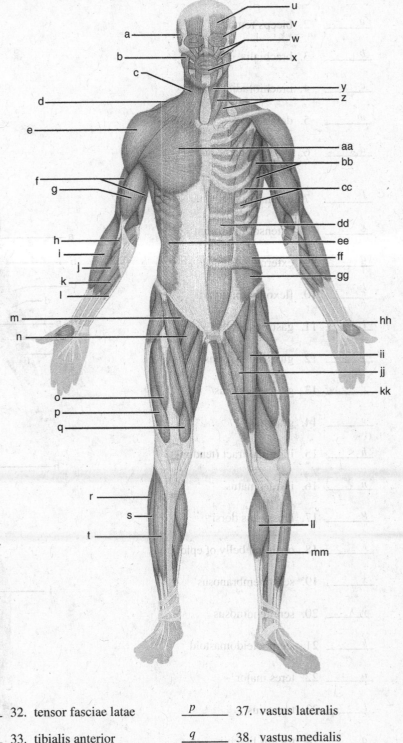

hh	32. tensor fasciae latae
t	33. tibialis anterior
gg	34. transversus abdominis
d	35. trapezius
f	36. triceps brachii
p	37. vastus lateralis
q	38. vastus medialis
w	39. zygomaticus

12. Identify each lettered muscle in this diagram of the human posterior superficial musculature by matching its letter with one of the following muscle names:

_t_   1. adductor magnus

_u_   2. biceps femoris

_b_   3. brachialis

_c_   4. brachioradialis

_m_   5. deltoid

_d_   6. extensor carpi radialis longus

_f_   7. extensor carpi ulnaris

_g_   8. extensor digitorum

_q_   9. external oblique

_e_   10. flexor carpi ulnaris

_i_   11. gastrocnemius

_s_   12. gluteus maximus

_r_   13. gluteus medius

_v_   14. gracilis

_h_   15. iliotibial tract (tendon)

_n_   16. infraspinatus

_p_   17. latissimus dorsi

_j_   18. occipital belly of epicranius

_x_   19. semimembranosus

_w_   20. semitendinosus

_k_   21. sternocleidomastoid

_o_   22. teres major

_l_   23. trapezius

_a_   24. triceps brachii

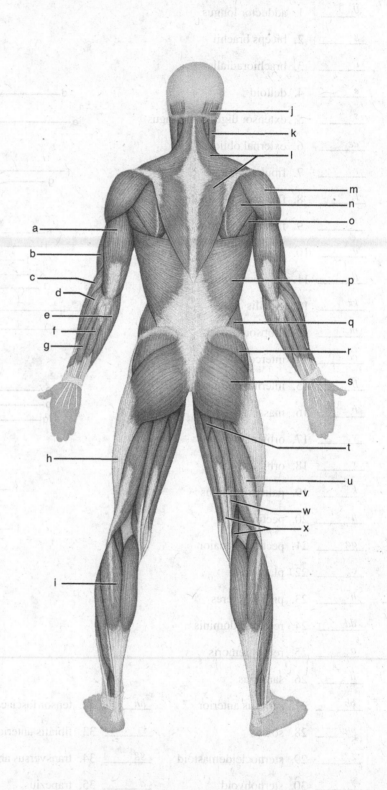

General Review: Muscle Descriptions

13. Identify the muscles described by completing the following statements. Use an appropriate reference as needed.

1. The __deltoid__ , __vastus lateralis__ , __gluteus maximus__ , and __gluteus medius__

   are commonly used for intramuscular injections (four muscles).

2. The insertion tendon of the __quadriceps__ group contains a large sesamoid bone, the patella.

3. The triceps surae insert in common into the __calcaneal__ tendon.

4. The bulk of the tissue of a muscle tends to lie __proximal__ to the part of the body it causes to move.

5. The extrinsic muscles of the hand originate on the __humerus, radius, and ulna__ .

6. Most flexor muscles are located on the __anterior__ aspect of the body; most

   extensors are located __posteriorly__ . An exception to this

   generalization is the extensor-flexor musculature of the __thigh/lower limb__ .

Skeletal Muscle Physiology: Frogs and Human Subjects

This exercise may be divided into two parts. The first demonstrates muscle contraction at the cellular level, and the second investigates contraction of the muscle as a whole. If desired, this exercise can be done in conjunction with Exercise 16 (Neurophysiology of Nerve Impulses: Frog Subjects) to save animals. Alternatively, the instructor may prefer to have the class observe the computer simulation of this material (PhysioEx™ 9.1 Exercise 2, Skeletal Muscle Physiology).

Suggestion for Alternative Equipment

Instructions for using PowerLab equipment can be found on MasteringA&P.

Time Allotment:

ATP Muscle Kit: 1 hour+ (depends largely on dissecting dexterity of students)
Muscle Fatigue in Humans: 1/2 hour
Inducing Contraction in the Frog Gastrocnemius Muscle: 2 hours+.

Multimedia Resources: See Appendix B for Guide to Multimedia Resource Distributors.

PhysioEx™ 9.1 Exercise 2 (PE: CD-ROM, website)
Interactive Physiology® 10-System Suite: Muscular System (BC: CD-ROM, Website)
Muscles and Joints: Muscle Power (FHS: 26 minutes, VHS, DVD, 3-year streaming webcast)
Muscular System at Work: The Inner Athlete (FHS: 25 minutes, VHS, DVD, 3-year streaming webcast)

Solutions:

Ringer's Solution, Frog

• 6.50 grams sodium chloride
• 0.14 gram potassium chloride
• 0.12 gram calcium chloride
• 0.20 gram sodium bicarbonate

Combine salts in a flask and add distilled water to make 1 liter of solution.

Laboratory Materials

Ordering information is based on a lab size of 24 students, working in groups of 4. A list of supply house addresses appears in Appendix A.

1 or 2 ATP muscle kits
6 petri dishes
1 box of microscope slides and coverslips
25 millimeter rulers
12–24 compound microscopes, lens paper, lens cleaning solution
6 watches or timers

Copies of textbooks or other heavy books
24–48 pointed glass probes (teasing needles)
6 glass marking pencils
6 100-milliliter beakers of distilled water
12–24 stereomicroscopes

6 50-milliliter beakers
Ringer's solution, frog
6 metal needle probes
6 medicine droppers
6 pairs of scissors
Cotton thread
6 forceps
6 glass or porcelain plates

6 live frogs (pithed)
Disposable gloves
6 sets of recording equipment and
    accessories (A or B)
    A: physiograph, paper and ink,
    force transducer, pin electrodes,
    stimulator, stimulator output

extension cable, transducer stand
and cable, straight pins, frog
board, laboratory stand, clamp
B: BIOPAC® BSL System for
Windows with BSL software version 3.7.5 to 3.7.7, or BSL System
for Mac OSX with BSL software

version 3.7.4 to 3.7.7, MP 36/35
or MP 45 data acquisition unit, PC
or Mac computer, BIOPAC Student Lab electrode lead set, hand
dynamometer, headphones, metric
tape measure, disposable vinyl
electrodes, and conduction gel

Advance Preparation—ATP Muscle Kit

1. Order the ATP muscle kits (Carolina) to be delivered no more than 7 days before the lab. One kit provides generously for eight students. Extra vials of the chemical solutions can be ordered separately (Carolina) and will reduce waiting time. Just before the lab begins, cut the muscle bundles into 4-centimeter lengths and place the accompanying glycerol in a petri dish.

2. Glass dissecting needles can be made from glass stirring rods. Use a Bunsen burner with a flame spreader attachment. Holding a stirring rod with oven mitts, heat the center while turning the rod until the flamed area glows orange. Pull the ends gently but firmly apart until the glass separates. With practice, fine-tipped needles can be made. Alternately, forceps may be used to separate the fibers.

Comments and Pitfalls

1. Students may have great difficulty separating the muscle bundles into individual fibers. Often two or three fibers remain together and that is the best they can do without shredding the muscle.

2. Remind the students to keep the fibers in a pool of glycerol to prevent them from drying out. However, when adding the solutions there shouldn't be too much glycerol on the muscle fibers.

3. Sometimes the fibers curl as they contract. Caution the students to measure the uncurled length of the fiber.

4. Occasionally there is great variability in the results (probably due to technical errors). Try rinsing the slides and glass needles in distilled water before use. This is a good exercise to collect class data and have the students compare individual results with the class results. You can discuss the importance of controlled experiments and repeated trials.

5. The magnesium included in the solution is thought to be needed for the ATPases that perform ATP hydrolysis which is needed to activate the myosin head (the cocking step).

Advance Preparation—Frog Gastrocnemius Muscle

1. If animal maintenance facilities are limited, order frogs to be delivered about 2–3 days prior to the date of the lab exercise. Healthy frogs can be maintained for a short time in a clean aquarium with a small amount of chlorinated water that is changed daily. Provide the frogs with a rock extending above the water line. Northern frogs require slightly cooler conditions (10–15°C) than southern frogs (15–20°C). One frog per lab group should be sufficient.

2. Designate a disposal area for the frogs. Have disposable gloves available for handling the frogs.

3. Pith frogs as needed, or if you prefer to have students pith their own frogs, provide them with copies of the pithing instructions on p. 238.

4. Set up work stations according to the amount of equipment available. Ideally there should be four students to a group. Each work station should include: a computer and associated equipment or a physiograph and associated equipment, a beaker of *frog Ringer's solution*, a medicine dropper, scissors, a glass needle, cotton thread, forceps, and a glass or porcelain plate.

5. Acquaint students with the operation of the recording equipment. Once the students are comfortable with the equipment, they should proceed with the experiment. Taking time here is worthwhile.

    a. *Physiograph.* There are several different brands of physiographs in use. It is best to consult the manual that comes with your equipment for specific details of operation. Have the students locate the switch regulating paper speed and practice running the paper at different speeds. The paper should then be rewound for future use. The students should also test the time marker at different settings with the paper running, and depress the event marker to observe the response. They should understand that the event marker will be automatically depressed when stimuli are applied to the muscle preparation. Be sure the ink is flowing smoothly through the writing tips, and be sure the tips are adjusted to record on horizontal lines of the paper grid.

b. BIOPAC®. It is helpful to have experienced student assistants to help with BIOPAC®. Introduce students to the basic features of BIOPAC® use before beginning this lab exercise.

Comments and Pitfalls

1. Students often fail to keep the muscle moist. Someone in each group should be in charge of keeping the muscle moist.

2. If the muscle is not lined up vertically on the equipment, it pulls at an angle.

3. Students may forget to record data. One person in each group should be the designated recorder.

4. Sometimes the ink does not flow smoothly. To help avoid this, test the equipment before beginning the experiment.

5. When determining the effect of load on skeletal muscle, remind students to loosen the afterload screw (if present) on the muscle lever.

6. If the sensitivity control or gain on the physiograph is at its most sensitive setting, you may have electrical interference.

7. If students are having trouble obtaining a muscle response, have them check to be sure that the connections are not loose and that the stimulator electrode is making contact with the muscle.

Advance Preparation for the Kymograph

1. Set up work stations according to the amount of equipment available. Ideally there should be four students to a group. Acquaint students with the operation of the equipment.

2. If smoked paper is to be used for kymograph recording, set up an area in a fume hood for smoking the paper, another hooded area with glazing fluid or fixative, and a line and clips for drying the paper.

Comments and Pitfalls

1. Kymograph paper is smoked in a fume hood using a smoky flame produced by passing natural gas through benzene. Because benzene is a known carcinogen, alternative recording methods should be sought. Muscle levers and signal magnets with ink recording tips can be purchased. If the budget is tight, small right-angled felt-tip markers can be attached to each smoke-writing stylus for satisfactory results. Students should practice putting paper tightly on the drum and lining up the signal magnet and muscle lever writing tips. If the muscle lever is equipped with an after load screw, have the students adjust it to bring the muscle lever to a horizontal position. Be sure the ink is flowing smoothly (if applicable). Have the students set the signal magnet to deliver one pulse per second, and calculate the drum speed in mm/sec for each setting.

2. Students may brush against the smoked paper before it has been fixed and destroy the recordings. If shellac is used as the glazing fluid, be sure students put paper into the shellac with the smoked side up. Spray lacquers are easier to use.

Answers to Pre-Lab Quiz (p. 237)

1. cations
2. c, repolarization
3. true
4. true
5. a, tetanus

Answers to Activity Questions

Activity 1: Observing Muscle Fiber Contraction (pp. 238–240)

8. The contracted fiber appears wider and the edges appear scalloped. The I band and H zone have disappeared.

10. Generally there is little or no contraction with ATP alone. There is no contraction with the salt solutions alone. Maximum contraction occurs in the presence of ATP and the proper concentrations of potassium and magnesium ions.

    It is expected that not all groups will obtain exactly the same results. The observed differences may be explained by inadvertent damage occurring to the muscle cells during separation, failure to separate completely into individual cells, and imprecision in measurements.

Activity 2: Inducing Contraction in the Frog Gastrocnemius Muscle (pp. 240–245)

Observing Graded Muscle Response to Increased Stimulus Intensity

4. As the voltage increases, more motor units respond. The name for this is recruitment or wave summation.

5. Once maximal stimulus is reached, all the motor units are contracting. Additional voltage has no effect.

Inducing Muscle Fatigue

4. After a period of rest, the muscle contracts again upon stimulation. The physiological basis for this may involve problems in excitation-contraction coupling. One theory suggests that buildup of inorganic phosphate from ATP and creatine phosphate breakdown may block calcium release from the SR. Another theory is that potassium accumulation in the T tubules may block calcium release from the SR and alter membrane potential of the muscle fiber.

Activity 3: Demonstrating Muscle Fatigue in Humans (p. 245)

7. As load increases, the period of contraction shortens as the muscle fatigues more quickly.

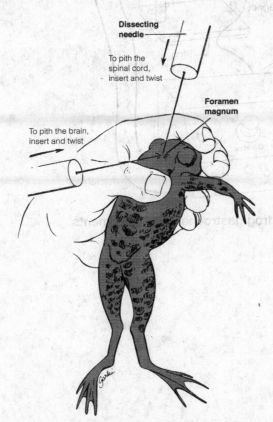

Procedure for pithing a frog

Activity 4: Electromyography in a Human Subject Using BIOPAC® (pp. 246–252)

Part 1: Temporal and Multiple Motor Unit Summation, Data Analysis

7. The intensity of each of the values increases with increasing force of muscle contraction.

The maximum voltage is reflective of the number of motor units being activated. The p-p value gradually increases, reflecting an increased number of active motor units.

Part 2: Force Measurement and Fatigue, Repeat Data Analysis for the Nondominant Forearm

4. There may or may not be a difference in the maximal force between the forearms, but usually the maximal force in the dominant forearm is 10–20% greater than in the nondominant forearm.

Muscle cells are amitotic. When a muscle gets larger in diameter, it is because of an increase in size (diameter) of the muscle cells, not because of an increase in the number of muscle cells.

One normally observes more rapid fatigue in the nondominant forearm.

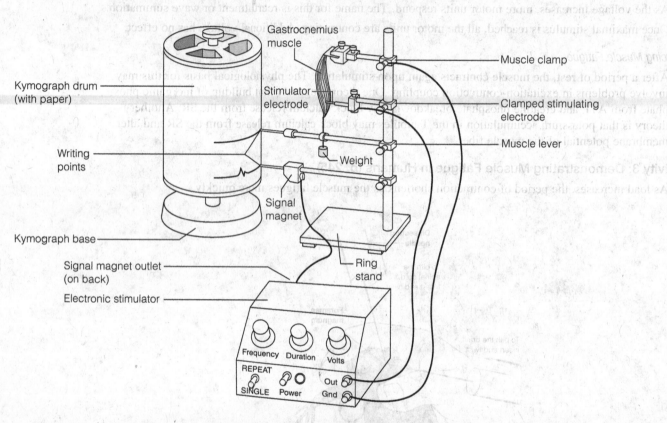

Kymograph setup for frog gastrocnemius experiments

Skeletal Muscle Physiology: Frogs and Human Subjects

Muscle Activity

1. The following group of incomplete statements begins with a description of a muscle fiber in the resting state just before stimulation. Complete each statement by choosing the correct response from the key items.

   Key:
   a. Na^+ diffuses out of the cell
   b. K^+ diffuses out of the cell
   c. Na^+ diffuses into the cell
   d. K^+ diffuses into the cell
   e. inside the cell
   f. outside the cell
   g. relative ionic concentrations on the two sides of the membrane
   h. electrical conditions
   i. activation of the sodium-potassium pump, which moves K^+ into the cell and Na^+ out of the cell
   j. activation of the sodium-potassium pump, which moves Na^+ into the cell and K^+ out of the cell

   There is a greater concentration of Na^+ __f__; there is a greater concentration of K^+ __e__. When the stimulus is delivered, the permeability of the membrane at that point is changed; and __c__, initiating the depolarization of the membrane. Almost as soon as the depolarization wave has begun, a repolarization wave follows it across the membrane. This occurs as __b__. Repolarization restores the __h__ of the resting cell membrane. The __g__ is (are) reestablished by __i__.

2. Number the following statements in the proper sequence to describe the contraction mechanism in a skeletal muscle fiber. Number 1 has already been designated.

   __1__ Depolarization occurs, and the action potential is generated.

   __5__ The muscle fiber relaxes and lengthens.

   __3__ The calcium ion concentrations at the myofilaments increase; the myofilaments slide past one another, and the cell shortens.

   __2__ The action potential, carried deep into the cell by the T tubules, triggers the release of calcium ions from the sarcoplasmic reticulum.

   __4__ The concentration of the calcium ions at the myofilaments decreases as they are actively transported into the sarcoplasmic reticulum.

3. Refer to your observations of muscle fiber contraction in Activity 1 to answer the following questions.

   a. Did your data support your hypothesis? *yes/no*

   b. *Explain* your observations fully. *Optimal muscle contraction requires Mg^{2+}, K^+, and ATP. Without ATP (the energy source) no contraction can occur once energy stores are exhausted. Mg^{2+} and K^+ are necessary for ATPase activity.*

c. Draw a relaxed and a contracted sarcomere below. Label the Z discs, thick filaments, and thin filaments.

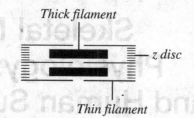

Thick filament — z disc — Thin filament

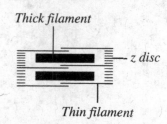

Thick filament — z disc — Thin filament

Induction of Contraction in the Frog Gastrocnemius Muscle

4. Why is it important to destroy the brain and spinal cord of a frog before conducting physiological experiments on muscle

   contraction? _Renders the frog unable to feel pain and prevents reflex movements that would confuse experimental results_

5. What kind of stimulus (electrical or chemical) travels from the motor neuron toward skeletal muscle? _Electrical_

   What kind of stimulus (electrical or chemical) travels from the axon terminal to the sarcolemma? _Chemical_

6. Give the name and duration of each of the three phases of the muscle twitch, and describe what is happening during each phase.

   a. _latent_ , _2.78_ msec, _electrical/chemical changes preparatory to contraction (i.e., depolarization,_

   release of Ca^{2+})

   b. _contraction_ , _23.33_ msec, _muscle shortens due to sliding of myofilaments_

   c. _relaxation_ , _174.90_ msec, _Ca^{2+} is reabsorbed by the sarcoplasmic reticulum, the muscle cells lengthen and relax._

7. Use the items in the key to identify the conditions described.

   Key:

   a. maximal stimulus   c. subthreshold stimulus   e. threshold stimulus
   b. recruitment   d. tetanus   f. wave summation

   ___d___ 1. sustained contraction without any evidence of relaxation

   ___f___ 4. increasingly stronger contractions owing to stimulation at a rapid rate

   ___c___ 2. stimulus that results in no perceptible contraction

   ___b___ 5. increasingly stronger contractions owing to increased stimulus strength

   ___e___ 3. stimulus at which the muscle first contracts perceptibly

   ___a___ 6. weakest stimulus at which all muscle fibers in the muscle are contracting

8. Complete the following statements by writing the appropriate words on the corresponding numbered blanks at the right.

   When a weak but smooth muscle contraction is desired, a few motor units are stimulated at a _1_ rate. Within limits, as the load on a muscle is increased, the muscle contracts _2_ (more/less) strongly.

   1. _very rapid_

   2. _more_

9. During the frog experiment on muscle fatigue, how did the muscle contraction pattern change as the muscle began to

fatigue? _The distance of the contraction peak from the baseline continued to decrease._

How long was stimulation continued before fatigue was apparent? _(student data)_

If the sciatic nerve that stimulates the living frog's gastrocnemius muscle had been left attached to the muscle and the stimulus had been applied to the nerve rather than the muscle, would fatigue have become apparent sooner, later, or at the same time?

At the same time

10. What will happen to a muscle in the body when its nerve supply is destroyed or badly damaged? _The muscle becomes flaccid,_

paralyzed, and eventually atrophies. Nerve stimulation is necessary for viable muscles.

11. Explain the relationship between the load on a muscle and its strength of contraction. _Strength of contraction increases as the_

load increases until the load becomes excessive.

12. The skeletal muscles are maintained in a slightly stretched condition for optimal contraction. How is this accomplished?

By the manner in which they are attached to the skeleton

Why does stretching a muscle beyond its optimal length reduce its ability to contract? (Include an explanation of the events

at the level of the myofilaments.) _Overstretching prevents myosin cross bridge interaction, since the myofilaments no longer overlap._

If the cross bridges cannot make contact, no force (contraction) can be generated.

13. If the length but not the tension of a muscle is changed, the contraction is called an isotonic contraction. In an isometric contraction, the tension is increased but the muscle does not shorten. Which type of contraction did you observe most often during

the laboratory experiments? _Isotonic_

Electromyography in a Human Subject Using BIOPAC®

14. If you were a physical therapist applying a constant voltage to the forearm, what might you observe if you gradually

increased the _frequency_ of stimulatory impulses, keeping the voltage constant each time? _One is likely to observe an increase_

in the duration of motor unit activation.

15. Describe what is meant by the term _recruitment_. _Recruitment refers to the process by which an increasing number of motor units_

in a muscle are activated by gradually increasing levels of stimulation (e.g., voltage).

16. Describe the physiological processes occurring in the muscle fibers that account for the gradual onset of muscle fatigue.

The specific causes of muscle fatigue are not well understood. Fatigue is likely due to a problem in excitation-contraction coupling, and

in rare cases a problem at the neuromuscular junction. Ionic imbalances also contribute to muscle fatigue. ATP availability declines,

but in moderate exercise, lack of ATP does not produce fatigue.

17. Most subjects use their dominant forearm far more than their nondominant forearm. What does this indicate about degree of activation of motor units and these factors: muscle fiber diameter, maximum muscle fiber force, and time to muscle fatigue? (You may need to use your textbook for help with this one.)

Generally, since people use their dominant forearm more, the muscle fibers in that arm are activated for more prolonged periods. Thus,

increase in muscle fiber diameter (muscular hypertrophy) usually results, allowing for increased force. Increased activity generally

leads to increased respiratory and contractual efficiency, resulting in a greater time to muscle fatigue.

18. Define *dynamometry*. *Dynamometry is the process of measuring force.*

19. How might dynamometry be used to assess patients in a clinical setting? *Dynamometry can assist the clinician in the assessment*

of muscle function by allowing for the study of contractual deficits and the recovery of muscle function.

Histology of Nervous Tissue

Time Allotment: 1 hour.

Multimedia Resources: See Appendix B for Guide to Multimedia Resource Distributors.

Interactive Physiology® 10-System Suite: Nervous System I (PE: CD-ROM, website)
The Nervous System: Nerves at Work (FHS: 27 minutes, DVD, 3-year streaming webcast)
Practice Anatomy Lab™ 3.0 (PAL) (PE: DVD, website)

Laboratory Materials

Ordering information is based on a lab size of 24 students, working in groups of 4. A list of supply house addresses appears in Appendix A.

24 compound microscopes, lens paper, immersion oil, lens cleaning solution

Model of neuron (if available)
24 slides of ox spinal cord smear, teased myelinated fibers, Purkinje

cells (cerebellum), pyramidal cells (cerebrum), dorsal root ganglion, and nerve cross section

Advance Preparation

1. Set out slides of ox spinal cord smear and teased myelinated fibers, Purkinje cells (cerebellum), pyramidal cells (cerebrum), dorsal root ganglion, and nerve cross section.

2. Set out lens paper, immersion oil, and lens cleaning solution. Have compound microscopes available.

3. Set out models of neurons, if available.

Comments and Pitfalls

1. Students may focus on the wrong cells. Encourage them to look at the histology images in Exercise 15, use histology atlases, and help each other.

2. Students may have difficulty with the connective tissue sheaths. Remind them of the similarities to muscle terminology.

Answers to Pre-Lab Quiz (p. 257)

1. two
2. c, satellite cells and Schwann cells
3. Neurons
4. c, dendrites
5. true

6. myelin
7. tracts
8. b, multipolar
9. Efferent
10. a, endoneurium

Answers to Activity Questions

Activity 1: Identifying Parts of a Neuron (pp. 260–261)

3. The gaps are at regular intervals. Action potentials will occur at regular intervals along the axon as local currents open voltage-gated sodium channels. This allows the electrical signal to jump from gap to gap and travel very fast.

Activity 2: Studying the Microscopic Structure of Selected Neurons (p. 262)

The Purkinje and pyramidal cells are multipolar. The dorsal root ganglion neurons are unipolar.

NAME _____

LAB TIME/DATE _____

Histology of Nervous Tissue

1. The basic functional unit of the nervous system is the neuron. What is the major function of this cell type?

To generate and transmit nerve impulses _____

2. Name four types of neuroglia in the CNS, and list a function for each of these cells. (You will need to consult your textbook for this.)

Types		**Functions**	
a.	_microglia_	a.	_clearing debris through phagocytosis (dead cells, bacteria, etc.)_
b.	_oligodendrocytes_	b.	_form myelin around axons in the CNS_
c.	_astrocytes_	c.	_support the neurons; may serve nutritive function and help regulate the chemical environment of the neurons_
d.	_ependymal cells_	d.	_line cavities of the brain (and spinal cord); aid in circulation of cerebrospinal fluid_

Name the PNS neuroglial cell that forms myelin. _Schwann cell_ _____

Name the PNS neuroglial cell that surrounds neuron cell bodies in ganglia. _Satellite cell_ _____

3. Match each description with a term from the key.

Key:
a. afferent neuron
b. central nervous system
c. efferent neuron
d. ganglion
e. interneuron
f. neuroglia
g. neurotransmitters
h. nerve
i. nuclei
j. peripheral nervous system
k. synaptic cleft
l. tract

_b_   1. the brain and spinal cord collectively

_f_   2. specialized supporting cells in the nervous system

_k_   3. junction or point of close contact between neurons

_l_   4. a bundle of axons inside the CNS

_e_   5. neuron serving as part of the conduction pathway between sensory and motor neurons

_j_   6. ganglia and spinal and cranial nerves

_d_   7. collection of nerve cell bodies found outside the CNS

_c_   8. neuron that conducts impulses away from the CNS to muscles and glands

_a_   9. neuron that conducts impulses toward the CNS from the body periphery

_g_   10. chemicals released by neurons that stimulate or inhibit other neurons or effectors

Neuron Anatomy

4. Match the following anatomical terms (column B) with the appropriate description or function (column A).

Column A

    c   1. region of the cell body from which the axon originates

    b   2. secretes neurotransmitters

    f, d   3. receptive regions of a neuron (2 terms)

    g   4. insulates the nerve fibers

    d   5. site of the nucleus and most important metabolic area

    h   6. involved in the transport of substances within the neuron

    e   7. essentially rough endoplasmic reticulum, important metabolically

    a   8. impulse generator and transmitter

Column B

a. axon

b. axon terminal

c. axon hillock

d. cell body

e. chromatophilic substance

f. dendrite

g. myelin sheath

h. neurofibril

5. Draw a "typical" multipolar neuron in the space below. Include and label the following structures on your diagram: cell body, nucleus, nucleolus, chromatophilic substance, dendrites, axon, myelin sheath, myelin sheath gaps, and axon terminals.

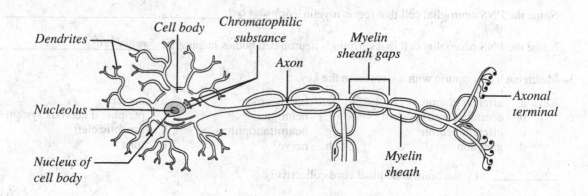

6. What substance is found in synaptic vesicles of the axon terminal? <u>*Neurotransmitters*</u>

7. What anatomical characteristic determines whether a particular neuron is classified as unipolar, bipolar, or multipolar?

The number of processes issuing from the cell body

Make a simple line drawing of each type here.

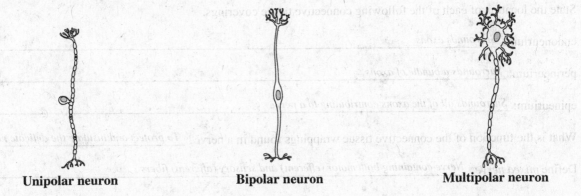

Unipolar neuron   **Bipolar neuron**   **Multipolar neuron**

8. Correctly identify the sensory (afferent) neuron, interneuron (association neuron), and motor (efferent) neuron in the figure below.

Which of these neuron types is/are unipolar? *Sensory neuron*

Which is/are most likely multipolar? *Motor neuron, interneuron*

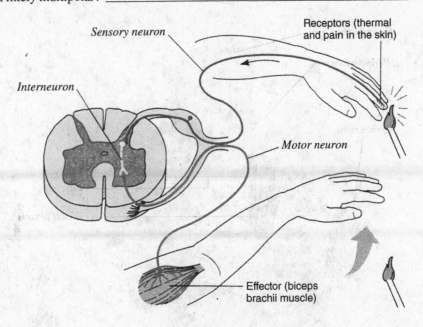

9. Describe how the Schwann cells form the myelin sheath encasing the nerve fibers.

Schwann cells begin to wrap themselves around the axon in jelly roll fashion, thus forming a tight coil of membranous

material, which forms the myelin sheath.

Structure of a Nerve

10. What is a nerve? *A bundle of axons wrapped in connective tissue. It extends to and/or from the CNS and body viscera or peripheral structures.*

11. State the location of each of the following connective tissue coverings.

    endoneurium: *Surrounds axons*

    perineurium: *Surrounds a bundle of axons*

    epineurium: *Surrounds all of the axons contributing to a nerve*

12. What is the function of the connective tissue wrappings found in a nerve? *To protect and insulate the delicate nerve fibers*

13. Define *mixed nerve*. *Nerve containing both motor (efferent) and sensory (afferent) fibers*

14. Identify all indicated parts of the nerve section.

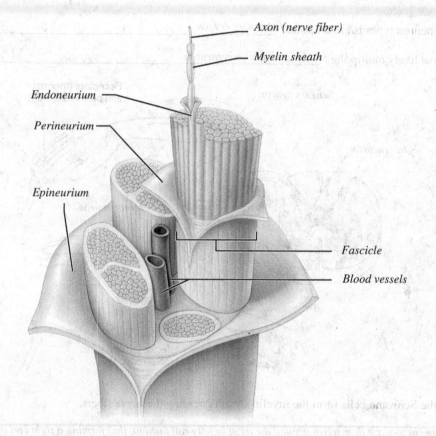

Axon (nerve fiber)

Myelin sheath

Endoneurium

Perineurium

Epineurium

Fascicle

Blood vessels

Neurophysiology of Nerve Impulses: Frog Subjects

If desired, part of this investigation of the nerve impulse may be done in conjunction with Exercise 14 (Skeletal Muscle Physiology) to save animals.

Time Allotment: 1–1¹/2 hours (more if oscilloscope is used).

Multimedia Resources: See Appendix B for Guide to Multimedia Resource Distributors.

See Exercise 6 for histology listings.

Brain and Nervous System: Your Information Superhighway (FHS: 31 minutes, DVD, 3-year streaming webcast)

Interactive Physiology® 10-System Suite: Nervous System I and II (PE: CD-ROM, website)

PhysioEx™ 9.1 Exercise 3 (PE: CD-ROM, website)

Solutions:

Hydrochloric Acid (HCl), 0.01%
Add 0.27 milliliter of 1 *N* HCl (Carolina) to 90 milliliters of distilled water. Add distilled water to a final volume of 100 milliliters. *Or*, beginning with 37% HCl (d 1.2), prepare a 1 *N* solution by adding 8 milliliters of 37% HCl to 90 milliliters of distilled water. Add distilled water to a final volume of 100 milliliters.

Ringer's Solution, Frog
• 6.50 grams sodium chloride
• 0.14 gram potassium chloride
• 0.12 gram calcium chloride
• 0.20 gram sodium bicarbonate

Combine salts in flask and add distilled water to make 1 liter of solution.

Tubocurarine, 0.5%
Weigh out 0.125 gram of D-tubocurarine chloride. Add distilled water to make 25 milliliters. **Label: Poison. Use extreme care. Note: Solution should be placed in a serum bottle** (Aldrich) **for use.**

Laboratory Materials

Ordering information is based on a lab size of 24 students, working in groups of 4. A list of supply house addresses appears in Appendix A.

12 live frogs *(Rana pipiens)*
Disposable gloves
12 dropper bottles of Ringer's solution, frog
6 small ice baths

6 dissecting trays and dissection kits
6 stimulators
Filter paper
6 dropper bottles of 0.01% HCl
NaCl crystals

Absorbent cotton
Ether
Disposable pipettes
1-cc syringes with small-gauge needle
12 glass rods or probes

Thread
6 ring stands and 12 clamps
12 glass slides or glass plates
6 platinum electrodes

6 slide holders or heat-resistant mitts
Oscilloscope
Nerve chambers
Bunsen burners

Serum bottle of 0.5% tubocurarine
Frog boards
24 safety glasses
6 forceps

Advance Preparation

1. Order frogs to be delivered 2–3 days prior to the date of the lab, if animal maintenance facilities are limited. Frogs may be pithed just prior to the lab to save time (see Exercise 14). Each group will need two to three frogs. Have disposable gloves available for handling the frogs.

2. Set out for each group dissecting instruments and tray, safety glasses, two dropper bottles of *Ringer's solution, frog* (at room temperature and iced), a small ice bath, thread, several glass rods or glass probes, a laboratory stand and two clamps, several glass slides or glass plates, platinum electrode, stimulator, filter paper, a dropper bottle of *0.01% HCl solution*, NaCl crystals, heat-resistant mitts or a slide holder, a Bunsen burner, absorbent cotton, and a disposable pipet and bulb. Have a small container of ether available. **Note: Ether is highly flammable and should be used with care in a fume hood.**

3. For Claude Bernard's experiment, set out disposable gloves, a frog board, thread, and a 1-cc syringe with small-gauge needle. Have a small container of *0.5% tubocurarine solution* available. **Note: Tubocurarine is extremely toxic. Wear disposable gloves when handling the tubocurarine.**

4. If oscilloscopes are to be used, set out nerve chambers, set up the oscilloscopes, and provide instructions. Allow time for the students to become familiar with the equipment.

Comments and Pitfalls

1. Be sure the muscle nerve preparation is kept moist and not touched by metal dissection equipment. Be careful that the nerve does not get stretched or damaged during dissection and setup.

2. Ether has a very low ignition temperature. Conduct ether experiments in a lab hood. If a hood is not available, do this part of the experiment with the windows open and after all Bunsen burners have been put out. Do not attempt to put out an ether fire with water; use a CO_2 extinguisher. Order ether in small amounts and do not store it for long periods of time. Keep it in an explosion-proof refrigerator when not in use.

3. When performing Claude Bernard's experiment, students may need to increase the stimulus intensity when testing the muscles, as muscle threshold is generally higher than nerve threshold.

Answers to Pre-Lab Quiz (p. 269)

1. conductivity
2. a, depolarization
3. b, K⁺
4. a, absolute refractory period
5. a, gastrocnemius and sciatic

Answers to Activity Questions

Activity 1: Stimulating the Nerve (p. 272)

2. Repeated stimuli should cause the muscle to contract to tetanus.

3. Mechanical stimulation should result in muscle contraction.

4. HCl and NaCl should both cause muscle contraction.

5. Thermal stimulation also results in muscle contraction. These experiments indicate that a variety of stimuli can result in conduction of an impulse.

Activity 2: Inhibiting the Nerve (pp. 273–274)

2. (Ether) The anesthetized part of the nerve does not respond, but the unanesthetized area distal to the anesthetized area responds to the stimulus, resulting in muscle contraction.

3. (Ether) Ether exerts its blocking effect on the nerve fibers. The muscle was still able to contract when the nerve was stimulated beyond the anesthetized section.

4. (Curare) Eventually the nonligated muscle will show reduced or no contraction in response to the stimulus. Curare travels throughout the frog's circulatory system and eventually finds its way to neuromuscular junctions. The left muscle is not affected because the ligation cuts off circulation to the tissue in that area. The right muscle does not respond to nervous stimulation because the curare blocks the acetylcholine receptor sites in the neuromuscular junction.

5. (Curare) Both gastrocnemius muscles should respond to direct stimulation, as direct stimulation of the muscle does not require action at the neuromuscular junction. The difference between the right and left nerve response is the result of the curare block to the acetylcholine receptor sites. When the muscles are stimulated directly, the stimulus bypasses the chemically gated channels that respond to acetylcholine. Curare acts at the neuromuscular junction by blocking the acetylcholine receptor sites. **Note: It is beyond the scope of this lab to prove that the nerve to the right muscle is still conducting an impulse.**

Activity 3: Visualizing the Compound Action Potential with an Oscilloscope (pp. 274–275)

7. The amplitude of the compound action potential will increase until maximal amplitude is reached.

9. Reversing the nerve (distal to proximal) should still give a recording on the oscilloscope. Action potentials can travel in either direction along an axon. The usual "forward" direction of the action potential is determined by the site of origin of the signal and the refractory period that follows the passage of the action potential.

Neurophysiology of Nerve Impulses: Frog Subjects

The Action Potential

1. Match the terms in column B to the appropriate definition in column A.

   Column A

   _a_ 1. period of depolarization of the neuron membrane during which it cannot respond to a second stimulus

   _c_ 2. reversal of the resting potential due to an influx of sodium ions

   _d, e_ 3. period during which potassium ions diffuse out of the neuron because of a change in membrane permeability

   _d_ 4. period of repolarization when only a strong stimulus will elicit an action potential

   _f_ 5. mechanism in which ATP is used to move sodium out of the cell and potassium into the cell; restores the resting membrane voltage and intracellular ionic concentrations

   Column B

   a. absolute refractory period

   b. action potential

   c. depolarization

   d. relative refractory period

   e. repolarization

   f. sodium-potassium pump

2. Define the term *depolarization*. _A decrease in the membrane potential as the membrane becomes less negative inside, moving toward zero at a specific site on an axon or muscle cell membrane_

   How does an action potential differ from simple depolarization? _An action potential is a large transient depolarization event that is conducted along the membrane of a neuron or muscle cell. It does not decrease in amplitude as it travels away from the site of stimulation._

3. Would a substance that decreases membrane permeability to sodium increase or decrease the probability of generating an action potential? Why?

   Decrease; with stimulation, sodium enters the cell, causing depolarization, and anything that blocks sodium's entry prevents the change in membrane potential toward zero that is necessary to generate an action potential.

4. The diagram here represents a section of an axon. Complete the figure by illustrating an area of resting membrane potential, an area of depolarization, and local current flow. Indicate the direction of the depolarization wave.

$[Na^+]$ $[K^+]$

$[Na^+]$ $[K^+]$

Physiology of Nerves Stimulating and Inhibiting the Nerve

5. Respond appropriately to each question posed below. Insert your responses in the corresponding numbered blanks to the right.

1–3. Name three types of stimuli that resulted in action potential generation in the sciatic nerve of the frog.

4. Which of the stimuli resulted in the most effective nerve stimulation?

5. Which of the stimuli employed in that experiment might represent types of stimuli to which nerves in the human body are subjected?

6. What is the usual mode of stimulus transfer in neuron-to-neuron interactions?

7. Since the action potentials themselves were not visualized with an oscilloscope during this initial set of experiments, how did you recognize that impulses were being transmitted?

1. _electrical shock_

2. _chemical (acid or salt)_

3. _thermal (heat) or mechanical (pinching)_

4. _electrical shock_

5. _all of them_

6. _chemical or electrochemical_

7. _contraction of the gastrocnemius muscle_

6. How did the site of action of ether and tubocurarine differ? _Ether exerts its blocking effect on the nerve, while tubocurarine blocks the ACh receptor site of the muscle._

In the tubocurarine experiment, why was one of the frog's legs ligated? _As a control to prevent the tubocurarine (in the blood) from reaching that muscle_

Visualizing the Compound Action Potential with an Oscilloscope

7. Explain why the amplitude of the compound action potential recorded from the frog sciatic nerve increased when the voltage of the stimulus was increased above the threshold value. _More and more nerve fibers were being recruited._

8. What was the effect of cold temperature (flooding the nerve with iced frog Ringer's solution) on the functioning of the sciatic nerve tested? _Cold temperature increases the threshold for excitation and may result in complete inexcitability of the nerve._

9. When the nerve was reversed in position, was the impulse conducted in the opposite direction? _Yes_

How can this result be reconciled with the concept of one-way conduction in neurons? _Action potentials can travel in either direction along an axon. The usual "forward" direction of the action potential is determined by the site of origin of the signal and the refractory period that follows the passage of the action potential._

Gross Anatomy of the Brain and Cranial Nerves

Time Allotment: 2 hours.

Multimedia Resources: See Appendix B for Guide to Multimedia Resource Distributors.

Anatomy of the Human Brain (FHS: 35 minutes, DVD, 3-year streaming webcast)
Animated Neuroscience and the Action of Nicotine, Cocaine, and Marijuana in the Brain
(FHS: 25 minutes, DVD, 3-year streaming webcast)
The Brain (FHS: 20 minutes, DVD, 3-year streaming webcast)
The Brain (NIMCO: 30 minutes, DVD)
Brain and Nervous System: Your Information Superhighway (FHS: 31 minutes, DVD, 3-year
streaming webcast)
The Human Brain in Situ (FHS: 19 minutes, DVD, 3-year streaming webcast)
The Human Nervous System: The Brain and Cranial Nerves Videotape (PE: 28 minutes, DVD.
See Lab Manual Preface for details.)
Practice Anatomy Lab™ 3.0 (PAL) (PE: DVD, website)
Sheep Brain Dissection (WNS: 22 minutes, DVD)

Laboratory Materials

*Ordering information is based on a lab size of 24 students, working in groups of 4. A list of supply
house addresses appears in Appendix A.*

Human brain models (dissectable)	12 dissecting kits	safety pins; blunt probes (hot and
3-D model of ventricles	Disposable gloves	cold); cotton swabs; ammonia;
Preserved human brains (if available)	24 pairs of safety glasses	tuning forks; tongue depressors;
Frontally sectioned human brain slice	Soap, sponges, and disinfectant	and solutions of 10% sugar, 10%
(if available)	Materials as needed for cranial	salt, vinegar (1% acetic acid), and
12 preserved sheep brains with menin-	nerves testing: aromatic oils	0.1% quinine
ges and cranial nerves intact	(e.g., vanilla and cloves); eye	
12 dissecting trays	chart; ophthalmoscope; penlight;	

Advance Preparation

1. Make arrangements for appropriate storage, disposal, and cleanup of dissection materials. Check with
   the Department of Health or the Department of Environmental Protection, or their counterparts, for state
   regulations.

2. Designate a disposal container for organic debris, and a dishwashing area with hot soapy water, sponges, and
   a lab disinfectant such as 10% bleach solution or Wavicide-01 (Carolina) for washing down the lab benches.

3. Set out disposable gloves and safety glasses.

4. Set out dissectible human brain models (ideally one per group), and preserved human brains.

5. Set out dissection kits, dissection trays, and sheep brains with meninges and cranial nerves intact.

6. For testing cranial nerve function, set out dropper bottles of oil of cloves and vanilla; eye chart; ophthalmoscope; penlight; safety pins; blunt probes (hot and cold); cotton swabs; salty, sweet, sour, and bitter solutions; ammonia; tuning forks; and tongue depressors. Set out autoclave bag for disposables.

Comments and Pitfalls

1. Students who are not careful readers confuse or do not distinguish between cerebellar and cerebral.

2. Hasty removal of the meninges removes the pituitary gland before its connection to the brain by the infundibulum can be established; occasionally even the optic chiasma is lost. Encourage the students to go slowly and use the scalpel sparingly.

3. The arachnoid meninx may be hard to identify, as it is usually poorly preserved

Answers to Pre-Lab Quiz (pp. 279–280)

1. central nervous system
2. cerebral hemispheres
3. false
4. b, diencephalon
5. medulla oblongata

6. b, cerebellum
7. gray matter
8. b, meninges
9. false
10. Twelve

Answers to Activity and Dissection Questions

Activity 3: Identifying and Testing the Cranial Nerves (pp. 288–290)

3. The trigeminal ganglion, associated with the trigeminal nerve (CN V), is located between the pons and the greater wing of the sphenoid bone. The geniculate ganglion, associated with the facial nerve (CN VII), is in the inner ear cavity. The inferior ganglion, associated with the glossopharyngeal nerve (CN IX), is near the parotid salivary gland. The superior ganglion, associated with the glossopharyngeal nerve (CN IX), is just external to the jugular foramen. The spiral ganglion, associated with the vestibulocochlear nerve (CN VIII), is in the cochlea. The vestibular ganglion, associated with the vestibulocochlear nerve (CN VIII), is in the inner ear.

Dissection: The Sheep Brain (pp. 292–296)

3. The cerebral hemispheres are relatively much larger in the human brain than in the sheep brain.

Ventral Structures

1. The olfactory bulbs are larger in the sheep. The sense of smell is more important to sheep than it is to humans for both protection and locating food.

Dorsal Structures

1. The sheep cerebral fissures are not as deep.
2. The falx cerebelli is not present in the sheep.
4. The corpora quadrigemina are reflex centers for visual and auditory stimuli.

Internal Structures

2. The sheep fornix is large in relation to the size of the sheep's brain when compared with the fornix of the human brain. The fornix links regions of the limbic system, which provides strong emotional response to odors, among other things. Sheep have a more acute sense of smell than humans and rely more on smell to alert them to danger, food sources, etc.

Answers to Group Challenge (p. 296)

Some possible answers to the questions are listed below. Student answers may vary.

1. Which is the "odd" nerve?	Why is it the odd one out?
Optic nerve (II) (Oculomotor nerve (III)) Olfactory nerve (I) Vestibulocochlear nerve (VIII)	*The oculomotor nerve is a primarily motor cranial nerve. Cranial nerves I, II, and VIII are either purely, or mostly, sensory cranial nerves.*
2. Which is the "odd" nerve?	Why is it the odd one out?
Oculomotor nerve (III) Trochlear nerve (IV) Abducens nerve (VI) (Hypoglossal nerve (XII))	*Cranial nerves III, IV, and VI innervate extrinsic eye muscles that move the eye-ball. The hypoglossal nerve does not innervate an extrinsic eye muscle, and is not tested using the same procedure as cranial nerves III, IV, and VI.*
3. Which is the "odd" nerve?	Why is it the odd one out?
Facial nerve (VII) Hypoglossal nerve (XII) (Trigeminal nerve (V)) Glossopharyngeal nerve (IX)	*Cranial nerves VII and IX carry the sensation of taste from the tongue. Cranial nerve XII is a motor nerve to the tongue. The trigeminal nerve does not provide sensory or motor function to the tongue.*

Exercise 17

Copyright © 2016 Pearson Education, Inc.

Gross Anatomy of the Brain and Cranial Nerves

The Human Brain

1. Match the letters on the diagram of the human brain (right lateral view) to the appropriate terms listed at the left.

_h_   1. frontal lobe

_b_   2. parietal lobe

_j_   3. temporal lobe

_f_   4. precentral gyrus

_c_   5. parieto-occipital sulcus

_a_   6. postcentral gyrus

_i_   7. lateral sulcus

_g_   8. central sulcus

_e_   9. cerebellum   _d_   11. occipital lobe

_l_   10. medulla   _k_   12. pons

2. In which of the cerebral lobes are the following functional areas found?

primary auditory cortex: _temporal_   olfactory cortex: _temporal_

primary motor cortex: _frontal_   primary visual cortex: _occipital_

primary somatosensory cortex: _parietal_   Broca's area: _frontal_

3. Which of the following structures are not part of the brain stem? (Circle the appropriate response or responses.)

(cerebral hemispheres)   pons   midbrain   (cerebellum)   medulla oblongata   (diencephalon)

4. Complete the following statements by writing the proper word or phrase on the corresponding blanks at the right.

A(n) _1_ is an elevated ridge of cerebral tissue. The convolutions seen in the cerebrum are important because they increase the _2_. Gray matter is composed of _3_. White matter is composed of _4_. A fiber tract that provides for communication between different parts of the same cerebral hemisphere is called a(n) _5_ tract, whereas one that carries impulses from the cerebrum to lower CNS areas is called a(n) _6_ tract. The caudate nucleus, putamen, and globus pallidus are collectively called the _7_.

1. _gyrus_

2. _surface area_

3. _neuron cell bodies_

4. _myelinated fibers_

5. _association_

6. _projection_

7. _basal nuclei (basal ganglia)_

5. Identify the structures on the following medial view of the human brain stem and diencephalon by matching the numbered areas to the proper terms in the list.

_4___ a. anterior commissure

_18__ b. cerebellum

_15__ c. cerebral aqueduct

_14__ d. cerebral peduncle

_10__ e. choroid plexus

_13__ f. corpora quadrigemina

_1___ g. corpus callosum

_3___ h. fornix

_16__ i. fourth ventricle

_6___ j. hypothalamus

_5___ k. interthalamic adhesion

_8___ l. mammillary bodies

_19__ m. medulla oblongata

_7___ n. optic chiasma

_12__ o. pineal gland

_9___ p. pituitary gland

_17__ q. pons

_2___ r. septum pellucidum

_11__ s. thalamus

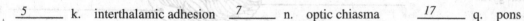

6. Using the letters in front of the terms from question 5, match the appropriate structures with the descriptions given below.

_j___ 1. site of regulation of body temperature and water balance; most important autonomic center

_n___ 2. site where medial fibers of the optic nerves cross

_f___ 3. located in the midbrain; contains reflex centers for vision and audition

_b___ 4. responsible for regulation of posture and coordination of complex muscular movements

_s___ 5. important synapse site for afferent fibers traveling to the sensory cortex

_m___ 6. contains autonomic centers regulating blood pressure, heart rate, and respiratory rhythm, as well as coughing, sneezing, and swallowing centers

_g___ 7. large commissure connecting the cerebral hemispheres

_h___ 8. fiber tract involved with olfaction

_c___ 9. connects the third and fourth ventricles

_s___ 10. encloses the third ventricle

7. Embryologically, the brain arises from the rostral end of a tubelike structure that quickly becomes divided into three major regions. Groups of structures that develop from the embryonic brain are listed below. Designate the embryonic origin of each group as the hindbrain, midbrain, or forebrain.

forebrain 1. the diencephalon, including the thalamus, optic chiasma, and hypothalamus

hindbrain 2. the medulla oblongata, pons, and cerebellum

forebrain 3. the cerebral hemispheres

8. What is the function of the basal nuclei? _They are involved in the regulation, modulation, and refinement of voluntary motor activity._

9. What is the striatum, and how is it related to the fibers of the internal capsule? _The striatum consists of the caudate and putamen nuclei that are part of the basal nuclei (basal ganglia). The fibers of the internal capsule pass through the striatum, giving it a striped or striated appearance, hence the name striatum._

10. A brain hemorrhage within the region of the right internal capsule results in paralysis of the left side of the body.

    Explain why the left side (rather than the right side) is affected. _Because most of the motor fibers cross over to the opposite side at the level of the medulla oblongata_

11. Explain why trauma to the brain stem is often much more dangerous than trauma to the frontal lobes.

    Trauma to the brain stem might damage the medulla oblongata, which contains vital respiratory, cardiac, and vasomotor centers. Also, the reticular activating system, which helps to maintain consciousness, spans the length of the brain stem.

Why This Matters

12. Explain how patients in a vegetative state can have no damage to their cerebral cortex and yet lack awareness of their environment. _These patients lack awareness of their environment because the relay to the cerebral cortex, the thalamus, is damaged and so the sensory signals can't reach the cerebral cortex._

13. Patients in a vegetative state will often reflexively respond to visual and auditory stimuli. Where in the brain are the centers for these reflexes located?

    The superior colliculi contain the centers for visual stimuli and the inferior colliculi contain the centers for auditory stimuli.

    Explain how this phenomenon relates to the unaffected parts of their brain. _The corpora quadrigemina are located in the brain stem which is not affected in the vegetative state._

Meninges of the Brain

14. Identify the meningeal (or associated) structures described below:

dura mater   1. outermost meninx covering the brain; composed of tough fibrous connective tissue

pia mater   2. innermost meninx covering the brain; delicate and highly vascular

arachnoid villi   3. structures instrumental in returning cerebrospinal fluid to the venous blood in the dural venous sinuses

choroid plexus   4. structure that produces the cerebrospinal fluid

arachnoid mater   5. middle meninx; like a cobweb in structure

dura mater   6. its outer layer forms the periosteum of the skull

falx cerebri   7. a dural fold that attaches the cerebrum to the crista galli of the skull

tentorium cerebelli   8. a dural fold separating the cerebrum from the cerebellum

Cerebrospinal Fluid

15. Label the structures involved with circulation of cerebrospinal fluid on the accompanying diagram.

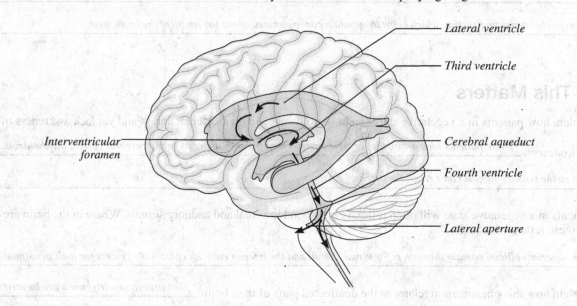

Lateral ventricle

Third ventricle

Interventricular foramen

Cerebral aqueduct

Fourth ventricle

Lateral aperture

Add arrows to the figure above to indicate the flow of cerebrospinal fluid from its formation in the lateral ventricles to the site of its exit from the fourth ventricle. Then fill in the blanks in the following paragraph.

Cerebrospinal fluid flows from the fourth ventricle into the <u>1</u> space surrounding the brain and spinal cord. From this space it drains through the <u>2</u> into the <u>3</u>.

1. _subarachnoid_

2. _arachnoid villi_

3. _dural venous sinuses_

Cranial Nerves

16. Using the terms below, correctly identify all structures indicated by leader lines on the diagram.

a. abducens nerve (VI)

b. accessory nerve (XI)

c. cerebellum

d. cerebral peduncle

e. decussation of the pyramids

f. facial nerve (VII)

g. frontal lobe of cerebral hemisphere

h. glossopharyngeal nerve (IX)

i. hypoglossal nerve (XII)

j. longitudinal fissure

k. mammillary body

l. medulla oblongata

m. oculomotor nerve (III)

n. olfactory bulb

o. olfactory tract

p. optic chiasma

q. optic nerve (II)

r. optic tract

s. pituitary gland

t. pons

u. spinal cord

v. temporal lobe of cerebral hemisphere

w. trigeminal nerve (V)

x. trochlear nerve (IV)

y. vagus nerve (X)

z. vestibulocochlear nerve (VIII)

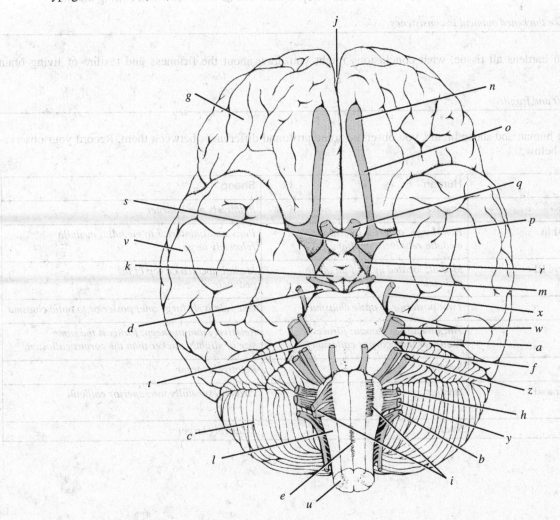

Copyright © 2016 Pearson Education, Inc.

17. Provide the name and number of the cranial nerves involved in each of the following activities, sensations, or disorders.

accessory (XI)   1. rotating the head

olfactory (I)   2. smelling a flower

oculomotor (III)   3. raising the eyelids; pupillary constriction

faci vagus (X)   4. slowing the heart; increasing motility of the digestive tract

facial (VII)   5. involved in Bell's palsy (facial paralysis)

trigeminal (V)   6. chewing food

vestibulocochlear (VIII)   7. listening to music; seasickness

facial (VII)   8. secretion of saliva; tasting well-seasoned food

III, IV, VI   9. involved in "rolling" the eyes (three nerves—provide numbers only)

trigeminal (V)   10. feeling a toothache

optic (II)   11. reading the newspaper

I, II, VIII   12. purely or mostly sensory in function (three nerves—provide numbers only)

Dissection of the Sheep Brain

18. In your own words, describe the firmness and texture of the sheep brain tissue as observed when cutting into it.

Very soft; much like thickened oatmeal in consistency

Because formalin hardens all tissue, what conclusions might you draw about the firmness and texture of living brain tissue?

It must be very soft and fragile.

19. When comparing human and sheep brains, you observed some profound differences between them. Record your observations in the chart below.

Structure	Human	Sheep
Olfactory bulb	*Smaller*	*Relatively much larger*
Pons/medulla relationship	*Pons large; anterior to medulla; medulla relatively smaller*	*Pons small; anterior to medulla; medulla relatively large*
Location of cranial nerve III	*Medial; located in the fold of the peduncle*	*Medial; located on top of the peduncle*
Mammillary body	*Two; posterior to optic chiasma*	*One relatively large one; posterior to optic chiasma*
Corpus callosum	*Thick bundle in human; fornix is thinner than corpus callosum*	*Relatively thin in sheep; fornix is the same size or slightly thicker than the corpus callosum*
Interthalamic adhesion	*Smaller*	*Relatively larger*
Relative size of superior and inferior colliculi	*Smaller*	*Larger, especially the superior colliculi*
Pineal gland	*Smaller*	*Relatively larger*

Electroencephalography

 Time Allotment: 30 minutes for each subject. Allow additional time if students are not acquainted with the recording equipment.

Laboratory Materials

Ordering information is based on a lab size of 24 students, working in groups of 4. A list of supply house addresses appears in Appendix A.

6 oscilloscopes and EEG lead-selector boxes or 6 physiographs and high-gain preamplifiers
6 containers of electrode gel
6 sets of EEG electrodes and leads
6 containers of collodion gel *or* long elastic EEG straps

BIOPAC® BSL System for Windows with BSL software version 3.7.5 to 3.7.7, or BSL System for Mac OS X with BSL software version 3.7.4 to 3.7.7, MP36/35 or MP45 data acquisition unit, PC or Mac computer, electrode lead set, disposable

vinyl electrodes, Lycra® swim cap (such as Speedo® brand) or supportive wrap (such as 3M Coban™ Self-adhering Support Wrap) to press electrodes against head for improved contact, and a cot or lab bench and pillow

Advance Preparation

1. Prepare a set of instructions for the particular recording equipment you will be using. If you are using a physiograph or BIOPAC®, students may be familiar with it from Exercise 14. Be sure to include instructions on correct calibration of the equipment so that meaningful recordings can be made.
2. Set out recording equipment. This can be either an oscilloscope and EEG selector box, a physiograph and high-gain preamplifier, or a BIOPAC® data acquisition unit.
3. Prepare a quiet, dimly lit space with a cot. Have electrodes, electrode leads, electrode gel, and collodion gel available. Long elastic EEG straps or adhesive bandages may be used in place of the collodion.

Comments and Pitfalls

1. It is very important to choose subjects who can relax.
2. Clean the area where the electrode will be attached to provide a better contact.

Answers to Pre-Lab Quiz (p. 303)

1. a, electrical activity of the brain
2. beta waves
3. true
4. a, the earlobe
5. b, breathe rapidly

Answers to Activity Questions

Activity 1: Observing Brain Wave Patterns Using an Oscilloscope or Physiograph (pp. 304–305)

5. The frequency of the brain waves should increase and the amplitude should decrease. It may be characterized as a beta rhythm if the amplitude decreases and the frequency is in the range of 15 to 30 cycles per second.

6. The frequency of the brain waves should increase to become beta waves.

7. Hyperventilation results in alkalosis, which causes overexcitability of the nervous system. The tracings may resemble those of an epileptic seizure.

Activity 2: Electroencephalography Using BIOPAC® (pp. 305–308)

6. The alpha rhythm is observed when the subject is relaxed with the eyes closed, and it usually diminishes when the eyes are open.

The beta rhythm is usually most pronounced when the eyes are open and attentive, or when the subject is performing mental tasks.

The alpha waveforms are greater during the segments recorded when the subject's eyes are closed; the beta waveforms are slightly more pronounced during the signal recorded when the subject's eyes are opened as well as during the segment when the subject's eyes are reclosed. The alpha signal appears more varied than the beta signal.

The delta and theta rhythms are the most varied, especially under these subject conditions. They are most easily observed when the subject makes the transition from mild sleep to deep sleep. It is unlikely that a significant difference can be discerned under these conditions.

NAME _____

LAB TIME/DATE _____

Electroencephalography

Brain Wave Patterns and the Electroencephalogram

1. Define *EEG*. *A record of the electrical activity of the brain* _____

2. Identify the type of brain wave pattern described in each statement below.

_____*delta*_____ below 4 Hz; slow, large waves; normally seen during deep sleep

_____*alpha*_____ rhythm generally apparent when an individual is in a relaxed, nonattentive state with the eyes closed

_____*beta*_____ correlated to the alert state; usually about 14 to 30 Hz

3. What is meant by the term *alpha block*? *A change from an alpha rhythm to increased frequency waves as a result of increased*

alertness, mental concentration, excitement, etc. _____

4. List at least four types of brain lesions that may be determined by EEG studies. *Epileptic foci, infections, tumors, abscesses,*

blood clots _____

5. What is the common result of hypoactivity or hyperactivity of the brain neurons? *Unconsciousness* _____

Observing Brain Wave Patterns

6. How was alpha block demonstrated in the laboratory experiment? *By clapping your hands, which caught the attention of the*

subject. _____

7. What was the effect of mental concentration on the brain wave pattern? *(Should have) increased the frequency of the brain*

waves from the level of the alpha rhythm _____

8. What effect on the brain wave pattern did hyperventilation have? *Produced a fast, irregular pattern.* _____

Electroencephalography Using BIOPAC®

9. Observe the average frequency of the waves you measured for each rhythm. Did the calculated average for each fall within the specified range indicated in the introduction to encephalograms? *The average should fall within the normal range.*

10. Suggest the possible advantages and disadvantages of using electroencephalography in a clinical setting.

    EEG is a useful tool in the clinical setting to assess cerebral activity in generalized brain regions. Because EEG is indirectly recording,

    via the scalp, the activity of millions of nerve cells simultaneously, it is less effective in assessing the function of very specific regions of

    the brain.

The Spinal Cord and Spinal Nerves

 Time Allotment: 1¹/₂ hours.

 Multimedia Resources: See Appendix B for Guide to Multimedia Resource Distributors.

Brain and Nervous System: Your Information Superhighway (FHS: 31 minutes, DVD, 3-year streaming webcast)

The Human Nervous System: The Spinal Cord and Nerves Videotape (PE: 28 minutes, DVD. *See Lab Manual Preface for details.*)

Practice Anatomy Lab™ 3.0 (PAL) (PE: DVD, website)

Laboratory Materials

Ordering information is based on a lab size of 24 students, working in groups of 4. A list of supply house addresses appears in Appendix A.

Spinal cord model (cross section)
3-D cord and spinal of spinal nerves
24 red pencils
24 blue pencils
12–24 preserved spinal cord sections
 with meninges and roots intact

(cow, or maybe saved from sheep
 brain dissection in Exercise 17)
12–24 dissecting trays and dissecting kits
12–24 dissecting microscopes
24 compound microscopes, lens paper,
 lens cleaning solution

24 slides of spinal cord (cross section)
Disposable gloves
24 pairs of safety glasses
Soap, sponges, disinfectant
Post-it Notes

Advance Preparation

1. Make arrangements for appropriate storage, disposal, and cleanup of dissection materials. Check with the Department of Health or the Department of Environmental Protection, or their counterparts, for state regulations.

2. Designate a disposal container for organic debris, and a dishwashing area with hot soapy water and sponges. Provide a lab disinfectant such as Wavicide-01 (Carolina) for washing down the lab benches.

3. Set out disposable gloves and safety glasses.

4. Set out dissection tools, trays, and spinal cord sections from cow specimens or saved from the sheep brain dissection.

5. Set out charts and models of the spinal cord, and red and blue pencils.

6. Set out slides of spinal cord cross section, lens paper, and lens cleaning solution.

7. Set out dissecting microscopes. Have compound microscopes available.

8. Check to be sure that the diagram of the spinal tracts in the text you are using is similar to that in Figure 19.4. If there are differences, decide which you will use and make the appropriate adjustments to the assignment if necessary.

Comments and Pitfalls

1. Students may have trouble distinguishing between gray and white matter in the spinal cord dissection. A drop or two of methylene blue stain with a water rinse may help.

Answers to Pre-Lab Quiz (pp. 311–312)

1. a, conus medullaris
2. c, 31
3. gray
4. false
5. sensory

6. true
7. c, plexuses
8. a, brachial
9. false
10. common fibular

Answers to Activity Questions

Activity 2: Identifying Spinal Cord Tracts (p. 315)

Labels for Figure 19.4:

Left (top to bottom): Ascending (sensory) tracts

Dorsal columns

    Fasciculus gracilis

Dorsal columns

    Fasciculus cuneatus

Dorsal spinocerebellar tract

Ventral spinocerebellar tract

Lateral spinothalamic tract

Ventral spinothalamic tract

Right (top to bottom): Descending (motor) tracts

Lateral reticulospinal tract

Lateral corticospinal tract

Rubrospinal tract

Medial reticulospinal tract

Ventral corticospinal tract

Vestibulospinal tract

Tectospinal tract

Dorsal columns—joint, muscle position sense, fine touch localization

    Fasciculus gracilis—lower trunk and limbs

    Fasciculus cuneatus—neck, upper trunk and limbs

Dorsal spinocerebellar—proprioception

Ventral spinocerebellar—proprioception

Lateral spinothalamic—pain and temperature

Ventral spinothalamic—pressure and crude touch

Lateral corticospinal—cross in medulla, stimuli to skeletal muscles (pyramidal)

Ventral corticospinal—cross at level of synapse, stimuli to skeletal muscles (pyramidal)

Rubrospinal—some upper limb movement

Tectospinalmediate head movements toward visual targets

Vestibulospinal—posture and balance

Medial reticulospinal—muscle tone and visceral motor functions

Lateral reticulospinal—muscle tone and visceral motor functions

Dissection: Spinal Cord (p. 316)

1. The third meninx is the pia mater, which adheres closely to the surface of the brain and spinal cord.

3. The central canal is more oval than circular. It is lined with ependymal cells. Students may observe that the dorsal medial sulcus touches the gray commissure of the spinal cord.

Answers to Group Challenge: Fix the Sequence (p. 322)

Student answers may vary because there may be more than one way to correct a sequence.

1. Cervical plexus, phrenic nerve, diaphragm _____*All correct*_____

2. Brachial plexus, ulnar nerve, palmaris longus _____*Change palmaris longus to any of the following: flexor carpi ulnaris, flexor digitorium profundus, or an intrinsic hand muscle. Or change ulnar nerve to median nerve.*_____

3. Brachial plexus, radial nerve, triceps brachii _____*All correct*_____

4. Cervical plexus, axillary nerve, deltoid _____*Change cervical plexus to brachial plexus.*_____

5. Lumbar plexus, femoral nerve, gracilis _____*Change gracilis to sartorius, pectineus, iliacus, or any of the quadriceps muscles. Or change femoral nerve to obturator nerve.*_____

6. Lumbar plexus, sciatic nerve, common fibular nerve, tibialis anterior _____*Change lumbar plexus to sacral plexus.*_____

7. Sacral plexus, superior gluteal nerve, gluteus maximus _____*Change gluteus maximus to gluteus medius, gluteus minimus, or tensor fasciae latae. Or change superior gluteal nerve to inferior gluteal nerve.*_____

The Spinal Cord and Spinal Nerves

Anatomy of the Spinal Cord

1. Match each anatomical term in the key to the descriptions given below.

   Key: a. cauda equina   b. conus medullaris   c. filum terminale   d. foramen magnum

   _d___ 1. most superior boundary of the spinal cord

   _c___ 2. meningeal extension beyond the spinal cord terminus

   _b___ 3. spinal cord terminus

   _a___ 4. collection of spinal nerves traveling in the vertebral canal below the terminus of the spinal cord

2. Match the key letters on the diagram with the following terms.

   _k___ 1. arachnoid mater

   _a___ 2. central canal

   _c___ 3. dorsal horn

   _h___ 4. dorsal ramus of spinal nerve

   _g___ 5. dorsal root ganglion

   _n___ 6. dorsal root of spinal nerve

   _j___ 7. dura mater

   _o___ 8. gray commissure

   _d___ 9. lateral horn

   _l___ 10. pia mater

   _f___ 11. spinal nerve

   _m___ 12. ventral horn

   _i___ 13. ventral ramus of spinal nerve

   _e___ 14. ventral root of spinal nerve

   _b___ 15. white matter

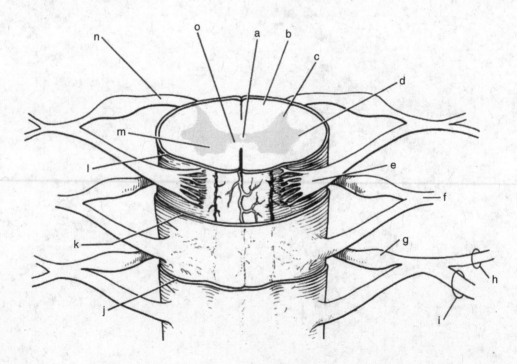

3. Choose the proper answer from the following key to respond to the descriptions relating to spinal cord anatomy. Some terms are used more than once.

Key: a. sensory   b. motor   c. both sensory and motor   d. interneurons

<u>d</u>   1. primary neuron type found in dorsal horn

<u>b</u>   2. primary neuron type found in ventral horn

<u>a</u>   3. neuron type in dorsal root ganglion

<u>b</u>   4. fiber type in ventral root

<u>a</u>   5. fiber type in dorsal root

<u>c</u>   6. fiber type in spinal nerve

4. Where in the vertebral column is a lumbar puncture generally done? *Between L₃ and L₄ or L₄ and L₅.*

Why are these the sites of choice? *The spinal cord ends at the level of L₂; thus there is little chance of damaging it below that level.*

5. The spinal cord is enlarged in two regions, the *cervical* and the *lumbar* regions.

What is the significance of these enlargements? *Nerves serving the limbs issue from these regions of the spinal cord.*

6. How does the position of the gray and white matter differ in the spinal cord and the cerebral hemispheres?

In the spinal cord, the white matter surrounds the gray matter. In the cerebral hemisphere, there is an outer "rind" of gray matter and

deep to that is white matter with a few scattered islands of gray matter.

Why This Matters

7. Where in the body does the varicella-zoster virus lie dormant? *The varicella-zoster virus lies dormant in the cell body of sensory*

neurons in the dorsal root ganglion.

8. Do you think it is possible to get shingles more than once? *Yes.* Explain. *It is possible to get shingles more than once*

because there are multiple nerves (levels) that the virus can be found latent (dormant) in.

9. From the key, choose the name of the tract that might be damaged when the following conditions are observed. Some terms are used more than once.

<u>d, e, f</u>   1. uncoordinated movement

<u>b, c</u>   2. lack of voluntary movement

<u>d, e, f</u>   3. tremors, jerky movements

<u>g</u>   4. diminished pain perception

<u>a, h</u>   5. diminished sense of touch

Key: a. dorsal columns (fasciculus cuneatus and fasciculus gracilis)
b. lateral corticospinal tract
c. ventral corticospinal tract
d. tectospinal tract
e. rubrospinal tract
f. vestibulospinal tract
g. lateral spinothalamic tract
h. ventral spinothalamic tract

Dissection of the Spinal Cord

10. Compare and contrast the meninges of the spinal cord and the brain. *Both the spinal cord and the brain have three meninges:*

   pia mater, arachnoid mater, and dura mater. In the brain, the dura mater has two layers—periosteal and meningeal. The spinal cord

   has only the meningeal layer. In the spinal cord there exists an epidural space between the vertebral bone and the dura, but the dura

   of the brain is tightly adhered to the skull.

11. How can you distinguish the dorsal from the ventral horns? *The ventral horns are wider than the dorsal horns. The dorsal*

   horns extend closer to the edge of the spinal cord.

Spinal Nerves and Nerve Plexuses

12. In the human, there are 31 pairs of spinal nerves, named according to the region of the vertebral column from which they issue. The spinal nerves are named below. Indicate how they are numbered.

   cervical nerves $C_1–C_8$ sacral nerves $S_1–S_5$

   lumbar nerves $L_1–L_5$ thoracic nerves $T_1–T_{12}$

13. The ventral rami of spinal nerves C_1 through T_1 and T_{12} through S_4 take part in forming *plexuses*,

   which serve the *limbs and anterior trunk* of the body. The ventral rami of T_2 through T_{12} run

   between the ribs to serve the *intercostal muscles*. The dorsal rami of the spinal nerves

   serve *the posterior body trunk*.

14. What would happen if the following structures were damaged or transected? Use the key choices for responses.

   Key: a. loss of motor function   b. loss of sensory function   c. loss of both motor and sensory function

   b   1. dorsal root of a spinal nerve   *c*   3. ventral ramus of a spinal nerve

   a   2. ventral root of a spinal nerve

15. Define *nerve plexus.* *A complex network of joining and diverging nerves*

16. Name the major nerves that serve the following body areas.

cervical _____ 1. head, neck, shoulders (name plexus only)

phrenic _____ 2. diaphragm

sciatic _____ 3. posterior thigh

common fibular, tibial, sural, medial, and lateral plantar _____ 4. leg and foot (name two)

median, ulnar _____ 5. anterior forearm muscles (name two)

radial, musculocutaneous _____ 6. arm muscles (name two)

lumbar _____ 7. abdominal wall (name plexus only)

femoral _____ 8. anterior thigh

ulnar _____ 9. medial side of the hand

The Autonomic Nervous System

 Time Allotment: 1 1/2 hours (1 hour).

 Multimedia Resources: See Appendix B for Guide to Multimedia Resource Distributors.

Brain and Nervous System: Your Information Superhighway (FHS: 31 minutes, DVD, 3-year streaming webcast)
Practice Anatomy Lab™ 3.0 (PAL) (PE: DVD website)

Laboratory Materials

Ordering information is based on a lab size of 24 students, working in groups of 4. A list of supply house addresses appears in Appendix A.

Laboratory charts or models of spinal cord, spinal nerves, and sympathetic chain
BIOPAC® BSL System for Windows with BSL software version 3.7.5 to 3.7.7, or BSL System for Mac OS X with BSL software

version 3.7.4 to 3.7.7, MP36/35 or MP45 data acquisition unit, PC or Mac computer, respiratory transducer belt, EDA/GSR finger leads or disposable finger electrodes with EDA pinch leads, electrode lead set, disposable

vinyl electrodes, conduction gel, and nine 8 1/2 by 11 inch sheets of paper of different colors (white, black, red, blue, green, yellow, orange, brown, and purple) to be viewed in this sequence

Advance Preparation

1. Set out charts and/or models of the spinal cord and sympathetic chain.
2. Set out equipment and materials for the BIOPAC® activity. Introduce your students to the basic features of the equipment prior to beginning the lab activity.

Answers to Pre-Lab Quiz (p. 327)

1. autonomic
2. craniosacral
3. false
4. sympathetic
5. false

Activity 2: Comparing Sympathetic and Parasympathetic Effects (p. 330)

Organ	Parasympathetic effect	Sympathetic effect
Heart	*Decreases rate*	*Increases rate and force*
Bronchioles of lungs	*Constricts*	*Dilates*
Digestive tract	*Increases motility; stimulates secretion*	*Decreases activity; closes sphincters*
Urinary bladder	*Contracts wall; relaxes sphincter*	*Relaxes wall; constricts sphincter*
Iris of the eye	*Constricts pupil*	*Dilates pupil*
Blood vessels (most)	*Little or no effect*	*Constricts most vessels*
Penis/clitoris	*Causes erection*	*Causes ejaculation*
Sweat glands	*No effect*	*Stimulates secretion*
Adrenal medulla	*No effect*	*Stimulates medulla to secrete epinephrine and norepinephrine*
Pancreas	*Stimulates insulin secretion*	*Decreases insulin secretion*

Activity 3: Exploring the Galvanic Skin Response (Electrodermal Activity) within a Polygraph Using BIOPAC® (pp. 330–336)

Data Analysis

12. It is likely that the most significant changes will be observed when the face is touched.

There may or may not be a significant change after each color presentation.

The responses will vary from student to student, depending on the affective nature of the question.

Colors can affect mood, which can be observed through a subsequent change in autonomic activity.

Specific questions might elicit an emotional response that can be observed through a subsequent change in autonomic activity.

NAME _____

LAB TIME/DATE _____

The Autonomic Nervous System

Parasympathetic and Sympathetic Divisions

1. List the names of the two motor neurons of the autonomic nervous system. *Preganglionic neuron and postganglionic neuron*

2. List the names and numbers of the four cranial nerves that the parasympathetic division of the ANS arises from.

   Cranial nerves III (oculomotor), VII (facial), IX (glossopharyngeal), and X (vagus)

3. List two types of sympathetic ganglia that contain postganglionic cell bodies. *Sympathetic trunk ganglia and collateral ganglia*

4. List two types of parasympathetic ganglia that contain postganglionic cell bodies. *Terminal ganglia and intramural ganglia*

5. Which part of the rami communicantes contains nonmyelinated fibers? *The gray ramus communicans contains nonmyelinated fibers (axons).*

6. The following chart states a number of characteristics. Use a check mark to show which division of the autonomic nervous system is involved in each.

Sympathetic division	Characteristics	Parasympathetic division
✓	Postganglionic axons secrete norepinephrine; adrenergic fibers	
	Postganglionic axons secrete acetylcholine; cholinergic fibers	✓
	Long preganglionic axon; short postganglionic axon	✓
✓	Short preganglionic axon; long postganglionic axon	
	Arises from cranial and sacral nerves	✓
✓	Arises from spinal nerves T_1 through L_3	
	Normally in control	✓
✓	"Fight-or-flight" system	
	Has more specific effects	✓
✓	Has rami communicantes	
✓	Has extensive branching of preganglionic axons	

Galvanic Skin Response (Electrodermal Activity) Within a Polygraph Using BIOPAC®

7. Describe exactly how, from a physiological standpoint, EDA/GSR can be correlated with activity of the autonomic nervous system. *The autonomic nervous system controls sweat glands of the skin. Increased moisture on the skin decreases its electrical resistance, which can be recorded.*

8. Based on this brief exposure to a polygraph, explain why this might not be an exact tool for testing the sincerity and honesty of a subject. Refer to your data to support your conclusions.

   It is not possible to state with certainty that every subject who lies will have an absolutely predictable autonomic nervous system response.

   For this reason, although GSR is useful as an investigative tool, it is not accepted as an exact measurement tool.

Human Reflex Physiology

Suggestion for Alternative Equipment

Intelitool®, PowerLab®, and iWorks® may be used as alternatives to this traditional exercise. Instructions for these software programs can be found in the Instructor's Resources section of the MasteringA&P course.

Time Allotment: 1 hour.

Multimedia Resources: See Appendix B for Guide to Multimedia Resource Distributors.

Decision (FHS: 28 minutes, DVD, 3-year streaming webcast)

Solutions:

Bleach Solution, 10%
Measure out 100 milliliters of bleach. Add water (undistilled) to a final volume of 1 liter.

Laboratory Materials

Ordering information is based on a lab size of 24 students, working in groups of 4. A list of supply house addresses appears in Appendix A.

6 reflex hammers
6 sharp pencils
6 small pieces of sterile absorbent cotton
6 tongue depressors
6 metric rulers
6 reaction time rulers (if available)
6 flashlights
6 beakers (100 or 250 milliliter)

6 10- or 25-milliliter graduated cylinders
6 dropper bottles of lemon juice
6 packages of wide-range pH paper
Disposable autoclave bag
6 wash bottles of 10% bleach
Large laboratory bucket of 10% bleach
Cot (if available)

BIOPAC® BSL System for Windows with BSL software version 3.7.5 to 3.7.7, or BSL System for Mac OS X with BSL software version 3.7.4 to 3.7.7, MP36/35 or MP45 data acquisition unit, PC or Mac computer, hand switch, and headphones

---

Advance Preparation

1. Fill a large laboratory bucket with *10% bleach solution* and set out an autoclave bag for disposable items. Set out wash bottles of *10% bleach solution.*

2. For each group, set out a reflex hammer, a sharp pencil, a small piece of sterile absorbent cotton, a tongue depressor, a metric ruler, a 12-inch ruler or reaction time ruler, a flashlight, a 100- or 250-milliliter beaker, a 10- or 25-milliliter graduated cylinder, a dropper bottle of lemon juice, and wide-range pH paper.

3. Set out equipment and materials for the BIOPAC® activity. Introduce your students to the basic features of the equipment prior to beginning the lab activity.

Comments and Pitfalls

1. Be sure that the same student does all parts of the stretch reflex experiment.

2. Pupillary reflexes are more easily tested on subjects with light-colored irises.

3. Students do not always distinguish between the general term *pupillary reflexes* and the pupillary light reflex. Emphasize that the pupillary light reflex and the consensual response are both examples of pupillary reflexes.

4. Students often erroneously try to catch the ruler with their hands rather than between the thumb and forefinger in Activity 9. Also, be sure that the same subject does all four parts of this experiment.

Answers to Pre-Lab Quiz (p. 339)

1. A reflex is a rapid, predictable, involuntary motor response to a stimulus.
2. somatic
3. d, sensory neuron
4. false
5. c, tendon or ligament
6. d, salivary
7. true
8. pupillary light reflex, consensual reflex
9. glands
10. false

Answers to Activity Questions

Activity 1: Initiating Stretch Reflexes (pp. 341–343)

1. The leg swings forward as the quadriceps muscles contract. (The hamstrings are reciprocally inhibited.) The femoral nerve is carrying the impulses.

2. The response is usually greater than the first response. Mental distraction seems to increase the reflex response.

3. The response during other muscle activity is usually more vigorous due to increased facilitation in the spinal cord.

4. Fatigue results in a less vigorous response. Muscle function is responsible. Fatigue likely results from a problem with excitation-contraction coupling, or possibly a problem at the neuromuscular junction. Either could reduce the response of muscle to nervous stimulation.

5. Plantar flexion due to the contraction of the triceps surae (gastrocnemius and soleus muscles) is the result. Contraction of the gastrocnemius muscle usually results in plantar flexion of the foot.

Activity 2: Initiating the Crossed-Extensor Reflex (p. 343)

The subject withdraws the pricked hand by flexion of the elbow. Then the other elbow extends. The extensor part of the reflex is relatively slow, probably because many association neurons are involved.

Activity 3: Initiating the Plantar Reflex (p. 343)

The normal response is downward flexion (curling) and adduction of the toes.

Activity 4: Initiating the Corneal Reflex (p. 344)

The subject blinks. The function is to protect the eye. The subject experiences discomfort (if not pain) because the cornea lacks pressure receptors but is richly supplied with pain receptors.

Activity 5: Initiating the Gag Reflex (p. 344)

The posterior pharyngeal walls elevate as pharyngeal muscles contract, and the subject gags.

Activity 6: Initiating Pupillary Reflexes (pp. 344–345)

3. The left pupil contracts (the pupillary light reflex).

4. The right pupil also contracts. The contralateral (consensual) reflex indicates that there is some connection between the pathways for each eye.

Activity 7: Initiating the Ciliospinal Reflex (p. 345)

1. The left pupil dilates; the right pupil does not.

2. Sympathetic innervation of the irises does not seem to be as closely integrated as parasympathetic innervation, since a contralateral response was not observed.

Activity 8: Initiating the Salivary Reflex (p. 345)

3. The volume of saliva is much greater after stimulation with lemon juice. The final saliva pH should be close to the initial reading (usually pH 6–7). It is much less acidic than the reading 10 seconds after the application of lemon juice, as saliva contains sodium bicarbonate.

Activity 9: Testing Reaction Time for Intrinsic and Learned Reflexes (p. 346)

3. Addition of a signal word should increase reaction time because it takes time to discriminate the words.

4. Student data.

Activity 10: Measuring Reaction Time Using BIOPAC® (pp. 347–348)

Data Analysis

5. It is possible that there will be a difference between Segment 1 and Segment 2. If Segment 2 appears to be faster, this is likely due to the learning that occurred from the experience acquired during Segment 1. Responses may be more rapid during Segment 4 than in Segment 3 for the same reason.

Human Reflex Physiology

The Reflex Arc

1. Define *reflex*. _A rapid, predictable, involuntary motor response to a stimulus that is mediated over a neural pathway called a reflex arc_

2. Name five essential components of a reflex arc: _receptor_, _sensory neuron_, _integration center_, _motor neuron_, and _effector_

3. In general, what is the importance of reflex testing in a routine physical examination? _Allows the condition of the nervous system to be assessed. Pathology is indicated by exaggeration, distortion, or absence of reflexes normally present._

Somatic and Autonomic Reflexes

4. Use the key terms to complete the statements given below. Some terms are used more than once.

   Key: a. abdominal reflex   d. corneal reflex   g. patellar reflex
         b. calcaneal tendon reflex   e. crossed-extensor reflex   h. plantar reflex
         c. ciliospinal reflex   f. gag reflex   i. pupillary light reflex

   Reflexes classified as somatic reflexes include _a_, _b_, _d_, _e_, _f_, _g_, and _h_.

   Of these, the stretch reflexes are _b_ and _g_, and the superficial reflexes are _a_ and _h_.

   Reflexes classified as autonomic reflexes include _c_ and _i_.

5. Name three cord-mediated reflexes. _Calcaneal tendon reflex, patellar reflex, and crossed-extensor reflex_

   Name three somatic spinal reflexes in which the higher brain centers participate. _Abdominal, cremaster, and plantar reflexes_

6. Can the stretch reflex be elicited in a pithed animal (that is, an animal in which the brain has been destroyed)? _Yes, in a singly pithed frog in which the cord is intact_

   Explain your answer. _It is a cord-mediated reflex (initiated and executed at the spinal cord level)._

7. Trace the reflex arc, naming efferent and afferent nerves, receptors, effectors, and integration centers for the two reflexes listed. (*Hint:* Remember which nerve innervates the anterior thigh and which nerve innervates the posterior thigh.)

   patellar reflex: _Proprioceptors (stretch receptors) in the quadriceps muscle → afferent fibers of femoral nerve → spinal cord → efferent fibers of femoral nerve → quadriceps muscle_

   calcaneal tendon reflex: _Proprioceptors (stretch receptors) in the gastrocnemius muscle → afferent fibers of sciatic nerve → spinal cord → efferent fibers of sciatic nerve → gastrocnemius (triceps surae) muscle_

8. Three factors that influence the speed and effectiveness of reflex arcs were investigated in conjunction with patellar reflex testing—mental distraction, effect of simultaneous muscle activity in another body area, and fatigue.

Which of these factors increase(s) the excitatory level of the spinal cord? *Simultaneous muscle activity, mental distraction*

Which factor decreases the excitatory level of the muscles? *Muscle fatigue (exercise)*

When the subject was concentrating on an arithmetic problem, did the change noted in the patellar reflex indicate that brain activity is necessary for the patellar reflex or only that it may modify it? *Only that it may modify it. It will occur in any case.*

9. Name the division of the autonomic nervous system responsible for each of the reflexes listed.

ciliospinal reflex: *sympathetic*   salivary reflex: *parasympathetic*

pupillary light reflex: *parasympathetic*

10. The pupillary light reflex, the crossed-extensor reflex, and the corneal reflex illustrate the purposeful nature of reflex activity. Describe the protective aspect of each.

pupillary light reflex: *It protects the retina from excessive illumination, which is damaging to the photoreceptors.*

corneal reflex: *It protects the eye from trauma.*

crossed-extensor reflex: *It withdraws the injured limb from the painful stimulus while simultaneously extending the opposite limb. If the upper limbs are involved, extension of the opposite limb acts to push away the stimulus. If the lower limbs are involved, extension of the opposite limb prepares the limb to receive the body weight.*

11. Was the pupillary consensual response contralateral or ipsilateral? *Contralateral*

Why would such a response be of significant value in this particular reflex? *Usually, if a light source is intense, both eyes are illuminated.*

12. Differentiate between the types of activities accomplished by somatic and autonomic reflexes. *Autonomic reflexes involve the activation of smooth or cardiac muscle and glands. Somatic reflexes involve the activation of skeletal muscles.*

13. Several types of reflex activity were not investigated in this exercise. The most important of these are autonomic reflexes, which are difficult to illustrate in a laboratory situation. To rectify this omission, complete the following chart, using references as necessary.

Reflex	Organ involved	Receptors stimulated	Action
Micturition (urination)	*Bladder*	*Stretch receptors in the bladder wall*	*Impulse goes to cord (afferent fibers) and returns (efferent fibers), causing bladder contraction and relaxation of its internal sphincter*
Defecation	*Rectum*	*Stretch receptors in the rectal walls (colon terminus)*	*Afferent impulses to the sacral region of the cord followed by efferent impulses to the muscles of the rectum and the anal sphincters to initiate feces evacuation*
Carotid sinus	*Carotid artery*	*Pressure receptors in the carotid sinus*	*When arterial pressure increases excessively, sensory impulses travel to the cardioinhibitory center in the medulla oblongata, which in turn sends efferent impulses via the vagus nerve to slow the heart, thus decreasing its rate and the blood pressure.*

Reaction Time of Intrinsic and Learned Reflexes

14. How do intrinsic and learned reflexes differ? *Although there is no clear-cut distinction, intrinsic reflexes are generally inborn and use a simple reflex arc. Learned reflexes are the result of practice and repetition, involving more neural pathways and higher intellectual activities.*

15. Name at least three factors that may modify reaction time to a stimulus. *Receptor sensitivity, nerve conduction velocity, and the number of neurons and synapses involved.*

16. In general, how did the response time for the learned activity performed in the laboratory compare to that for the simple patellar reflex? *The response time for the learned activity was much longer.*

17. Did the response time without verbal stimuli decrease with practice? *Yes* Explain the reason for this. *The subject was anticipating the stimulus.*

18. Explain, in detail, why response time increased when the subject had to react to a word stimulus. *Choice and decision making about the response involved and the large number of synapses involved increased the response time.*

19. When you were measuring reaction time in the BIOPAC® activity, was there a difference in reaction time when the stimulus was predictable versus unpredictable? Explain your answer. *It is most likely that the reaction time will be shorter during the segments with predictable, evenly spaced stimuli than during the random segments. The subject can more easily predict the onset of the stimulus, reducing reaction time.*

22 EXERCISE

General Sensation

Time Allotment: 1 1/2 hours.

Multimedia Resources: See Appendix B for Guide to Multimedia Resource Distributors.

Touch (part of the NOVA Mystery of the Senses series) (IM: 60 minutes each, 5-piece DVD set)

Laboratory Materials

Ordering information is based on a lab size of 24 students, working in groups of 4. A list of supply house addresses appears in Appendix A.

24 compound microscopes, lens paper, lens cleaning solution, immersion oil

24 slides (longitudinal sections) of lamellar corpuscles, tactile corpuscles, tendon organs, and muscle spindles

Large beaker of ice water with chipped ice

Hot water bath set at 45°C, laboratory thermometer

6 sets of red, black, and blue fine-point felt-tipped markers

6 calipers or esthesiometers

6 millimeter rulers

18 large finger bowls or 1000-milliliter beakers

24 coins (nickels or quarters)

6 towels

Advance Preparation

1. Set out prepared slides of lamellar corpuscles, tactile corpuscles, tendon organs, and muscle spindles. If time is a problem, set these up as a demonstration.

2. Set out lens paper, lens cleaning solution, and immersion oil. Have compound microscopes available.

3. Set out black, red, and blue felt-tipped markers, calipers or two-point discriminators or esthesiometers (sometimes called anesthesiometers), and millimeter rulers (one each per group).

4. Prepare a small water bath set at 45°C.

5. Set out beakers containing chipped ice and water.

6. Have at least four nickels or quarters available.

7. For each group, set out three large finger bowls or beakers, a thermometer, and paper towels. Have ice water available.

Comments and Pitfalls

1. Remind the students to use caution when adjusting the width of the calipers or two-point discriminators in the two-point discrimination test. Caution the students against dragging the sharp tips along the surface of the skin. Wooden toothpicks may be substituted for calipers.

2. If a student has Raynaud's disease and is the subject in the Referred Pain experiment (Activity 6), he or she may experience temporary numbness of the hand. This experiment works best on subjects with thin arms.

3. Use water-based, felt-tipped pens or have some sort of stain remover available.

4. Adaptation of the hand to ice water may take longer than two minutes. You may wish to warn students that it may be painful to keep their hands in the ice water long enough to experience adaptation.

Answers to Pre-Lab Quiz (pp. 353–354)

1. sight, hearing, equilibrium, smell, or taste
2. a, exteroceptors
3. true
4. b, in the dermal papillae of hairless skin
5. a, deep pressure and vibrations
6. true
7. tactile localization
8. b, adaptation
9. false
10. b, elbow in ice water to test the ulnar nerve response

Answers to Activity Questions

Activity 2: Determining the Two-Point Threshold (p. 356)

Fingertips and lips usually have the greatest density of touch receptors.

Activity 3: Testing Tactile Localization (p. 357)

2. The ability to locate the stimulus should not improve with repeated trials because the receptor density remains unchanged.

Activity 4: Demonstrating Adaptation of Touch Receptors (p. 357)

3. The pressure sensation returns when coins are added to the stack. The same receptors are probably being used. Generator potentials are graded and stronger stimuli produce larger potentials and thus increased frequency of nerve impulses.

Activity 5: Demonstrating Adaptation of Temperature Receptors (pp. 357–358)

1. The water will feel warm to the left hand. After the left hand has been in the warm water for one minute the water will feel much less warm; the water will feel very warm to the right hand. Yes, adaptation has occurred in the left hand.

3. After two minutes the warm water will begin to feel lukewarm to the right hand. The hand in the ice water may hurt and the experiment may have to go longer than two minutes to observe adaptation. Adaptation to the cold seems to take longer. The right hand adapts more quickly.

4. The water feels cool to the right hand and warm to the left hand.

Activity 6: Demonstrating the Phenomenon of Referred Pain (p. 358)

Initially the elbow feels cold and then begins to hurt. After a while a tingling sensation can be felt in the fingers and the palm of the hand. The fingers may then begin to ache. The ulnar nerve serves several hand and finger muscles as well as the skin of a portion of the hand. All above sensations fade during the three minutes after removal.

General Sensation

Structure of General Sensory Receptors

1. Differentiate between interoceptors and exteroceptors relative to location and stimulus source.

interoceptor: *In viscera or deep in body tissues; internal stimuli*

exteroceptor: *At or close to the body surface; stimuli in external environment*

2. A number of activities and sensations are listed in the chart below. For each, check whether the receptors would be exteroceptors or interoceptors; and then name the specific receptor types. (Because specific visceral receptors were not described in detail in this exercise, you need only indicate that the receptor is a visceral receptor if it falls into that category.)

Activity or sensation	Exteroceptor	Interoceptor	Specific receptor type
Backing into a sun-heated iron railing	✓		*Thermoreceptors or pain receptors depending upon the temperature*
Someone steps on your foot	✓ ✓		*Pain receptors* *Lamellar corpuscles*
Reading a street sign	✓		*Rods/cones of the eye (photoreceptors)*
Leaning on your elbows	✓	✓	*Lamellar corpuscles Proprioceptors*
Doing sit-ups		✓	*Proprioceptors*
The "too full" sensation		✓	*Visceral receptors (stretch)*

Receptor Physiology

3. Explain how the sensory receptors act as transducers. *They convert other energy types (e.g., pressure [mechanical energy], to the electrical nerve impulse).*

4. Define *stimulus*. *A change in the environment of a sensory receptor*

5. What was demonstrated by the two-point discrimination test? *The relative density of touch receptors in various body areas (lips, fingertips, etc.)*

How well did your results correspond to your predictions? *Answers may vary.*

What is the relationship between the accuracy of the subject's tactile localization and the results of the two-point discrimination test? *Areas with the most accurate tactile localization were demonstrated to have the smallest two-point thresholds.*

6. Define *punctate distribution*. _Having specific localization or found at certain discrete points_

7. Several questions regarding general sensation are posed below. Answer each by placing your response in the appropriately numbered blanks to the right.

1. Which cutaneous receptors are the most numerous?   1. _pain receptors_

2–3. Which two body areas tested were most sensitive to touch?   2–3. _lips, fingertips_

4–5. Which two body areas tested were least sensitive to touch?   4–5. _ventral forearm, back of neck_

6–8. Where would referred pain appear if the following organs were receiving painful stimuli: (6) gallbladder, (7) kidneys, and (8) appendix? (Use your textbook if necessary.)

6. _right inferior thorax_

7. _lumbar region_

8. _right lower quadrant of abdominal surface_

9. Where was referred pain felt when the elbow was immersed in ice water during the laboratory experiment?   9. _medial aspect of hand (medial aspect of upper arm)_

10. What region of the cerebrum interprets the kind and intensity of stimuli that cause cutaneous sensations?   10. _somatosensory association cortex_

8. Define *adaptation of sensory receptors*. _Decline in receptor sensitivity and stimulation with prolonged unchanging stimuli_

9. Why is it advantageous to have pain receptors that are sensitive to all vigorous stimuli, whether heat, cold, or pressure? _Because all of these stimuli, if excessive, cause tissue damage._

Why is the nonadaptability of pain receptors important? _Pain is a warning of actual or potential tissue damage._

10. Imagine yourself without any cutaneous sense organs. Why might this be very dangerous? _Many external stimuli (heat, cold, pressure) that can threaten homeostasis might go undetected, and proper protective measures might not be taken._

Why This Matters

11. Explain why "brain freeze" is a type of referred pain. _The location where the pain is felt is different than the location of the stimulus._

12. Describe the location of the stimulus for "brain freeze" and the location of the pain as interpreted by the brain. _The cold stimulus is located on the palate and the throat, but the pain is felt in the forehead._

23 EXERCISE

Special Senses: Anatomy of the Visual System

Time Allotment: 1 1/2 hours.

Multimedia Resources: See Appendix B for Guide to Multimedia Resource Distributors.

The Eye: Structure, Function, and Control of Movement (FHS: 54 minutes, DVD)
Eyes and Ears (FHS: 28 minutes, DVD, 3-year streaming webcast)
Practice Anatomy Lab™ 3.0 (PAL) (PE: DVD, website)
The Senses (FHS: 20 minutes, DVD, 3-year streaming webcast)
Sheep Eye Dissection (WNS: 15 minutes, VHS, DVD)
Vision (part of the NOVA Mystery of the Senses series) (IM: 60 minutes each, 5-piece DVD set)

Solutions:

Bleach Solution, 10%
Measure out 100 milliliters of bleach. Add water (undistilled) to a final volume of 1 liter.

Laboratory Materials

Ordering information is based on a lab size of 24 students, working in groups of 4. A list of supply house addresses appears in Appendix A.

Dissectible eye model and/or chart of eye anatomy
12–24 preserved cow or sheep eyes
12–24 dissecting pans and dissecting kits

24 compound microscopes, lens paper, lens cleaning solution
24 slides (longitudinal section) of eye showing retinal layers

Disposable gloves
24 pairs of safety glasses
Soap, sponges, and disinfectant

Advance Preparation

1. Make arrangements for appropriate storage and disposal of dissection materials. Check with the Department of Health or the Department of Environmental Protection for state regulations.

2. Designate a disposal container for organic debris and a dishwashing area with hot soapy water and sponges. Provide lab disinfectant such as Wavicide-01 (biology supply company) or *10% bleach solution* for washing down the lab benches.

3. Set out disposable gloves and safety glasses.

4. Set out dissecting kits, dissecting pans, and preserved cow or sheep eyes. Plan for groups of two or individual dissections.

5. Set out dissectible eye models and/or eye anatomy charts.

6. Set out slides of the eye showing retinal layers, lens paper, and lens cleaning solution. Have compound microscopes available. As an alternative, set up a demonstration slide of the retina.

Comments and Pitfalls

1. Preserved cow eyes are often misshapen, and inexperienced students may need help locating and identifying the cornea at the beginning of the dissection.

Answers to Pre-Lab Quiz (p. 361)

1. conjunctiva
2. d, six
3. c, cornea
4. aqueous humor
5. true

Answers to Activity Questions

Activity 1: Identifying Accessory Eye Structures (p. 363)

Right eye: medial rectus

Left eye: lateral rectus (and on occasion the superior or inferior oblique)

Dissection: The Cow (Sheep) Eye (pp. 365–367)

6. The optic disc

Activity 4: Predicting the Effects of Visual Pathway Lesions (p. 368)

A lesion in the right optic nerve affects medial and lateral vision of the right eye. (The person is blind in the right eye.)

A sagittal lesion through the optic chiasma affects medial vision in both eyes. (The lateral peripheral vision is diminished.) Sagittal lesions also eliminate binocular vision.

A lesion in the left optic tract affects left lateral and right medial vision. (While looking straight ahead, nothing is seen in the far right visual field.)

A lesion in the right primary visual cortex affects right lateral and left medial vision. (While looking straight ahead, nothing is seen in the far left visual field.)

23 REVIEW SHEET
EXERCISE

Special Senses:
Anatomy of the Visual System

Anatomy of the Eye

1. Name five accessory eye structures that contribute to the formation of lacrimal fluid (tears) and/or help lubricate the eyeball, and then describe the major secretory product of each.

Accessory structures	Product
lacrimal glands	*saline solution; lysozyme*
conjunctiva	*mucus*
tarsal glands	*oily secretion*
caruncle	*whitish, oily secretion*
ciliary glands	*sweat*

2. The eyeball is wrapped in adipose tissue within the bony orbit. What is the function of the adipose tissue?

   To package, protect, and cushion the eyeball in the bony orbit

3. Why does one often have to blow one's nose after crying? *Because tears drain into the nasal cavities via the nasolacrimal ducts*

4. Identify the extrinsic eye muscle predominantly responsible for each action described below.

   lateral rectus _____ 1. turns the eye laterally

   medial rectus _____ 2. turns the eye medially

   inferior oblique _____ 3. turns the eye up and laterally

   inferior rectus _____ 4. turns the eye down and medially

   superior rectus _____ 5. turns the eye up and medially

   superior oblique _____ 6. turns the eye down and laterally

5. What is a sty? *Inflammation of a small oil or sweat gland associated with the eye exterior* _____

   Conjunctivitis? *Inflammation of the conjunctiva* _____

6. Correctly identify each lettered structure in the diagram by writing the letter next to its name in the numbered list. Use an appropriate reference if necessary.

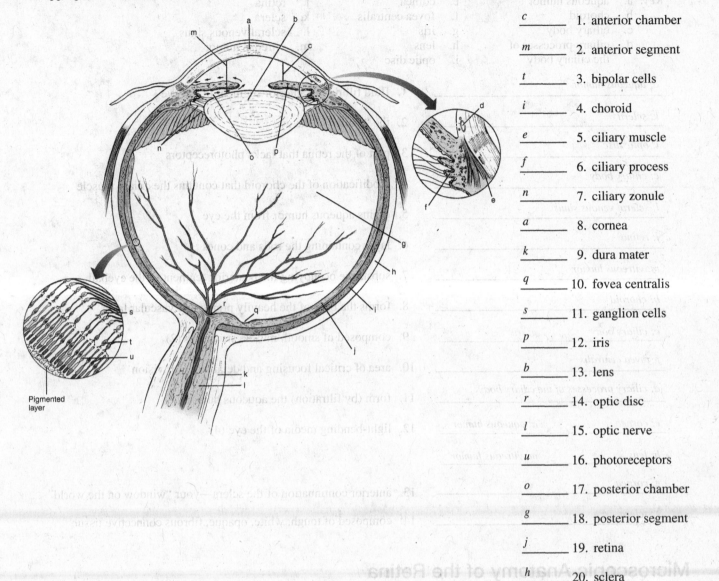

c		1. anterior chamber
m		2. anterior segment
t		3. bipolar cells
i		4. choroid
e		5. ciliary muscle
f		6. ciliary process
n		7. ciliary zonule
a		8. cornea
k		9. dura mater
q		10. fovea centralis
s		11. ganglion cells
p		12. iris
b		13. lens
r		14. optic disc
l		15. optic nerve
u		16. photoreceptors
o		17. posterior chamber
g		18. posterior segment
j		19. retina
h		20. sclera
d		21. scleral venous sinus

Notice the arrows drawn close to the left side of the iris in the diagram on page 362. What do they indicate?

The flow of aqueous humor from the ciliary processes of the ciliary body to the scleral venous sinus

7. The iris is composed primarily of two smooth muscle layers.
Which muscle layer dilates the pupil? *The dilator pupillae*

8. You would expect the pupil to be dilated in which of the following circumstances? Circle the correct response.

a. in bright light b. in dim light

9. The intrinsic eye muscles are controlled by (circle the correct response):

autonomic nervous system somatic nervous system

10. Match the key responses with the descriptive statements that follow. Some choices will be used more than once.

Key: a. aqueous humor   e. cornea   j. retina
        b. choroid   f. fovea centralis   k. sclera
        c. ciliary body   g. iris   l. scleral venous sinus
        d. ciliary processes of   h. lens   m. vitreous humor
            the ciliary body   i. optic disc

a; aqueous humor   1. fluid filling the anterior segment of the eye

k; sclera   2. the "white" of the eye

i; optic disc   3. part of the retina that lacks photoreceptors

c; ciliary body   4. modification of the choroid that contains the ciliary muscle

l; scleral venous sinus   5. drains aqueous humor from the eye

j; retina   6. layer containing the rods and cones

m; vitreous humor   7. substance occupying the posterior segment of the eyeball

b; choroid   8. forms the bulk of the heavily pigmented vascular layer

c; ciliary body   , *g; iris*   9. composed of smooth muscle structures (2)

f; fovea centralis   10. area of critical focusing and detailed color vision

d; ciliary processes of the ciliary body   11. form (by filtration) the aqueous humor

e; cornea   , *a; aqueous humor*   12. light-bending media of the eye (4)

h; lens   , *m; vitreous humor*

e; cornea   13. anterior continuation of the sclera—your "window on the world"

k; sclera   14. composed of tough, white, opaque, fibrous connective tissue

Microscopic Anatomy of the Retina

11. The two major layers of the retina are the pigmented and neural layers. In the neural layer, the neuron populations are arranged as follows from the pigmented layer to the vitreous humor. (Circle the proper response.)

bipolar cells, ganglion cells, photoreceptors   photoreceptors, ganglion cells, bipolar cells

ganglion cells, bipolar cells, photoreceptors   (photoreceptors, bipolar cells, ganglion cells)

12. The axons of the ___*ganglion*___ cells form the optic nerve, which exits from the eyeball.

13. Complete the following statements by writing either *rods* or *cones* on each blank.

The dim light receptors are the ___*rods*___. Only ___*cones*___ are found in the fovea centralis, whereas

mostly ___*rods*___ are found in the periphery of the retina. ___*Cones*___ are the photoreceptors that operate best

in bright light and allow for color vision.

Dissection of the Cow (Sheep) Eye

14. What modification of the choroid that is not present in humans is found in the cow eye? _Tapetum lucidum_

What is its function? _To reflect light that enters the eye, thus increasing light stimulation of the retina under dim light conditions_

15. What does the retina look like? _Thin yellowish white or tan membrane (often becomes crumpled during dissection of the eye)_

At what point is it attached to the posterior aspect of the eyeball? _At the optic disc_

Visual Pathways to the Brain

16. The visual pathway to the occipital lobe of the brain consists most simply of a chain of five cells. Beginning with the photoreceptor cell of the retina, name them, and note their location in the pathway.

1. _photoreceptor cell; retina_

2. _bipolar cell; retina_

3. _ganglion cell; retina_

4. _neuron; lateral geniculate nucleus of the thalamus_

5. _cortical neuron; primary visual cortex of the cerebral hemisphere(s)_

17. Visual field tests are done to reveal destruction along the visual pathway from the retina to the optic region of the brain. Note where the lesion is likely to be in the following cases.

Normal vision in left eye visual field; absence of vision in right eye visual field: _Right optic nerve_

Normal vision in both eyes for right half of the visual field; absence of vision in both eyes for left half of the visual field:

Right optic tract (or right primary visual cortex)

18. How is the right optic _tract_ anatomically different from the right optic _nerve_? _The right optic nerve contains fibers from the right eye only. The right optic tract contains fibers from the lateral aspect of the right eye and the medial aspect of the left eye._

Special Senses: Visual Tests and Experiments

Time Allotment: 1 1/2 hours.

Multimedia Resources: See Appendix B for Guide to Multimedia Resource Distributors.

The Eye: Structure, Function, and Control of Movement (FHS: 54 minutes, DVD)
Eyes and Ears (FHS: 28 minutes, DVD, 3-year streaming webcast)
Practice Anatomy Lab™ 3.0 (PAL) (PE: DVD, website)
The Senses (FHS: 20 minutes, DVD, 3-year streaming webcast)
Sheep Eye Dissection (WNS: 15 minutes, VHS, DVD)
Vision (part of the NOVA Mystery of the Senses series) (IM: 60 minutes each, 5-piece DVD set)

Laboratory Materials

Ordering information is based on a lab size of 24 students, working in groups of 4. A list of supply house addresses appears in Appendix A.

6 laboratory lamps, penlights, or flashlights	6–12 Ishihara's color plates	6 test tubes
Snellen eye chart and chalk or masking tape	Ophthalmoscope (if available)	6 common (straight) pins
	6 metric rulers/meter sticks	6 pencils

Advance Preparation

1. Hang up a Snellen eye chart in a well-lit part of the room. Measure back 20 feet from the chart and mark the distance on the floor with chalk or masking tape.

2. Set out Ishihara's color plates.

3. Set out a box of common pins.

4. Set out test tubes, pencils, metric rulers, and meter sticks (one each per group).

5. Set out several laboratory lamps, penlights, or bright flashlights.

6. Set out the ophthalmoscopes (check to be sure ophthalmoscope batteries are working).

Comments and Pitfalls

1. Some students will have difficulty with the ophthalmoscope. Remind the subject to look straight ahead at a fixed object while the examiner looks through the pupil at a slight angle. Caution the examiner to limit illuminating the retina to *one minute or less*. Switch to the other eye if necessary. *Do not examine the macula for more than one second at a time.*

2. For demonstration of the blind spot, emphasize that the dot disappears when the right eye is tested, and the X disappears when the left eye is tested. Some student is sure to claim that he or she has no blind spot in the left eye as the dot never disappeared!

Answers to Pre-Lab Quiz (pp. 373–374)

1. optic disc
2. true
3. b, presbyopia
4. cones
5. intrinsic

Answers to Activity Questions

Activity 6: Testing for Depth Perception (p. 377)

It is much easier to put the pencil in the test tube with both eyes open.

Activity 7: Demonstrating Reflex Activity of Intrinsic and Extrinsic Eye Muscles (p. 377)

Photopupillary Reflex

When exposed to bright light, the pupil constricts. The pupil of the opposite eye will also be slightly constricted.

Accommodation Pupillary Reflex

As the eye focuses on printed material, the pupil constricts. This reduces divergent light rays and aids in formation of a sharper image. It also restricts the amount of light entering the eye.

Convergence Reflex

The eyeballs will both move medially to focus on the object. This reflex keeps the image focused on the fovea.

Special Senses: Visual Tests and Experiments

The Optic Disc, Refraction, Visual Acuity, and Astigmatism

1. Explain why vision is lost when light hits the blind spot. *This area lacks photoreceptors.* _____

2. Match the terms in column B with the descriptions in column A.

	Column A		Column B
g; refraction	1. light bending	a.	accommodation
a; accommodation	2. ability to focus for close (less than 20 feet) vision	b.	astigmatism
d; emmetropia	3. normal vision	c.	convergence
e; hyperopia	4. inability to focus well on close objects (farsightedness)	d.	emmetropia
f; myopia	5. nearsightedness	e.	hyperopia
b; astigmatism	6. blurred vision due to unequal curvatures of the lens or cornea	f.	myopia
c; convergence	7. medial movement of the eyes during focusing on close objects	g.	refraction

3. Complete the following statements:

In farsightedness, the light is focused _1_ the retina. The lens required to treat myopia is a(n) _2_ lens. The "near point" of vision increases with age because the _3_ of the lens decreases as we get older. A convex lens, like that of the eye, produces an image that is upside down and reversed from left to right. Such an image is called a(n) _4_ image.

1. *behind*
2. *concave*
3. *elasticity*
4. *real*

4. Use terms from the key to complete the statements concerning near and distance vision. Some choices will be used more than once.

Key: a. contracted   b. decreased   c. increased   d. loose   e. relaxed   f. taut

During distance vision, the ciliary muscle is _e_, the ciliary zonule is _f_, the convexity of the lens is _b_, and light refraction is _b_. During close vision, the ciliary muscle is _a_, the ciliary zonule is _d_, lens convexity is _c_, and light refraction is _c_.

5. Using your Snellen eye test results, answer the following questions.

Is your visual acuity normal, less than normal, or better than normal? _The answers may vary._

Explain your answer. _____

Explain why each eye is tested separately when an examiner is using the Snellen eye chart. _There is usually a slight difference in the visual acuity of the two eyes._

Explain 20/40 vision. _Poorer than normal vision. Able to read #40 letters at 20 feet. The normal eye reads these letters at 40 feet._

Explain 20/10 vision. _Better than normal vision. Can read #10 letters at 20 feet. The normal eye would have to be 10 feet away to read these letters._

6. Define _astigmatism_. _Blurred vision due to unequal curvatures of the lens or cornea_

How can it be corrected? _With specially ground (circularly ground) lenses_

7. Define _presbyopia_. _"Old vision"; a hyperopia resulting from decreasing lens elasticity with advancing age_

What causes it? _Decreased function of an increasingly inelastic lens_

Color Blindness

8. To which wavelengths of light do the three cone types of the retina respond maximally?

red _____, _blue_ _____, and _green_ _____

9. How can you explain the fact that we see a great range of colors even though only three cone types exist?

When more than one cone type is stimulated simultaneously, intermediate colors (of the visible spectrum) are seen.

Binocular Vision

10. Explain the difference between binocular and panoramic vision. _Binocular—visual fields overlap considerably but not completely; therefore, slightly different views are received by each eye. Panoramic—little or no overlap of visual fields; therefore, each eye "sees" a different view._

What is the advantage of binocular vision? _Allows for depth perception_

What factor(s) is (are) responsible for binocular vision? _The slight difference between the visual fields of the two eyes and the partial crossover at the optic chiasma_

Eye Reflexes

11. In the experiment on the convergence reflex, what happened to the position of the eyeballs as the object was moved closer

to the subject's eyes? *Eyeballs turned medially*

Which extrinsic eye muscles control the movement of the eyes during this reflex? *Medial recti*

What is the value of this reflex? *Allows the image to be precisely focused on the fovea of each eye*

12. In the experiment on the photopupillary reflex, what happened to the pupil of the eye exposed to light? *It constricted.*

What happened to the pupil of the nonilluminated eye? *It constricted.*

Explanation? *Regulation of pupil constriction by the parasympathetic division of the autonomic nervous system is coordinated*

(i.e., consensual) and prevents overillumination of the delicate retinal cells.

Ophthalmoscopic Examination

13. Why is the ophthalmoscopic examination an important diagnostic tool? *Allows noninvasive examination of the retinal condition*

and vasculature

14. Many college students struggling through mountainous reading assignments are told that they need glasses for "eyestrain."

Why is it more of a strain on the extrinsic and intrinsic eye muscles to look at close objects than at far objects?

No accommodation or convergence is required for distant vision.

Special Senses:
Hearing and Equilibrium

Time Allotment: 1 hour.

Multimedia Resources: See Appendix B for Guide to Multimedia Resource Distributors.

Eyes and Ears (FHS: 28 minutes, DVD, 3-year streaming webcast)
Hearing (FHS: 30 minutes, DVD, 3-year streaming webcast)
Hearing (part of the NOVA Mystery of the Senses series) (IM: 60 minutes each, 5-piece DVD set)
Practice Anatomy Lab™ 3.0 (PAL) (PE: DVD, website)
The Senses (FHS: 20 minutes, DVD, 3-year streaming webcast)

Laboratory Materials

Ordering information is based on a lab size of 24 students, working in groups of 4. A list of supply house addresses appears in Appendix A.

3-D dissectible ear models and/or chart of ear anatomy
24 compound microscopes, lens paper, lens cleaning solution
24 slides of the cochlea
1 slide of crista ampullaris receptor of a semicircular canal

6 sets of tuning forks (range of frequencies)
6 rubber mallets
Absorbent cotton
Otoscope (if available), disposable otoscope tips, and alcohol swabs
Disposable autoclave bag
6 metric rulers

6 pocket watches or clocks that tick
White chalk and blackboard or markers and whiteboard
Audiometer (if available)
Red and blue pencils
Rotating stool or chair
Three coins of different sizes

Advance Preparation

1. Set out dissectible ear models and/or chart of ear anatomy.

2. Set out slides of the cochlea, lens paper, and lens cleaning solution. Have compound microscopes available. Set up a demonstration slide of the crista ampullaris receptor of a semicircular canal.

3. For each group, set out tuning forks, rubber mallet, absorbent cotton, a pocket watch or small clock that ticks, a piece of white chalk or a whiteboard marker, and a metric ruler.

4. If an audiometer is available it can be used instead of the tuning forks to test frequency range of hearing. If necessary, prepare instructions for the use of the audiometer. Set out red and blue pencils.

5. Set out otoscopes (if available), disposable otoscope tips, alcohol swabs, and an autoclave bag.

6. Have a sturdy rotating chair or stool available for the Barany test.

Comments and Pitfalls

1. It is often difficult to find an area quiet enough to get good results with the acuity and sound localization tests. An empty lab or a quiet corner of the hallway might be used.

2. Students should be reminded to simulate conductive deafness while performing the Weber test. Although it is not a specific assignment, they'll be asked for results in the Review Sheets.

3. Remind the students to strike the tuning forks with the rubber mallet and not against the lab bench.

4. Be sure the students understand how to evaluate the direction of nystagmus before the subject spins. Also remind the subject to keep his or her eyes open! Instruct students who are standing around the stool to place their foot firmly against the stool leg to prevent the stool from tipping over.

Answers to Pre-Lab Quiz (pp. 383–384)

1. three
2. a, auricle
3. tympanic membrane
4. stapes
5. cochlea
6. otoscope
7. b, Rinne
8. b, internal ear
9. macula/vestibule
10. c, involuntary trailing of eyes in one direction, then rapid movement in the other

Answers to Activity Questions

Activity 4: Conducting Laboratory Tests of Hearing (pp. 387–389)
Acuity Test

The threshold is indefinite.

Sound Localization

No, the sound is less easily located if the source is equidistant from both ears. Sound arriving from spots equidistant from both ears arrives at each ear at the same time and with equal loudness. This does not provide enough information to adequately locate the position of the source.

Frequency Range of Hearing

Generally, high-frequency sounds are heard less clearly, but results depend on the loudness of each of the tuning forks.

Activity 7: Conducting Laboratory Tests on Equilibrium (pp. 391–393)
Balance Tests

1. Nystagmus should not be present.
2. The cerebellum integrates input from receptors in the vestibule and semicircular canals, the eyes and somatic receptors, and coordinates skeletal muscle activity and regulates muscle tone.

Barany Test

4. When rotation stops, the direction of nystagmus reverses. If the chair is rotated clockwise, the nystagmus will be counterclockwise. For a few seconds after the chair is stopped, the subject reports a feeling of movement in the same direction and the same speed in which the chair was spun.

Romberg Test

2. Gross swaying movements are not usually observed when the eyes are open.

3. Side-to-side movement increases.

4. Front-to-back swaying occurs.

   The equilibrium apparatus and proprioceptors are probably functioning normally.

   Visual information is lacking and the result is increased swaying.

   Equilibrium and balance require input from a number of receptors, including proprioceptors, the vestibular apparatus, and the eyes.

Special Senses:
Hearing and Equilibrium

Anatomy of the Ear

1. Select the terms from column B that apply to the column A descriptions. Some terms are used more than once.

Column A		Column B
_a_, _d_, _m_	1. structures composing the external ear	a. auricle (pinna)
_b_, _k_, _n_	2. structures composing the internal ear	b. cochlea
_e_, _f_, _l_	3. collectively called the auditory ossicles	c. endolymph
_i_	4. involved in equalizing the pressure in the middle ear with external air pressure	d. external acoustic meatus
_m_	5. vibrates at the same frequency as sound waves hitting it; transmits the vibrations to the ossicles	e. incus (anvil)
		f. malleus (hammer)
_k_, _n_	6. contain receptors for the sense of balance	g. oval window
_g_	7. transmits the vibratory motion of the stapes to the fluid in the scala vestibuli of the internal ear	h. perilymph
		i. pharyngotympanic (auditory) tube
_j_	8. acts as a pressure relief valve for the increased fluid pressure in the scala tympani; bulges into the tympanic cavity	j. round window
_i_	9. passage between the throat and the tympanic cavity	k. semicircular canals
_c_	10. fluid contained within the membranous labyrinth	l. stapes (stirrup)
_h_	11. fluid contained within the bony labyrinth and bathing the membranous labyrinth	m. tympanic membrane
		n. vestibule

Why This Matters

2. List the structures typically affected by acute labyrinthitis. *Semicircular ducts, utricle, saccule, and the cochlear duct*

3. In some cases, inflammation of a cranial nerve accompanies acute labyrinthitis. Which cranial nerve is the most likely to be

    affected? *Vestibulocochlear (VIII)*

4. Identify all indicated structures and ear regions in the following diagram.

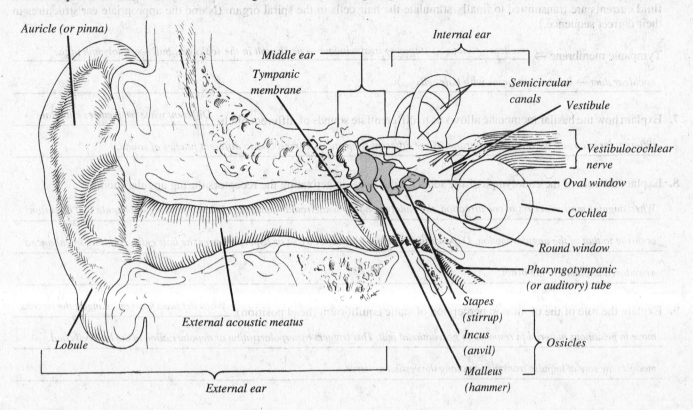

5. Match the membranous labyrinth structures listed in column B with the descriptive statements in column A. Some terms are used more than once.

Column A		Column B
_g_ , _j_ 1. sacs found within the vestibule		a. ampulla
_d_ 2. contains the spiral organ		b. ampullary cupula
_g_ , _j_ 3. sites of the maculae		c. basilar membrane
_h_ 4. positioned in all spatial planes		d. cochlear duct
_c_ 5. hair cells of spiral organ rest on this membrane		e. cochlear nerve
_i_ 6. gelatinous membrane overlying the hair cells of the spiral organ		f. otoliths
_a_ 7. contains the crista ampullaris		g. saccule
_f_ , _g_ , _j_ , _k_ 8. function in static equilibrium		h. semicircular ducts
_a_ , _b_ , _h_ , _k_ 9. function in dynamic equilibrium		i. tectorial membrane
_e_ 10. carries auditory information to the brain		j. utricle
_b_ 11. gelatinous cap overlying hair cells of the crista ampullaris		k. vestibular nerve
_f_ 12. grains of calcium carbonate in the maculae		

6. Sound waves hitting the tympanic membrane initiate its vibratory motion. Trace the pathway through which vibrations and fluid currents are transmitted to finally stimulate the hair cells in the spiral organ. (Name the appropriate ear structures in their correct sequence.)

Tympanic membrane → *malleus → incus → stapes → oval window → perilymph in the scala vestibuli → endolymph in the*

cochlear duct → basilar membrane with hair cells

7. Explain how the basilar membrane allows us to differentiate sounds of different pitch. *Different wave frequencies stimulate*

different locations on the basilar membrane. These different frequencies correspond to different pitches of sound.

8. Explain the role of the endolymph of the semicircular ducts in activating the receptors during angular motion.

When angular motion occurs in one direction, the endolymph in a semicircular canal lags behind, pushing the cupula in a direction

opposite to that of the angular motion. Depending on the ear, this depolarizes or hyperpolarizes the hair cells, resulting in enhanced

or reduced impulses to the brain.

9. Explain the role of the otoliths in perception of static equilibrium (head position). *When the head position changes, the otoliths*

move in gelatinous material in response to gravitational pull. This triggers hyperpolarization or depolarization of the hair cells and

modifies the rate of impulse transmission along the vestibular nerve.

Laboratory Tests

10. Was the auditory acuity measurement made in Activity 4 (on page 387) the same or different for both ears?

(student response)

What factors might account for a difference in the acuity of the two ears? *Earwax, middle/external ear infection, cochlear*

nerve damage, etc.—anything that affects sound conduction or nervous system structures associated with hearing

11. During the sound localization experiment in Activity 4 (on page 387) note the position(s) in which the sound was least easily located.

How can this phenomenon be explained? *The usual cues that allow sound to be localized (slight differences in loudness in the two*

ears and in the time the sound reaches each ear) are missing.

12. In the frequency experiment in Activity 4 (on page 388) note which tuning fork was the most difficult to hear. *Answers may vary.*

What conclusion can you draw? *High-frequency sounds are heard less well at low intensity.*

13. When the tuning fork handle was pressed to the forehead during the Weber test, where did the sound seem to originate?

From the ears

Where did it seem to originate when one ear was plugged with cotton? *From the plugged ear*

How do sound waves reach the cochlea when conduction deafness is present? *By vibration through bones of the skull*

14. Indicate whether the following conditions relate to conduction deafness (C), sensorineural deafness (S), or both (C and S).

_c_____ 1. can result from the fusion of the ossicles

_s_____ 2. can result from a lesion on the cochlear nerve

_s_____ 3. sound heard in one ear but not in the other during bone and air conduction

_c, s_____ 4. can result from otitis media

_c_____ 5. can result from impacted cerumen or a perforated eardrum

_s_____ 6. can result from a blood clot in the primary auditory cortex

15. The Rinne test evaluates an individual's ability to hear sounds conducted by air or bone. Which is more indicative of normal hearing? _Air-conducted sound_

16. Define *nystagmus*. _Involuntary rolling or trailing of the eyes in one direction and then rapid movement in the opposite direction_

Define *vertigo*. _Sensation of dizziness and rotational movement when such movement is not occurring_

17. The Barany test investigated the effect that rotatory acceleration had on the semicircular canals. Explain *why* the subject still had the sensation of rotation immediately after being stopped. _The fluids of the inner ear had not yet stopped moving._

18. What is the usual reason for conducting the Romberg test? _To determine if proprioceptive impulses are being transmitted up the spinal cord to the brain properly_

Was the degree of sway greater with the eyes open or closed? Why? _Closed. Visual cues (input) were lacking._

19. Normal balance, or equilibrium, depends on input from a number of sensory receptors. Name them. _Proprioceptors of the muscles and tendons, vestibular apparatus of the ears, retina of the eye (photoreceptors)_

26 EXERCISE

Special Senses:
Olfaction and Taste

Time Allotment: 1 hour.

Multimedia Resources: See Appendix B for Guide to Multimedia Resource Distributors.

The Senses of Smell and Taste (NIMCO: 28 minutes, DVD)
The Senses: Skin Deep (FHS: 28 minutes, DVD, 3-year streaming webcast)
Smell (part of the NOVA Mystery of the Senses series) (IM: 60 minutes each, 5-piece DVD set)
Smell and Taste (FHS: 30 minutes, DVD)
Taste (part of the NOVA Mystery of the Senses series) (IM: 60 minutes each, 5-piece DVD set)
Taste (FHS: 30 minutes, DVD, 3-year streaming webcast)

Laboratory Materials

Ordering information is based on a lab size of 24 students, working in groups of 4. A list of supply house addresses appears in Appendix A.

24 compound microscopes, lens paper, lens cleaning solution
24 slides of nasal olfactory epithelium (longitudinal section)
24 slides of tongue showing taste buds (cross section)
Paper towels
6 small mirrors
6 small packets of granulated sugar
Disposable autoclave bag
18 cotton-tipped swabs

6 dropper bottles of oil of cloves, oil of wintergreen, and oil of peppermint (or corresponding condiment flavors)
Absorbent cotton
Toothpicks
Disposable gloves
6 sets of 5 numbered vials containing common household substances with strong odors (herbs, spices, etc.)

6 flasks of distilled or tap water
6 paper plates
Chipped ice
6 opaque containers of equal-sized food cubes of apple, raw potato, dried prunes, banana, and raw carrot (at least 6 of each)
6 nose clips
6 paper cups

Advance Preparation

1. Set out slides of the tongue and the nasal epithelium, lens paper, and lens cleaning solution. Have compound microscopes available. (Or set up demonstration slides of the tongue and nasal epithelium.)

2. Set out for each group paper towels, a small mirror, a packet of granulated sugar, absorbent cotton, dropper bottles of oil of cloves, oil of wintergreen, and oil of peppermint (or corresponding flavorings from the condiment section of the supermarket), a flask of distilled water, a paper plate, and chipped ice.

3. Set out a disposable autoclave bag, toothpicks, and disposable gloves.

4. Prepare a plate of cubed food items such as apple, raw potato, dried prunes, banana, and raw carrot. These foods should be in an opaque container (a foil-lined egg carton works well). Keep covered and refrigerated until used.

5. Set out nose clips and five numbered vials containing common household substances with strong odors (such as cinnamon, garlic, ginger, rosemary, lemon peel, etc.).

6. Prepare an answer key for the five vials and have it available.

Comments and Pitfalls

1. Some students dislike putting cotton in their noses. Substitute good nose clips.

2. Some students may have difficulty getting their noses to adapt to the aromatic oil. Be sure they are following directions carefully and are patient.

3. Subjects for the food tests should not be allowed to see the food.

4. Remind students to use toothpicks to select food cubes. Caution students to alert the instructor and group members about food allergies.

Answers to Pre-Lab Quiz (p. 399)

1. true
2. c, olfactory epithelium
3. bipolar
4. c, papillae

5. posterior
6. two
7. sweet, sour, bitter, salty, and umami
8. true

9. false
10. b, adaptation

Answers to Activity Questions

Activity 3: Stimulating Taste Buds (p. 402)

3. Substances must be dissolved in aqueous solution to stimulate the taste buds.

Activity 4: Examining the Combined Effects of Smell, Texture, and Temperature on Taste (pp. 402–403)

Effects of Smell and Texture

3. No, some foods can be identified fairly easily by texture. The sense of smell is most important when foods do not have an easily recognizable and unique texture. For example, it is hard to differentiate between raw apple and raw potato.

Effect of Olfactory Stimulation

2. It is hard to distinguish the flavor with the nostrils closed.

3. With the nostrils open it is easy to identify the oil.

6. The subject usually identifies the oil held at the nostrils.

7. Smell seems to be more important for identification in this experiment.

Effect of Temperature

Identification by a chilled tongue is more difficult.

Activity 5: Assessing the Importance of Taste and Olfaction in Odor Identification (p. 404)

4. It is much easier to identify odors without the nose clips. There are only five basic tastes. Other taste sensations depend on olfaction.

Activity 6: Demonstrating Olfactory Adaptation (p. 404)

The adapted nostril should be able to detect the new oil. Adaptation is to the particular scent and not to aromatic oils in general.

NAME _____

LAB TIME/DATE _____

Special Senses: Olfaction and Taste

Olfactory Epithelium and Olfaction

1. Describe the location and cellular composition of the olfactory epithelium. _An area on the roof of the nasal cavity on each_ _side of the nasal septum; olfactory sensory neurons, supporting cells, and olfactory stem cells are located here._

2. How and why does sniffing increase your ability to detect an odor? _Draws air superiorly into contact with the olfactory mucosa._ _(Most air entering the nasal passages passes inferior to the receptors.)_

Taste Buds and Taste

3. Name five sites where receptors for taste are found, and circle the predominant site.

   (tongue papillae) , _epiglottis_ , _pharynx_ ,

   soft palate , and _cheek mucosa_

4. Describe the cellular makeup and arrangement of a taste bud. (Use a diagram, if helpful.) _A structure consisting of centrally_ _located gustatory (receptor) cells surrounded by supporting cells_

5. Taste and smell receptors are both classified as _chemoreceptors_ , because they both respond to _chemicals in aqueous solution._

6. Why is it impossible to taste substances if your tongue is dry? _Substances must be in aqueous solution._

7. The basic taste sensations are mediated by specific chemical substances or groups. Name them for the following taste modalities.

   salt: _metal ions, especially Na$^+$_   sour: _acids (e.g., lemon juice),_   umami: _the amino acids glutamate_

   specifically H$^+$ _and asparate_

   bitter: _alkaloids (e.g., caffeine),_   sweet: _sugars, saccharine, some amino_

   aspirin   _acids, some lead salts_

Laboratory Experiments

8. Name three factors that influence our enjoyment of foods. Substantiate each choice with an example from the laboratory experience.

1. _smell_ _____ Substantiation: _Answers may vary._ _____

2. _texture_ _____ Substantiation: _Answers may vary._ _____

3. _temperature_ _____ Substantiation: _Answers may vary._ _____

Which of the factors chosen is most important? _Smell_ _____ Substantiate your choice with an example from

everyday life. _Answers may vary._ _____

Expand on your explanation and choices by explaining why a cold, greasy hamburger is unappetizing to most people.

When hot, a hamburger is "juicy" and has an enticing aroma. When cold, the fat congeals, giving the hamburger a greasy taste

and texture.

9. How palatable is food when you have a cold? _It's not._ _____ Explain your answer. _Smell is half of taste._

When you have clogged nasal passages, you lack this added sensory input.

10. In your opinion, is olfactory adaptation desirable? _Yes._ _____ Explain your answer.

Continuous unimportant (unchanging) olfactory stimuli would be distracting and (probably) irritating.

Functional Anatomy of the Endocrine Glands

Time Allotment: 1 hour+ (depending on detail required for microscopic study); additional work may be completed outside of lab.

Multimedia Resources: See Appendix B for Guide to Multimedia Resource Distributors.

The Endocrine System (IM: 17 minutes, DVD)
Hormonally Yours (FHS: 50 minutes, DVD, 3-year streaming webcast)
Hormone Heaven? (FHS: 50 minutes, DVD, 3-year streaming webcast)
Hormone Hell (FHS: 50 minutes, DVD, 3-year streaming webcast)
Hormones: Messengers (FHS: 27 minutes, DVD, 3-year streaming webcast)
Interactive Physiology® 10-System Suite: Endocrine System (PE: CD-ROM, website)
The Neuroendocrine System (IM: 29 minutes, DVD)
Practice Anatomy Lab™ 3.0 (PAL) (PE: DVD, website)

Laboratory Materials

Ordering information is based on a lab size of 24 students, working in groups of 4. A list of supply house addresses appears in Appendix A.

Human torso model
Anatomical chart of human endocrine
   system
24 compound microscopes, lens paper,
   lens cleaning solution

24 slides of anterior pituitary
   and posterior pituitary
   (differential staining, if possible),
   thyroid gland, parathyroid

glands, adrenal gland, pancreas
   (differential staining, if possible)

Advance Preparation

1. Set out human torso models and anatomical charts.

2. Set out slides of the anterior pituitary, posterior pituitary, thyroid gland, parathyroid glands, adrenal gland, and pancreas tissue. The anterior and posterior pituitary gland and pancreas slides should be differentially stained, if possible. Set out lens paper and lens cleaning solution. Have compound microscopes available.

Answers to Pre-Lab Quiz (p. 407)

1. A hormone is a chemical messenger that enters the blood for transport throughout the body.

2. endocrine

3. a, hypophysis

4. true

5. d, thyroid

6. glucagon

7. true

8. c, thymus

9. pancreatic islets

10. b, zona glomerulosa

Answers to Group Challenge: Odd Hormone Out (p. 411)

Some possible answers to the questions are listed below. Student answers may vary.

1. Which is the "odd hormone"?	Why it is the odd one out?
ACTH (oxytocin) LH FSH	*Oxytocin is not a tropic hormone and is not produced by the anterior pituitary.*

2. Which is the "odd hormone"?	Why it is the odd one out?
aldosterone cortisol epinephrine (ADH)	*ADH is not produced by the adrenal gland.*

3. Which is the "odd hormone"?	Why it is the odd one out?
(PTH) testosterone LH FSH	*PTH does not regulate the reproductive system.*

4. Which is the "odd hormone"?	Why it is the odd one out?
insulin cortisol (calcitonin) glucagon	*Calcitonin doesn't regulate blood glucose levels.*

Functional Anatomy of the Endocrine Glands

Gross Anatomy and Basic Function of the Endocrine Glands

1. Both the endocrine and nervous systems are major regulating systems of the body; however, the nervous system has been compared to an airmail delivery system and the endocrine system to the Pony Express. Briefly explain this comparison.

   The nervous system uses rapidly propagated electrical "messages," whereas endocrine system "messages" (hormones) are liberated

   into the blood to travel much more slowly to the target organs.

2. Define *hormone*. *A chemical substance liberated into the extracellular fluid that enters blood for transport throughout the body.*

   Hormones alter "target cell" metabolism in a specific manner.

3. Chemically, hormones belong chiefly to two molecular groups, the ___steroids___ and the ___amino acid–based molecules___.

4. Define *target cell*. *Cell responding to a particular hormone in a specific way*

5. If hormones travel in the bloodstream, why don't all tissues respond to all hormones? *The proper "hormone" receptors must*

   be present on the plasma membrane or within the cells for the tissue cells to respond.

6. Identify the endocrine organ described by each of the following statements.

   thyroid gland _____ 1. located in the throat; bilobed gland connected by an isthmus

   adrenal gland _____ 2. found atop the kidney

   pancreas _____ 3. a mixed gland, located behind the stomach and close to the small intestine

   testes _____ 4. paired glands suspended in the scrotum

   parathyroids _____ 5. ride "horseback" on the thyroid gland

   ovaries _____ 6. found in the pelvic cavity of the female, concerned with ova and female hormone production

   thymus _____ 7. found in the upper thorax overlying the heart; large during youth

   pineal gland _____ 8. found in the roof of the third ventricle of the brain

7. The table below lists the functions of many of the hormones you have studied. From the keys below, fill in the hormones responsible for each function, and the endocrine glands that produce each hormone. Glands may be used more than once.

Hormones Key:

ACTH	glucagon	T_3/T_4
ADH	insulin	testosterone
aldosterone	LH	TSH
cortisol	oxytocin	
epinephrine	progesterone	
estrogens	prolactin	
FSH	PTH	

Glands Key:

adrenal cortex	parathyroid glands
adrenal medulla	posterior pituitary
anterior pituitary	testes
hypothalamus	thyroid gland
ovaries	
pancreas	

Function	Hormone(s)	Synthesizing gland(s)
Regulate the function of another endocrine gland (tropic)	1. *FSH* 2. *LH* 3. *ACTH* 4. *TSH*	*anterior pituitary*
Maintain salt and water balance in the extracellular fluid	1. *aldosterone*	*adrenal cortex*
	2. *ADH*	*hypothalamus*
Directly involved in milk production and ejection	1. *oxytocin*	*posterior pituitary*
	2. *prolactin*	*anterior pituitary*
Controls the rate of body metabolism and cellular oxidation	1. T_3/T_4	*thyroid*
Regulates blood calcium levels	1. *PTH*	*parathyroid gland*
Regulates blood glucose levels; produced by the same "mixed" gland	1. *insulin*	*pancreas*
	2. *glucagon*	
Released in response to stressors	1. *cortisol*	*adrenal cortex*
	2. *epinephrine*	*adrenal medulla*
Drives development of secondary sex characteristics in males	1. *testosterone*	*tests*
Directly responsible for regulation of the menstrual cycle	1. *estrogen*	*ovaries*
	2. *progesterone*	

8. Although the pituitary gland is sometimes referred to as the master gland of the body, the hypothalamus exerts control over the pituitary gland. How does the hypothalamus control both anterior and posterior pituitary functioning?

Produces "releasing and inhibiting hormones," which control the production and release of anterior pituitary hormones; forms

hormones ADH and oxytocin, which are transported to the posterior pituitary and later released on nervous stimulation from

the hypothalamus

9. Indicate whether the release of the hormones listed below is stimulated by (A) another hormone; (B) the nervous system (neurotransmitters, or neurosecretions); or (C) humoral factors (the concentration of specific nonhormonal substances in the blood or extracellular fluid).

_A_	1. ACTH	_C_	4. insulin	_A_	7. T_4/T_3
_C_	2. calcitonin	_B_	5. norepinephrine	_A_	8. testosterone
_A_	3. estrogens	_C_	6. parathyroid hormone	_A_	9. TSH, FSH

10. Name the hormone(s) produced in *inadequate* amounts that directly result in the following conditions.

PTH _____ 1. tetany

ADH _____ 2. excessive urine output without high blood glucose levels

insulin _____ 3. loss of glucose in the urine

growth hormone (GH) _____ 4. abnormally small stature, normal proportions

_T_4/T_3 (thyroid hormone)_ _____ 5. low BMR, mental and physical sluggishness

11. Name the hormone(s) produced in *excessive* amounts that directly result(s) in the following conditions.

growth hormone (GH) _____ 1. large hands and feet in the adult, large facial bones

_T_4/T_3 (thyroid hormone)_ _____ 2. nervousness, irregular pulse rate, sweating

PTH _____ 3. demineralization of bones, spontaneous fractures

Microscopic Anatomy of Selected Endocrine Glands

12. Choose a response from the key below to name the hormone(s) produced by the cell types listed.

Key: a. calcitonin   d. glucocorticoids   g. PTH
      b. GH, prolactin   e. insulin   h. T_4/T_3
      c. glucagon   f. mineralocorticoids   i. TSH, ACTH, FSH, LH

_a_	1. parafollicular cells of the thyroid	_d_	6. zona fasciculata cells
_h_	2. follicular cells of the thyroid	_f_	7. zona glomerulosa cells
_e_	3. beta cells of the pancreatic islets	_g_	8. parathyroid cells
_c_	4. alpha cells of the pancreatic islets	_b_	9. acidophil cells of the anterior pituitary
_i_	5. basophil cells of the anterior pituitary		

Why This Matters

13. Explain why growth hormone is an anabolic hormone. _Anabolism is the branch of metabolism that is involved in the synthesis of large molecules. Growth hormone stimulates the synthesis of larger molecules including proteins._

14. Considering the primary target organs of growth hormone, explain why growth hormone is not a tropic hormone.

The primary target organs for growth hormone are liver, muscle, bone, and cartilage. None of these organs are endocrine glands and therefore growth hormone would not be a tropic hormone.

15. Six diagrams of the microscopic structures of the endocrine glands are presented here. Identify each and <u>name all structures</u> indicated by a leader line or bracket.

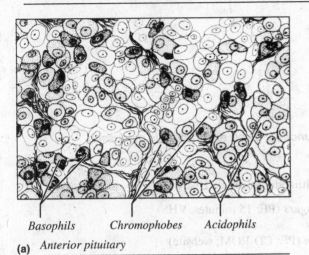

Basophils   Chromophobes   Acidophils

(a) _Anterior pituitary_

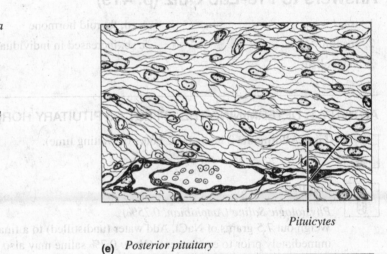

Colloid-filled follicles   Follicle cells

(d) _Thyroid gland_

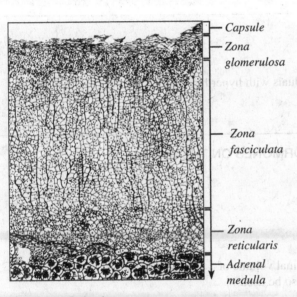

— Capsule
— Zona
  glomerulosa

— Zona
  fasciculata

— Zona
  reticularis
— Adrenal
  medulla

(b) _Adrenal gland_

Pituicytes

(e) _Posterior pituitary_

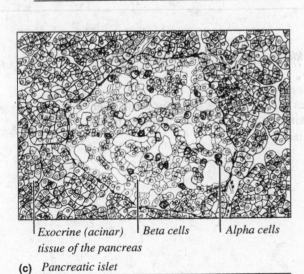

Exocrine (acinar)   Beta cells   Alpha cells
tissue of the pancreas

(c) _Pancreatic islet_

Parathyroid cells — Oxyphil cells

(f) _Parathyroid gland_

Endocrine Wet Labs and Human Metabolism

This exercise contains two experiments illustrating hormone function. Each experiment is discussed separately below.

Multimedia Resources: See Appendix B for Guide to Multimedia Resource Distributors.

Selected Actions of Hormones and Other Chemical Messengers (PE: 15 minutes, VHS)
PhysioEx™ 9.1 Exercise 4 (PE: CD-ROM, website)
Interactive Physiology® 10-System Suite: Endocrine System (PE: CD-ROM, website)

Answers to Pre-Lab Quiz (p. 419)

1. true
2. insulin
3. catabolism

4. d, thyroid hormone
5. b, increased in individuals with hyperthyroidism

ACTIVITY 1: DETERMINING THE EFFECT OF PITUITARY HORMONES ON THE OVARY

Time Allotment: 2 hours (1 1/2 hours of waiting time).

Solutions:

Physiologic Saline (Amphibian, 0.75%)
Weigh out 7.5 grams of NaCl. Add water (undistilled) to a final volume of 1 liter. Make fresh immediately prior to experiment. (*Note:* 0.7% saline may also be used.)

Laboratory Materials

Ordering information is based on a lab size of 24 students, working in groups of 4. A list of supply house addresses appears in Appendix A.

18 female frogs (*Rana pipiens*)
Disposable gloves
12 battery jars
12 syringes (2 ml)

12 20- to 25-gauge needles
6 vials of frog pituitary extract
6 small bottles of amphibian
physiologic saline

Spring or pond water
6 wax marking pencils

Advance Preparation

1. Order female frogs (two per group) to be delivered close to the date of the exercise (see preparation for the frog experiment in Exercise 14). Designate a frog disposal area. Set out disposable gloves.

2. For each group set out two syringes with 20- to 25-gauge needles, two battery jars, wax marking pencils, a small bottle of *amphibian physiologic saline*, pond or spring water, and a vial of frog pituitary extract (Carolina).

Comments and Pitfalls

1. Distilled water should be used as a control if the pituitary extract is suspended in water.

2. Injected frogs should be kept in a quiet area.

3. When introducing this exercise, caution students to hold the frog's body firmly and above its hind legs. Demonstrate the holding and carrying procedure.

Answers to Activity Questions (p. 420)

6. Ovulation is induced in the frog that received the pituitary extract injection. LH is the primary hormone stimulus for ovulation.

ACTIVITY 2: OBSERVING THE EFFECTS OF HYPERINSULINISM

 Time Allotment: 1/2 hour.

 Solutions:

Glucose, 20%
Weigh out 200 grams of glucose. Add distilled water to a final volume of 1 liter.

Laboratory Materials

Ordering information is based on a lab size of 24 students, working in groups of 4. A list of supply house addresses appears in Appendix A.

500- or 600-ml beakers
6 bottles of 20% glucose
  solution (250 ml)
Dropper bottle of commercial insulin
  (400 immunizing units [IU] per
  100 ml of H_2O)

12 finger bowls
6 small (1.5–2-inch) freshwater fish
  (listed in order of preference:
  guppy, bluegill, or sunfish)
6 wax marking pencils

Advance Preparation

1. Prepare a solution of *20% glucose* and store it in the refrigerator. Purchase or order enough small fish to supply one per group. Set up an aquarium or large beaker with an air stone to maintain the fish.

2. For each group set out a 250-milliliter bottle of *20% glucose*, a dropper bottle of *insulin*, a glass marking pencil, and two finger bowls.

Comments and Pitfalls

1. The fish may become very agitated and jump out of the bowl or beaker.
2. This exercise may be upsetting to some students, even though the fish recover.

Answers to Activity Questions (p. 421)

2. The fish often becomes very agitated, then loses its sense of balance just before becoming unconscious.
3. The fish will regain consciousness and right itself. The recovery time varies.

Answers to Group Challenge: Thyroid Hormone Case Studies (p. 422)

Case 1:

Marty is a 24-year-old male. He has noticed a bulge on his neck that has been increasing in size over the past few months. His physician orders a blood test, with the following results:

Component	Results	Normal range	Units
TSH	<0.1	0.1–5.5	µIU/ml
Free T₄	5.3	0.8–1.7	ng/dL

Does Marty have hypothyroidism or hyperthyroidism? *Marty's blood tests indicate hyperthyroidism.*

Name and briefly describe the most likely cause of his thyroid disorder. *Marty most likely has Graves' disease, indicated by the low level of TSH and the presence of a goiter.*

What other signs and symptoms might Marty be experiencing? *He might also be experiencing elevated metabolism; sweating; a rapid, more forceful heartbeat; nervousness; weight loss; difficulty concentrating; changes in skin texture; and protrusion of the eyeballs.*

Case 2:

Heather is a 60-year-old female. She complains of swelling in her limbs and fatigue. Her physician orders a blood test, with the following results:

Component	Results	Normal range	Units
TSH	5.7	0.1–5.5	µIU/ml
Free T₄	0.5	0.8–1.7	ng/dL

Does Heather have hypothyroidism or hyperthyroidism? *Heather's blood tests indicate hypothyroidism.*

Name and briefly describe the most likely cause(s) of her thyroid disorder. *Heather's thyroid disorder could be caused by primary failure of the thyroid gland or an iodine deficiency.*

Does Heather have a goiter? *Heather's TSH is elevated. So, she would most likely have a goiter.*

What other signs and symptoms might Heather be experiencing? *Heather might also be experiencing low metabolic rate; chills; constipation; thick, dry skin and puffy skin ("bags") beneath the eyes; and mental sluggishness.*

NAME _____

LAB TIME/DATE _____

Endocrine Wet Labs and Human Metabolism

Determining the Effect of Pituitary Hormones on the Ovary

1. In the experiment on the effects of pituitary hormones, two anterior pituitary hormones caused ovulation to occur in the experimental animal. Which of these actually triggered ovulation?

   LH _____ The normal function of the second hormone involved, *FSH* _____ is to *stimulate follicle (and oocyte) maturation.*

2. Why was a second frog injected with saline? *To provide a control* _____

Observing the Effects of Hyperinsulinism

3. Briefly explain what was happening within the fish's system when the fish was immersed in the insulin solution.

   Glucose was being swept out of the blood into the cells. This led to a hypoglycemic reaction, which affects nervous system functioning

   adversely.

4. What is the mechanism of the recovery process observed? *Glucose was added. Increased glucose levels in the blood reversed the*

   effects noted above.

5. What would you do to help a friend who had inadvertently taken an overdose of insulin? *Give him or her a glass of orange*

   juice or soda.

   Why? *A sugar source will increase blood glucose levels as explained in #4.* _____

Human Metabolism and Thyroid Hormones

6. Use an appropriate reference to indicate which of the following would be associated with increased or decreased BMR. Indicate increase by ↑ and decrease by ↓.

   increased exercise ___↑___   aging ___↓___   infection/fever ___↑___

   increased stress ___↑___   obesity ___↓___   sex (♂ or ♀) *Males generally have a higher BMR than females.*

7. What are some possible treatments for myxedema? (Use your textbook or another appropriate reference.)

Treatment for myxedema usually involves supplementing with oral thyroxine. If an iodine deficiency is suspected, increasing iodine in the diet may be all that is needed.

8. What are some possible treatments for Graves' disease? (Use your textbook or another appropriate reference.)

Treatment for Graves' disease includes surgical removal of all or part of the thyroid gland or therapy with radioactive iodine to destroy thyroid cells.

29

Blood

Note: For safety reasons, many instructors make the blood tests optional or try to provide alternative experiments. Substituting dog blood, as suggested below, is one option; using prepared slides or artificial blood are others.

Time Allotment: 2 hours.

Multimedia Resources: See Appendix B for Guide to Multimedia Resource Distributors.

Bleeding and Coagulation (FHS: 31 minutes, DVD, 3-year streaming webcast)
Blood (DE: 22 minutes, VHS, DVD)
Blood (FHS: 20 minutes, DVD, 3-year streaming webcast)
Practice Anatomy Lab™ 3.0 (*PAL*) (PE: DVD, website)
PhysioEx™ 9.1 Exercise 11 (PE: CD-ROM, website)

Solutions:

Bleach Solution, 10%
Measure out 100 milliliters of household bleach. Add water (undistilled) to a final volume of 1 liter.

Laboratory Materials

Ordering information is based on a lab size of 24 students, working in groups of 4. A list of supply house addresses appears in Appendix A.

Disposable gloves
24 pairs of safety glasses
Bucket or 6 beakers containing 10% household bleach solution
6 spray bottles containing 10% bleach solution
Autoclave bag
Designated lancet (sharps) disposable container
6 animal plasma samples (obtained from an animal hospital or prepared by centrifuging animal blood obtained from a biological supply house)
24 test tubes and test tube racks
6 packages of wide-range pH paper
Stained smears of human blood from a biological supply house or heparinized animal blood obtained from a biological supply house or animal hospital or EDTA-treated red cells (reference cells) with

blood type labels obscured (available from Immucor, Inc.). The blood in these kits (each containing four blood cell types—A1, A2, B, and O—individually supplied in 10-milliliter vials) is used to calibrate cell counters and other automated clinical laboratory equipment. This blood has been carefully screened and can be safely used by students for blood typing and determining hematocrits. It is not usable for hemoglobin determinations or coagulation studies.
2 boxes of clean microscope slides
Glass stirring rods
6–12 dropper bottles of Wright's stain
6–12 dropper bottles of distilled water
6 boxes sterile lancets, alcohol swabs, absorbent cotton balls
Paper towels

24 compound microscopes, lens paper, lens cleaning solution
Immersion oil
3-D models and/or charts of blood cells
Assorted slides of white blood count pathologies labeled "Unknown Sample # _____"
6 timers
24 heparinized capillary tubes
Microhematocrit centrifuge and reading gauge (if reading gauge is not available, a millimeter ruler may be used)
24 millimeter rulers
Capillary tube sealer or modeling clay
Hemoglobinometer, hemolysis applicator, and lens paper; or Tallquist hemoglobin scale and test paper
24 capillary tubes (nonheparinized)
6–12 fine triangular files
6 bottles of each blood typing sera (anti-A, anti-B, and anti-Rh [anti-D])

183

Rh typing box
24 wax marking pencils
Toothpicks and 24 clean glass slides
   or 24 test cards and blood-mixing
   sticks

Medicine dropper
Prepared slides demonstrating
   macrocytic hypochromic anemia,
   microcytic hypochromic anemia,
   sickle cell anemia, lymphocytic

leukemia (chronic), and
   eosinophilia
24 cholesterol test cards and color
   scale

Advance Preparation

1. Set out safety glasses, lens paper, lens cleaning solution, and immersion oil. Have compound microscopes available. Set out any available models and charts of blood cells.

2. Set out prepared slides of macrocytic hypochromic anemia, microcytic hypochromic anemia, sickle cell anemia, lymphocytic leukemia (chronic), and eosinophilia.

3. Set up the following supply areas (if all tests are to be done). Ideally there should be at least one set of solutions for each lab bench and enough of the other supplies for each student to do each test. If equipment must be shared, it should be washed in hot soapy water and rinsed in *10% bleach solution* after each use.

   General supply area:

   a. For instructors using student blood samples, set out sterile blood lancets, designated lancet (sharps) disposal containers, alcohol wipes, and absorbent cotton balls. Set up a disposable autoclave bag for all disposable items, and a laboratory bucket or battery jar of *10% bleach solution* for glassware. For each lab group, set out a 250-milliliter beaker of *10% bleach solution* (for used slides), spray bottles of 10% *bleach solution*, clean microscope slides (two per member of the group), a dropper bottle of Wright's stain (Carolina), a dropper bottle of distilled water, wide-range pH paper, test tube and test tube rack, nonhemolyzed plasma obtained fresh from an animal hospital or prepared by centrifuging animal (e.g., cattle or sheep) blood obtained from a biological supply house, timers, and disposable gloves.

   b. For instructors using heparinized dog blood, set out heparinized dog blood, glass rods, and all the materials listed in paragraph a, except the sterile lancets and alcohol wipes.

   c. EDTA-treated red cells (reference cells) with blood type labels obscured (available from Immucor, Inc.) could also be used.

   d. For instructors using stained smears of human blood, set out prepared slides of human blood stained with Wright's stain.

   e. Set out slides of WBC pathologies with the labels covered and marked "Unknown sample # _____." Suggestions include eosinophilia, neutrophilia, and various leukemias.

   Hematocrit supply area:

   Set out heparinized capillary tubes, microhematocrit centrifuge and reading gauge or millimeter ruler, and BD Seal-Ease™ or capillary tube sealer (Carolina) or modeling clay.

   Hemoglobin-determination supply area:

   Set out hemoglobinometer and hemolysis applicator or Tallquist scales.

   Coagulation time supply area:

   Set out nonheparinized capillary tubes, fine triangular files, and paper towels.

   Blood-typing supply area:

   Set out blood-typing sera, Rh-typing boxes (if used), wax markers, toothpicks, and blood test cards or slides (Carolina). If you are using WARD'S artificial blood, set out simulated blood and antibodies provided with the kit.

   Cholesterol-measurement supply area:

   Set out cholesterol test cards and color scale (Craig Medical).

Comments and Pitfalls

1. If human blood samples are provided, disposable gloves and safety glasses should be worn at all times. If student samples are used, be sure students use only their own blood. Emphasize instructions for proper care or disposal of items used in the blood tests (see Anatomy and Physiology Laboratory Safety Procedures in the preface of this Instructor Guide and page 426 of the laboratory manual). Be sure that sharp objects such as lancets are discarded only in a designated lancet or sharps disposal container.

2. If student blood samples are used, have the students plan their work so that a minimum number of pricks are necessary. Obtaining enough blood is the usual problem. Be sure that students' hands are warm before trying to obtain blood, and that they follow the advice in the laboratory manual. Emphasize that the capillary tube should be held in a horizontal position with the tip in the drop of blood.

3. It is nearly impossible to prick your own finger to draw blood unless an automatic device is used (available in many pharmacies or online at www.walgreens.com). Students are often careless with the lancets, since they are concentrating on obtaining blood for several different tests. Emphasize the importance of proper disposal. This is particularly important when using an automatic device, as it is difficult to distinguish a used lancet with a replaced cap from a new, unused one.

4. Obviously, heparinized blood samples may not be used for the coagulation time experiment.

5. Several problems may arise with the slides. Student-prepared blood smears tend to be too thick; be sure they understand the technique before starting. Warn against allowing the slide to dry with the stain on it. Avoid using old Wright stain, which may develop sediment that interferes with reading the slides.

6. A good color plate of the blood cells will help with identification. It may help to have some prepared slides available for demonstration. Also, point out the typical percentages of each cell type. Many students initially identify large numbers of cells as basophils.

7. Emphasize that the coagulation-time test must be started as soon as blood is drawn up into the capillary tube. To avoid cuts, have students hold the tubes with paper towels when breaking them.

8. Blood typing may be done here, but it may be easier to explain if it is done after the immune system has been discussed.

Answers to Pre-Lab Quiz (p. 425)

1. false
2. c, platelets
3. erythrocytes
4. c, monocyte
5. a, basophils
6. platelets
7. hematocrit
8. males
9. antigens
10. true

Blood

Composition of Blood

1. What is the blood volume of an average-sized adult male? _5–6_ liters; an average adult female? _4–5_ liters

2. What determines whether blood is bright red or a dull brick red? _Its degree of oxygenation. The more oxygen it carries, the brighter red it is._

3. Use the key to identify the cell type(s) or blood elements that fit the following descriptive statements. Some terms will be used more than once.

   Key: a. red blood cell   d. basophil   g. lymphocyte
         b. megakaryocyte   e. monocyte   h. formed elements
         c. eosinophil   f. neutrophil   i. plasma

   f; neutrophil   1. most numerous leukocyte

   c; eosinophil , _d; basophil_ , and _f; neutrophil_   2. granulocytes (3)

   a; red blood cell   3. also called an erythrocyte; anucleate formed element

   e; monocyte , _f; neutrophil_ , _c; eosinophil_   4. phagocytic leukocytes (3)

   e; monocyte , _g; lymphocyte_   5. agranulocytes

   b; megakaryocyte   6. precursor cell of platelets

   h; formed elements   7. (a) through (g) are all examples of these

   c; eosinophil   8. involved in destroying parasitic worms

   d; basophil   9. releases histamine; promotes inflammation

   g; lymphocyte   10. produces antibodies

   a; red blood cell   11. transports oxygen

   i; plasma   12. primarily water, noncellular; the fluid matrix of blood

   e; monocyte   13. exits a blood vessel to develop into a macrophage

   c; eosinophil , _d; basophil_ , _e; monocyte_ ,

   f; neutrophil , and _g; lymphocyte_   14. the five types of white blood cells

4. List four classes of nutrients normally found in plasma. _Sugar (e.g., glucose)_,

amino acids, _lipids (fatty acids)_, and _vitamins_

Name two gases. _Oxygen_ and _carbon dioxide (nitrogen)_

Name three ions. _Na^+_, _Cl^-_, and _Mg^{2+} (HCO_3^-, K^+, Ca^{2+})_

5. Describe the consistency and color of the plasma you observed in the laboratory. _Viscous and sticky; straw colored_

6. What is the average life span of a red blood cell? How does its anucleate condition affect this life span?

100–120 days. When the RBC's ATP reserves have been exhausted, the membrane begins to fragment. Without DNA to direct mRNA

(therefore protein) synthesis, needed enzymes cannot be made.

7. From memory, describe the structural characteristics of each of the following blood cell types as accurately as possible, and note the percentage of each in the total white blood cell population.

eosinophils: _Large, red-staining cytoplasmic granules; figure 8 or bilobed nucleus; 1–4% of WBC_

neutrophils: _Pale pink cytoplasm with fine granules; nucleus is multilobed and stains deep purple; 40–70% of WBC_

lymphocytes: _Small cell with sparse pale blue cytoplasm and dark purple–staining spherical nucleus; 20–45% of WBC_

basophils: _Sparse dark blue cytoplasmic granules that may obscure the large U-shaped nucleus, which stains dark blue;_

0.5% or less of WBC

monocytes: _Abundant gray-blue cytoplasm, dark blue-purple nucleus (often kidney shaped); 4–8% of WBC_

8. Correctly identify the blood pathologies described in column A by matching them with selections from column B:

Column A		Column B
b; leukocytosis 1. abnormal increase in the number of WBCs		a. anemia
d; polycythemia 2. abnormal increase in the number of RBCs		b. leukocytosis
a; anemia 3. condition of too few RBCs or of RBCs with hemoglobin deficiencies		c. leukopenia
c; leukopenia 4. abnormal decrease in the number of WBCs		d. polycythemia

Hematologic Tests

9. Broadly speaking, why are hematologic studies of blood so important in the diagnosis of disease?

Specific changes from the normal numbers/types of formed elements and/or plasma constituents are characteristic of certain

disease states.

10. In the chart below, record information from the blood tests you read about or conducted. Complete the chart by recording values for healthy male adults and indicating the significance of high or low values for each test.

Test	Student test results	Normal values (healthy male adults)	Significance	
			High values	Low values
Total WBC count	No data	4000–11,000/mm³	infection, metabolic disease, hemorrhage, or poisoning	decreased body protection or chemical toxicity, or disease states
Total RBC count	No data	4–6 million/mm³	polycythemia due to high altitude or pulmonary disease	anemia or bone marrow cancer
Hematocrit		42–52 volume %	polycythemia, dehydration, congestive heart failure, shock, or surgery	anemia
Hemoglobin determination		13–18 g/100 ml blood	polycythemia or dehydration	anemia (particularly iron-deficiency anemia)
Bleeding time	No data	2–7 min (Ivy) 0–5 min (Duke)	deficient or abnormal platelets	high platelet count
Coagulation time		2–6 min	hemophilia, leukemia, increased clotting time	thromboembolytic disorders

11. Why is a differential WBC count more valuable than a total WBC count when trying to determine the specific source of pathology? *A differential count determines the relative percentage of each type of WBC. Increases or decreases in specific WBC or populations are often indicative (diagnostic) of specific pathologies.*

12. What name is given to the process of RBC production? (Consult an appropriate reference as necessary) *Erythropoiesis*

What hormone acts as a stimulus for this process? *Erythropoietin*

Why might patients with kidney disease suffer from anemia? *When kidneys fail, they also do not produce enough erythropoietin to sustain erythropoiesis.*

How can such patients be treated? *They can be given genetically engineered erythropoietin (EPO).*

13. Discuss the effect of each of the following factors on RBC count. Consult an appropriate reference as necessary, and explain your reasoning.

long-term effect of athletic training (for example, running 4 to 5 miles per day over a period of 6 to 9 months):

Increases the RBC count. An athlete has relatively large muscle mass and needs an efficient oxygen delivery to the muscles when they are working.

a permanent move from sea level to a high-altitude area: *Increased RBC count. The air is thinner at high altitudes and contains less*

O_2. The body compensates by producing more RBCs so that the same relative amount of O_2 can be picked up and transported by the blood.

14. Define *hematocrit*. *Packed cell volume; percentage of total blood volume occupied by RBC*

15. If you had a high hematocrit, would you expect your hemoglobin determination to be high or low? *High*

Why? *Assuming the RBCs have a normal hemoglobin content, the higher the RBC volume, the higher the hemoglobin determination.*

16. What is an anticoagulant? *A substance that inhibits blood clotting*

Name two anticoagulants used in conducting the hematologic tests. *Heparin (in capillary tubes)*

and *EDTA*

What is the body's natural anticoagulant? *Heparin*

17. If your blood clumped with both anti-A and anti-B sera, your ABO blood type would be *AB*

To what ABO blood groups could you give blood? *AB*

From which ABO donor types could you receive blood? *A, B, AB, O*

Which ABO blood type is most common? *O*   Least common? *AB*

18. What blood type is theoretically considered the universal donor? *O⁻*   Why? *These RBCs have no A, B,*

or Rh antigens on the cell membrane, reducing the chance of a transfusion reaction.

19. Assume the blood of two patients has been typed for ABO blood type.

Typing results
Mr. Adams:

Blood drop and anti-A serum   Blood drop and anti-B serum

Typing results
Mr. Calhoon:

Blood drop and anti-A serum   Blood drop and anti-B serum

On the basis of these results, Mr. Adams has type *O* blood, and Mr. Calhoon has type *A* blood.

20. Explain why an Rh-negative person does not have a transfusion reaction on the first exposure to Rh-positive blood but *does* have a reaction on the second exposure. *There are no spontaneously formed anti-Rh antibodies in his or her blood. After the first exposure to Rh⁺ blood, the immune system reacts and then starts making antibodies.*

What happens when an ABO blood type is mismatched for the first time? *A transfusion reaction occurs the first and every time.*

21. Record your observations of the five demonstration slides viewed.

a. Macrocytic hypochromic anemia: *RBCs are large and pale.*

b. Microcytic hypochromic anemia: *RBCs are small and pale.*

c. Sickle cell anemia: *RBCs are crescent shaped.*

d. Lymphocytic leukemia (chronic): *Large number of small abnormal lymphocytes*

e. Eosinophilia: *Increased number of eosinophils*

Which of the slides above (a through e) corresponds to the following conditions?

b 1. iron-deficient diet

d 2. a type of bone marrow cancer

c 3. genetic defect that causes hemoglobin to become sharp/spiky

a 4. lack of vitamin B₁₂

e 5. a tapeworm infestation in the body

b 6. a bleeding ulcer

22. Provide the normal, or at least "desirable," range for plasma cholesterol concentration. *130–200* mg/100 ml

23. Describe the relationship between high blood cholesterol levels and cardiovascular diseases such as hypertension, heart attacks, and strokes.

High LDL levels favor cholesterol uptake and deposit in arteriosclerotic plaques, which, in turn (1) narrow the vessel, reducing blood flow to more distal tissues, and (2) increase the risk of thrombus formation. Narrowing of blood vessels is one cause of hypertension.

Attached thrombi or detached thrombi (emboli) are common causes of heart attack and stroke.

Anatomy of the Heart

Time Allotment: 1 1/2 hours.

Multimedia Resources: See Appendix B for Guide to Multimedia Resource Distributors.

The Circulatory System: Two Hearts That Beat as One (FHS: 28 minutes, DVD, 3-year streaming webcast)
Interactive Physiology® 10-System Suite: Cardiovascular System (PE: CD-ROM, website)
Life Under Pressure (FHS: 26 minutes, DVD, 3-year streaming webcast)
Practice Anatomy Lab™ 3.0 (PAL) (PE: DVD, website)

Laboratory Materials

Ordering information is based on a lab size of 24 students, working in groups of 4. A list of supply house addresses appears in Appendix A.

X-ray film of human thorax
X-ray viewing box
3-D model of the heart
Chart showing heart anatomy
24 red pencils
24 blue pencils
24 highlighters
3-D models of cardiac and skeletal
    muscle

24 compound microscopes, lens paper,
    lens cleaning solution, immersion oil
24 prepared slides of cardiac muscle
    (longitudinal section)
6–12 preserved or fresh sheep hearts
    (with pericardial sacs intact, if
    possible)
6–12 dissecting instruments and tray
    sets

6–12 pointed glass rods for probes
    (or blunt probes)
6–12 millimeter rulers
Disposable gloves
Container for disposal of organic
    debris
Laboratory detergent
Spray bottle with 10% household
    bleach solution

Advance Preparation

1. Make arrangements for appropriate storage, disposal, and cleanup of dissection materials. Check with the Department of Health or the Department of Environmental Protection, or their counterparts, for state regulations.

2. Set out disposable gloves and safety glasses.

3. Set out dissecting kits, dissecting pans, glass or blunt probes, plastic metric rulers, and preserved (or fresh) sheep hearts (one or two for each group).

4. Set out dissectible heart and cardiac muscle models, red and blue pencils, highlighters, and heart anatomy charts.

5. Set out prepared slides of cardiac muscle (longitudinal section), lens paper, immersion oil, and lens cleaning solution. Have compound microscopes available.

6. Set out an X-ray film of the human thorax and an X-ray viewing box.

Comments and Pitfalls

1. Some sheep hearts are sold with the pericardial sac removed. If possible, order sheep hearts with intact pericardial sacs (biology supply companies).

2. Students often confuse the base and apex of the heart. Explain that it looks like an inverted triangle which is why the base is at the top.

3. Be sure students have correctly identified the left ventricle of the heart as a landmark before they begin the dissection. As with all dissections, urge students to be cautious with the scalpel.

4. Many preserved hearts have the venae cavae and pulmonary veins completely removed, leaving large holes in the walls of the atria. This will make it difficult for students to answer some of the questions in the lab text. Purchase a dissected pig heart that has all the major vessels intact (biology supply companies), or refer students to models if necessary.

5. Provide students with extra blunt probes to mark vessels as they are identified.

Answers to Pre-Lab Quiz (p. 445)

1. c, pericardium
2. c, four
3. atria
4. a, aorta
5. true

6. tricuspid
7. right
8. c, coronary arteries
9. a, intercalated discs
10. left

Answers to Dissection Questions

Dissection: The Sheep Heart (pp. 452–454)

2. The pericardium is attached to the base of the heart.

3. The visceral pericardium is much thinner than the tough two-layered serofibrous parietal pericardium. The visceral pericardium adheres tightly to the heart, while the parietal pericardium forms the outer sac surrounding the pericardial cavity.

6. The aorta is easier to stretch than either of the venae cavae. The aorta must stretch to accommodate the increased volume of blood that enters with each left ventricular contraction.

8. The lumen of the superior vena cava is larger. The aorta has thicker walls. The aorta is capable of stretching and elastic recoiling, which helps to maintain pressure in the vessels. This requires strength and resilience. The vena cava is a low-pressure vessel for blood return to the heart, and is not subjected to large pressure fluctuations.

9. The tricuspid valve has three cusps.

10. The pulmonary (semilunar) valve closes when fluid fills the collapsed cuplike valves, causing them to bulge out into the lumen. The atrioventricular valves are flaps that swing closed as pressure in the ventricle increases. They are prevented from opening backward into the atria by the chordae tendineae attached to the papillary muscles.

14. The left ventricular cavity is much narrower than the right ventricular cavity. Papillary muscles and chordae tendineae are present in both cavities. The mitral valve has two cusps; the tricuspid valve has three cusps. The sheep valves are very similar to their human counterparts.

Anatomy of the Heart

Gross Anatomy of the Human Heart

1. An anterior view of the heart is shown here. Match each structure listed on the left with the correct letter in the figure.

g ____ 1. right atrium

j ____ 2. right ventricle

r ____ 3. left atrium

u ____ 4. left ventricle

b ____ 5. superior vena cava

k ____ 6. inferior vena cava

d ____ 7. ascending aorta

n ____ 8. aortic arch

a ____ 9. brachiocephalic trunk

l ____ 10. left common carotid artery

m ____ 11. left subclavian artery

e ____ 12. pulmonary trunk

c ____ 13. right pulmonary artery

p ____ 14. left pulmonary artery

o ____ 15. ligamentum arteriosum

f ____ 16. right pulmonary veins

q ____ 17. left pulmonary veins

h ____ 18. right coronary artery

i ____ 19. anterior cardiac vein

t ____ 20. left coronary artery

s ____ 21. circumflex artery

w ____ 22. anterior interventricular artery

x ____ 23. apex of heart

v ____ 24. great cardiac vein

2. What is the function of the fluid that fills the pericardial sac? _To reduce friction during heart activity_

3. Match the terms in the key to the descriptions provided below. Some terms are used more than once.

_f_   1. location of the heart in the thorax

_a_   2. superior heart chambers

_h_   3. inferior heart chambers

_e_   4. visceral pericardium

_a_   5. receiving chambers of the heart

_g_   6. layer composed of cardiac muscle

_b_   7. provide nutrient blood to the heart muscle

_d_   8. lining of the heart chambers

_h_   9. actual "pumps" of the heart

_c_   10. drains blood into the right atrium

Key:

a. atria

b. coronary arteries

c. coronary sinus

d. endocardium

e. epicardium

f. mediastinum

g. myocardium

h. ventricles

4. What is the function of the valves found in the heart? _They enforce a one-way flow of blood through the heart._

5. What is the role of the chordae tendineae? _They anchor the AV valve flaps during ventricular systole, thus preventing backflow of blood into the atria._

Pulmonary, Systemic, and Coronary Circulations

6. A simple schematic of general circulation is shown below. Which circuit is missing from this diagram?

Pulmonary circulation is not distinct from systemic circulation. Add to the diagram as best you can to make it depict the two

circuits. Label the two circuits.

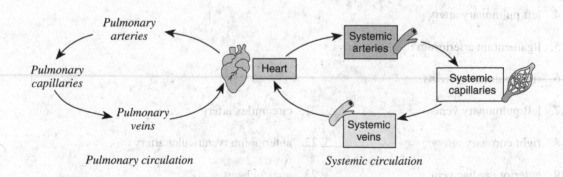

7. Differentiate clearly between the roles of the pulmonary and systemic circuits. *The pulmonary circuit provides for gas exchange only; the systemic circuit provides the functional supply of the body tissues.*

8. Complete the following scheme of circulation of a red blood cell in the human body.

Right atrium through the tricuspid valve to the *right ventricle* _____, through the *pulmonary semilunar* _____ valve to the pulmonary trunk, to the *right and left pulmonary arteries* _____, to the capillary beds of the lungs, to the *pulmonary veins* _____, to the *left atrium* _____ of the heart, through the *mitral/bicuspid* _____ valve to the *left ventricle* _____, through the *aortic semilunar* _____ valve to the *aorta* _____, to the systemic arteries, to the *capillary beds* _____ of the tissues, to the systemic veins, to the *inferior vena cava* _____, *superior vena cava* _____, and *coronary sinus* _____ entering the right atrium of the heart.

9. If the mitral valve does not close properly, which circuit is affected? *Systemic*

10. Why might a thrombus (blood clot) in the anterior descending branch of the left coronary artery cause sudden death?
This artery supplies blood to the interventricular septum and the anterior walls of both ventricles. Ventricular damage, particularly to the left ventricle, is very serious.

Microscopic Anatomy of Cardiac Muscle

11. How would you distinguish the structure of cardiac muscle from that of skeletal muscle? *Both tissue types are striated; thus, this is not a distinguishing feature. Skeletal muscle cells are long cylindrical cells with many peripherally located nuclei per cell. Cardiac cells have one (or two) centrally located nuclei per cell; their branched ends fit together at tight junctions called intercalated discs, which are not seen in skeletal muscle.*

12. Add the following terms to the photograph of cardiac muscle below.

   a. intercalated disc   b. nucleus of cardiac fiber   c. striations   d. cardiac muscle fiber

Describe the unique anatomical features of cardiac muscle. What role does the unique structure of cardiac muscle play in its function?

Cardiac muscle cells form a functional syncytium by virtue of their intercalated discs. This structural feature plus the special arrangement of cardiac muscle in the heart allows the pumping action of the heart to be carefully coordinated for maximal efficiency.

Dissection of the Sheep Heart

13. During the sheep heart dissection, you were asked initially to identify the right and left ventricles without cutting into the heart. During this procedure, what differences did you observe between the two chambers?

The left ventricle was firmer, thicker, and less compressible; the right ventricle felt "flabby."

When you measured thickness of ventricular walls, was the right or left ventricle thicker? *The left ventricle*

Knowing that structure and function are related, how would you say this structural difference reflects the relative functions of these two heart chambers? *The left ventricle pumps blood through the high-resistance systemic circulation; therefore, it has to be stronger than the right ventricle, which pumps blood through the short low-resistance pulmonary circuit.*

14. Semilunar valves prevent backflow into the *ventricles* ; mitral and tricuspid valves prevent backflow into the *atria* . Using your own observations, explain how the operation of the semilunar valves differs from that of the mitral and tricuspid valves. *When the ventricle was compressed (as in systole), the AV valve flaps moved superiorly into the closed position. When water was poured (as when blood backflows) into the semilunar valves, the cusps filled and closed the valve.*

15. Compare and contrast the structure of the atrioventricular valves. *Both have thin flaps secured to papillary muscles by chordae tendineae. The right valve has three cusps; the left valve has two.*

16. Two remnants of fetal structures are observable in the heart—the ligamentum arteriosum and the fossa ovalis. What were the fetal heart structures called, where was each located, and what common purpose did they serve as functioning fetal structures?

Ligamentum arteriosum—ductus arteriosus between the pulmonary trunk and the aorta. Fossa ovalis—foramen ovale, in the atrial septum. When they were open (and functional), they allowed blood to bypass the nonfunctional fetal lungs.

Conduction System of the Heart and Electrocardiography

Time Allotment: About 15 minutes of lab time for each group making ECG recordings.

Multimedia Resources: See Appendix B for Guide to Multimedia Resource Distributors.

Interactive Physiology® 10-System Suite: Cardiovascular System (PE: CD-ROM, website)

Laboratory Materials

Ordering information is based on a lab size of 24 students, working in groups of 4. A list of supply house addresses appears in Appendix A.

Millimeter ruler
Cot or lab table; pillow (optional)
Apparatus A or B:
 A: ECG recording apparatus, electrode paste, alcohol swabs, rubber straps

B: BIOPAC® BSL System for Windows with BSL software version 3.7.5 to 3.7.7, or BSL System for Mac OS X with BSL software version 3.7.4 to 3.7.7,

MP36/35 or MP45 data acquisition unit, PC or Mac computer, electrode lead set, disposable vinyl electrodes

Advance Preparation

1. Set out ECG recording apparatus, electrode paste, alcohol swabs, and a cot (or clear a section of the lab bench). Attach the leads to the recorder.

2. If you are using an ECG recording apparatus, turn it on, and allow it to warm up. Set the paper speed at 25 millimeters per second. Test the equipment as instructed by the manufacturer. Some equipment uses heat-sensitive paper. Be sure that the stylus produces a readable tracing. Adjust temperature setting accordingly. Test to see that a 1-millivolt signal causes a 10-millimeter vertical displacement of the stylus, and make any necessary adjustments. If the equipment uses a pen and ink, make sure the ink is flowing smoothly. Be sure the base line of the pen or stylus is on a horizontal line on the paper. If there is electrical interference, use the ground wire. Water or gas pipes are handy points for attachment.

3. Be sure the electrode plates are clean.

4. Set out equipment and materials for conducting the BIOPAC® activity. Introduce your students to the basic features of the equipment prior to beginning the lab activity.

Comments and Pitfalls

1. If leg leads are required, select student subjects with bare legs. Nylon stockings interfere with conduction.

2. Since electrode paste can be messy, try using electrode pads.

3. Have someone in the group double-check the arrangements of the electrodes before recording begins.

4. If the ECG is not clear, check to be sure electrodes are secure, remind the subject to remain still, and check the ground wire.

197

5. It is difficult to obtain good results when the student is running in place and attached to the electrodes. An alternate approach is to have the student run in place for 3 minutes and *then* connect the electrode to record the ECG immediately, and 2 and 4 minutes after exercise.

6. It is helpful to use a caliper and millimeter ruler when measuring the waves, intervals, and segments. These can be measured on screen with BIOPAC®.

7. If no ECG recording equipment is available, you can give the students a selection of ECG tracings and ask them to measure the waves, intervals, and segments.

Answers to Pre-Lab Quiz (p. 459)

1. true	6. a, P
2. c, sinoatrial	7. true
3. false	8. tachycardia
4. a, electrocardiogram	9. b, 4
5. three	10. true

Answers to Activity Questions

Activity 1A: Recording ECGs Using a Standard ECG Apparatus (pp. 463–464)
Recording the ECG after Running in Place

5. The Q-T interval is shortened and the interval between adjacent QRS complexes is shortened (the strength of contraction increases and the length of diastole decreases).

Recording the ECG During Breath Holding

4. The heart rate increases during breath holding. As the CO_2 level in the blood increases, the blood pH decreases, causing cerebral vasodilation. This may increase sympathetic tone, thereby increasing heart rate. There may be some connection between the medullary respiratory and cardiac centers. (Depending on the text you are using, this might be difficult for the students to track down.)

Activity 1B: Electrocardiography Using BIOPAC® (pp. 464–468)
Analysis of Segment 3: After Exercise with Deep Breathing

4. There is not likely to be a significant difference in Delta T between Segment 1 and Segment 3, although if there is a difference, some of the ECG components are likely to be of shorter duration in Segment 3. Postexercise heart rate should increase, so the bpm of Segment 3 should be greater than Segment 1.

There is an inverse relationship between time between R waves and heart rate. A shorter interval between R waves translates into a higher heart rate.

There is likely to be an increase in heart rate as the subject makes the transition from a lying to a sitting position.

If the P-R interval is of longer than normal duration, there may be first-degree heart block, a slowing of the electrical conduction through the AV node.

NAME _____

LAB TIME/DATE _____

Conduction System of the Heart and Electrocardiography

The Intrinsic Conduction System

1. List the elements of the intrinsic conduction system in order, starting from the SA node.

SA node → *AV node* _____ → *AV bundle (bundle of His)* _____ →

left and right bundle branches _____ → *subendocardial conducting network (Purkinje fibers)* _____

At what structure in the transmission sequence is the impulse temporarily delayed? *AV node* _____

Why? *Allows completion of atrial contraction before initiation of ventricular systole* _____

2. Even though cardiac muscle has an inherent ability to beat, the intrinsic conduction system plays a critical role in heart physiology.

What is that role? *Ensures that depolarization proceeds in an orderly manner from atria to ventricles; accelerates and coordinates*

heart activity to effectively pump blood _____

Electrocardiography

3. Define *ECG*. *Recording of electrical changes occurring during heart activity* _____

4. Draw an ECG wave form representing one heartbeat. Label the P wave, QRS complex, and T wave; the P-R interval; the S-T segment, and the Q-T interval.

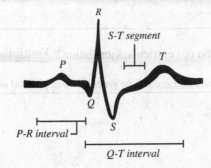

5. Why does heart rate increase during running? *Heart rate increases during running secondary to action of the sympathetic nervous*

system. Norepinephrine, released by sympathetic axons on the heart, and the hormone epinephrine released during a sympathetic discharge

stimulate pacemaker cells to fire more rapidly. _____

6. Describe what happens in the cardiac cycle in the following situations.

    1.   immediately before the P wave: *The heart is in diastole.*

    2.   during the P wave: *Depolarization of the atria*

    3.   immediately after the P wave: *Contraction of the atria*

    4.   during the QRS complex: *Depolarization of the ventricles and repolarization of the atria*

    5.   immediately after the QRS complex (S-T segment): *Contraction of the ventricles*

    6.   during the T wave: *Repolarization of the ventricles*

7. Define the following terms.

    1.   *tachycardia:* *Heart rate over 100 beats/min*

    2.   *bradycardia:* *Heart rate below 60 beats/min*

    3.   *fibrillation:* *Very rapid uncoordinated myocardial activity*

8. Abnormalities of heart valves can be detected more accurately by auscultation than by electrocardiography. Why is this so?

Most often serious valve problems cause turbulent blood flow, which can be detected (heard) with a stethoscope. Since the valves do not

have electrical activity (they are not part of the conduction system) no electrical signals can be recorded from them on the ECG.

Why This Matters

9. Given what you know about the correlation between the ECG waves and the electrical events in the heart, what wave of the ECG tracing would you expect to be affected by atrial fibrillation? Explain. *The P wave should be affected since this wave is*

generated by atrial depolarization.

10. Which is more serious, atrial fibrillation or ventricular fibrillation? *Ventricular fibrillation*

    Why? *Ventricular fibrillation is more serious because the ventricles pump blood to the lungs and through the systemic circuit.*

32

Anatomy of Blood Vessels

Time Allotment: 1¹/2 hours.

Multimedia Resources: See Appendix B for Guide to Multimedia Resource Distributors.

The Circulatory System (IM: 23 minutes, DVD)
Circulatory System: The Plasma Pipeline (FHS: 25 minutes, DVD, 3-year streaming webcast)
Human Biology (FHS: 58 minutes, DVD)
Interactive Physiology® 10-System Suite: Cardiovascular System (PE: CD-ROM, website)
Life Under Pressure (FHS: 26 minutes, DVD, 3-year streaming webcast)
Practice Anatomy Lab™ 3.0 (PAL) (PE: DVD, website)
Pumping Life—The Heart and Circulatory System Video (DE: 20 minutes, VHS)

Laboratory Materials

Ordering information is based on a lab size of 24 students, working in groups of 4. A list of supply house addresses appears in Appendix A.

Anatomical charts of human arteries and veins or a 3-D model of the human circulatory system
Anatomical charts and/or 3-D models of the following specialized

circulations: pulmonary circulation, hepatic portal circulation, arterial supply to the brain and cerebral arterial circle (Circle of Willis), fetal circulation

24 compound microscopes, lens paper, lens cleaning solution
24 prepared microscope slides showing cross sections of an artery and a vein

Advance Preparation

1. Set out anatomical charts and/or models of human arteries and veins and the human circulatory system.

2. Set out anatomical charts of special circulations.

3. Set out prepared slides of cross sections of arteries and veins, lens paper, and lens cleaning solution. Have compound microscopes available.

Answers to Pre-Lab Quiz (p. 471)

1. veins
2. true
3. a, aorta
4. superior mesenteric
5. dorsalis pedis

6. superior
7. c, great saphenous
8. hepatic
9. b, hepatic portal circulation
10. vein

Answers to Group Challenge: Fix the Blood Trace (p. 486)

1. aortic arch ↮R. subclavian artery → R. axillary artery → R. brachial artery → R. radial artery → R. superficial palmar arch (*Brachiocephalic artery* is missing between the aortic arch and the R. subclavian artery.)

2. abdominal aorta → R. common iliac artery ↮R. femoral artery → R. popliteal artery → R. anterior tibial artery → R. dorsalis pedis artery (*R. external iliac artery* is missing between the R. common iliac artery and the R. femoral artery.)

3. ascending aorta → aortic arch → L. common carotid artery → L. internal carotid artery → L. anterior cerebral artery (*all correct*)

4. R. median antebrachial vein → R. basilic vein → R. axillary vein ↮R. brachiocephalic vein → superior vena cava (*R. subclavian vein* is missing between the R. axillary vein and the R. brachiocephalic vein.)

Anatomy of Blood Vessels

Microscopic Structure of the Blood Vessels

1. Cross-sectional views of an artery and of a vein are shown here. Identify each; on the lines to the sides, note the structural details that enabled you to make these identifications:

artery
_____
(vessel type)

open, circular lumen
_____
(a)

thick tunica media
_____
(b)

vein
_____
(vessel type)

somewhat collapsed lumen
_____
(a)

thinner tunica media
_____
(b)

Now describe each tunic more fully by selecting its characteristics from the key below and placing the appropriate key letters on the answer lines.

Tunica intima _a, c, f_   Tunica media _d, e_   Tunica externa _b_

Key:

a. innermost tunic
b. most superficial tunic
c. thin tunic of capillaries

d. regulates blood vessel diameter
e. contains smooth muscle and elastin
f. has a smooth surface to decrease resistance to blood flow

2. Why are valves present in veins but not in arteries? _The high blood pressure in arteries propels the blood through them. The_

blood pressure in veins is low and often the blood is flowing against gravity. Valves prevent backflow.

3. Name two events *occurring within the body* that aid in venous return.

Skeletal muscle "milking action"   and _changes in thoracic cavity pressure during breathing_

4. Why are the walls of arteries proportionately thicker than those of the corresponding veins? _Arteries must withstand high_

pressure and pressure fluctuations. Veins are low-pressure vessels.

Major Systemic Arteries and Veins of the Body

5. Use the key on the right to identify the arteries or veins described on the left. Some terms are used more than once.

_d_ _____ 1. the arterial system has one of these; the venous system has two

_i_ _____ 2. these arteries supply the myocardium

_r_ ___, _z_ _____ 3. two paired arteries serving the brain

_o_ _____ 4. longest vein in the lower limb

_k_ _____ 5. artery on the dorsum of the foot checked after leg surgery

_j_ _____ 6. main artery that serves the thigh muscles

_t_ _____ 7. supplies the diaphragm

_c_ _____ 8. formed by the union of the radial and ulnar veins

_b_ ___, _f_ _____ 9. two superficial veins of the arm

_w_ _____ 10. artery serving the kidney

_p_ _____ 11. veins draining the liver

_q_ _____ 12. artery that supplies the distal half of the large intestine

_s_ _____ 13. drains the pelvic organs

_m_ _____ 14. what the external iliac artery becomes on entry into the thigh

_c_ _____ 15. artery that branches into radial and ulnar arteries

_y_ _____ 16. supplies most of the small intestine

_h_ _____ 17. join to form the inferior vena cava

_e_ _____ 18. an arterial trunk that has three major branches, which run to the liver, spleen, and stomach

_l_ _____ 19. major artery serving the tissues external to the skull

_a_ ___, _n_ ___, _o_ ___, _u_ _____ 20. four veins serving the leg

_v_ _____ 21. artery generally used to take the pulse at the wrist

Key:
a. anterior tibial
b. basilic
c. brachial
d. brachiocephalic
e. celiac trunk
f. cephalic
g. common carotid
h. common iliac
i. coronary
j. deep artery of the thigh
k. dorsalis pedis
l. external carotid
m. femoral
n. fibular
o. great saphenous
p. hepatic
q. inferior mesenteric
r. internal carotid
s. internal iliac
t. phrenic
u. posterior tibial
v. radial
w. renal
x. subclavian
y. superior mesenteric
z. vertebral

6. What is the function of the cerebral arterial circle? _Provides an alternate set of pathways for blood to reach brain tissue in case of impaired blood flow anywhere in the system_

7. The anterior and middle cerebral arteries arise from the _internal carotid_ artery. They serve the _cerebral hemispheres_ of the brain.

8. Trace the pathway of a drop of blood from the aorta to the left occipital lobe of the brain, noting all structures through which it flows. _Aorta → subclavian artery → vertebral artery → basilar artery → posterior cerebral artery → occipital brain tissue_

9. The human arterial and venous systems are diagrammed on pages 254–255. Identify all indicated blood vessels.

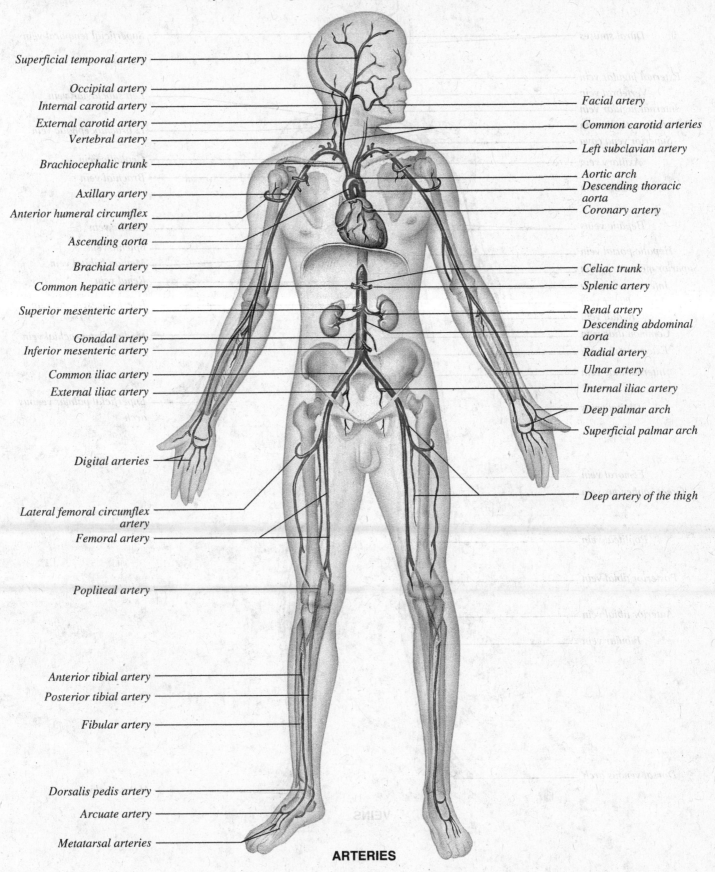

Superficial temporal artery

Occipital artery

Internal carotid artery

External carotid artery

Vertebral artery

Brachiocephalic trunk

Axillary artery

Anterior humeral circumflex artery

Ascending aorta

Brachial artery

Common hepatic artery

Superior mesenteric artery

Gonadal artery

Inferior mesenteric artery

Common iliac artery

External iliac artery

Digital arteries

Lateral femoral circumflex artery

Femoral artery

Popliteal artery

Anterior tibial artery

Posterior tibial artery

Fibular artery

Dorsalis pedis artery

Arcuate artery

Metatarsal arteries

Facial artery

Common carotid arteries

Left subclavian artery

Aortic arch

Descending thoracic aorta

Coronary artery

Celiac trunk

Splenic artery

Renal artery

Descending abdominal aorta

Radial artery

Ulnar artery

Internal iliac artery

Deep palmar arch

Superficial palmar arch

Deep artery of the thigh

ARTERIES

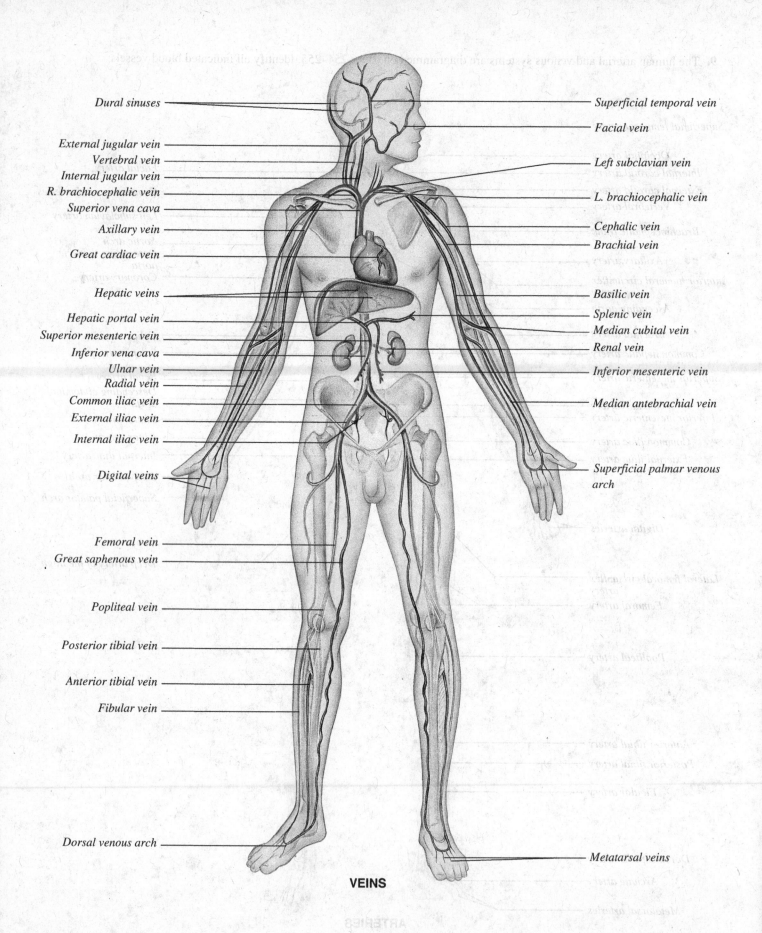

Dural sinuses

External jugular vein
Vertebral vein
Internal jugular vein
R. brachiocephalic vein
Superior vena cava
Axillary vein
Great cardiac vein

Hepatic veins

Hepatic portal vein
Superior mesenteric vein
Inferior vena cava
Ulnar vein
Radial vein
Common iliac vein
External iliac vein
Internal iliac vein

Digital veins

Femoral vein
Great saphenous vein

Popliteal vein

Posterior tibial vein

Anterior tibial vein

Fibular vein

Dorsal venous arch

Superficial temporal vein
Facial vein

Left subclavian vein

L. brachiocephalic vein

Cephalic vein
Brachial vein

Basilic vein
Splenic vein
Median cubital vein
Renal vein
Inferior mesenteric vein

Median antebrachial vein

Superficial palmar venous arch

Metatarsal veins

VEINS

10. Trace the blood flow for each of the following situations.

 a. from the capillary beds of the left thumb to the capillary beds of the right thumb: *Digital vein, L. radial vein, L. brachial vein, L. axillary vein, L. subclavian vein, L. brachiocephalic vein, superior vena cava, R. atrium, R. ventricle, pulmonary trunk, pulmonary artery, lobar artery, pulmonary capillaries of the lung, lobar veins, pulmonary veins, L. atrium, L. ventricle, aortic arch, brachiocephalic artery, R. subclavian artery, R. axillary artery, R. brachial artery, R. radial artery, digital artery*

 b. from the mitral valve to the tricuspid valve by way of the great toe: *Through mitral valve into left ventricle, aorta, common iliac artery, external iliac artery, femoral artery, posterior tibial artery, medial plantar artery, digital artery, capillary beds, digital vein, plantar arch, plantar vein, posterior tibial vein, femoral vein, external iliac vein, common iliac vein, inferior vena cava, right atrium, then through tricuspid valve*

Pulmonary Circulation

11. Trace the pathway of a carbon dioxide gas molecule in the blood from the inferior vena cava until it leaves the bloodstream. Name all structures (vessels, heart chambers, and others) passed through en route.

 Inferior vena cava → right atrium → tricuspid valve → right ventricle → pulmonary (semilunar) valve → pulmonary trunk → right or left pulmonary artery → lobar artery → pulmonary capillary beds in lungs → air sacs (alveoli) of lungs.

12. Trace the pathway of oxygen gas molecules from an alveolus of the lung to the right ventricle of the heart. Name all structures through which it passes. **Circle the areas of gas exchange.** *Alveolus →* (*alveolar/capillary walls*) *→ pulmonary vein → left atrium → mitral valve → left ventricle → aortic (semilunar) valve → aorta → systemic arteries →* (*capillary beds of tissues*) *→ systemic veins → superior or inferior vena cava → right atrium → tricuspid valve → right ventricle*

13. Most arteries of the adult body carry oxygen-rich blood, and the veins carry oxygen-poor blood. How does this differ in the pulmonary arteries and veins? *The pulmonary arteries carry oxygen-poor blood to the lungs, whereas the pulmonary veins carry oxygen-rich blood from the lungs to the left heart*

14. How do the arteries of the pulmonary circulation differ structurally from the systemic arteries? What condition is indicated by this anatomical difference? *The pulmonary arteries are more like veins anatomically. They have relatively thin walls, reflecting the fact that the pulmonary circulation is a low-pressure bed.*

Fetal Circulation

15. For each of the following structures, first indicate its function in the fetus; and then note its face (what happens to it or what it is converted to after birth). **Circle the blood vessel that carries the most oxygen-rich blood.**

Structure	Function in fetus	Fate and postnatal structure
Umbilical artery	Carries O_2-poor blood from the fetus to the placenta.	Obliterated. Becomes the medial umbilical ligament.
(Umbilical vein)	Carries O_2-rich blood from the placenta to the fetus.	Obliterated. Becomes the round ligament of the liver (ligamentum teres).
Ductus venosus	Shunts blood through the fetal liver, bypassing the bulk of its tissue.	Becomes the fibrous ligamentum venosum.
Ductus arteriosus	Bypasses the fetal lungs by shunting blood from the pulmonary trunk to the aorta.	Occludes. Becomes the ligamentum arteriosum.
Foramen ovale	Bypasses the lungs by shunting blood from the right atrium to the left atrium.	Closes. Becomes the fossa ovalis.

16. What organ serves as a respiratory/digestive/excretory organ for the fetus? _Placenta_

Hepatic Portal Circulation

17. What is the source of blood in the hepatic portal system? _Blood drained from the digestive viscera_

18. Why is this blood carried to the liver before it enters the systemic circulation? _This blood is rich in nutrients. The liver is the key_ _body organ responsible for maintaining proper blood concentrations of glucose, proteins, etc. Its phagocytes also cleanse the blood of_ _debris._

19. The hepatic portal vein is formed by the union of the _splenic vein_ and the _superior mesenteric vein_.
The _splenic_ vein carries blood from the _spleen, pancreas_, and _stomach_. The _superior mesenteric_ vein drains the _small intestine, large intestine_, and _stomach_.
The _inferior mesenteric_ vein empties into the splenic vein and drains the _large intestine_ and _rectum_.

20. Trace the flow of a drop of blood from the small intestine to the right atrium of the heart, noting all structures encountered or passed through on the way. _Capillaries of small intestine → superior mesenteric vein → hepatic portal vein → liver sinusoids_
→ hepatic vein → inferior vena cava → right atrium of heart

Human Cardiovascular Physiology: Blood Pressure and Pulse Determinations

 Time Allotment: 2 hours (with some shared small-group data).

 Multimedia Resources: See Appendix B for Guide to Multimedia Resource Distributors.

Human Biology (FHS: 58 minutes DVD)
Interactive Physiology® 10-System Suite: Cardiovascular System (PE: CD-ROM, website)
Life Under Pressure (FHS: 26 minutes, DVD, 3-year streaming webcast)
The Physiology of Exercise (FHS: 15 minutes, DVD)

A record, audiotape, or CD-ROM of *Interpreting Heart Sounds* (if available on free loan from the local chapters of the American Heart Association) or any suitable web resource featuring heart sounds.

Laboratory Materials

Ordering information is based on a lab size of 24 students, working in groups of 4. A list of supply house addresses appears in Appendix A.

12 stethoscopes
12 sphygmomanometers
Watch (or clock) with second hand
Alcohol swabs
6 felt-tipped pens
6 small basins or large finger bowls
6 laboratory thermometers
Ice

Audio recording of *Interpreting Heart Sounds* (if available on free loan from local chapters of the American Heart Association) and appropriate player, or any suitable web resource featuring heart sounds
BIOPAC® BSL System for Windows with BSL software version 3.7.6 to 3.7.7, or BSL System for

Mac OS X with BSL software version 3.7.6 to 3.7.7, MP36/35 data acquisition unit, PC or Mac computer, BIOPAC® pulse plethysmograph
Cot (if available)
6 meter sticks
Step stools (0.4 m [16 in.] and 0.5 m [20 in.] in height)

Advance Preparation

1. Set out stethoscopes (both bell and diaphragm) and sphygmomanometers (two per group). Check the valves on the bulbs of the cuffs to be sure that air is released from the cuff when the valves are opened (replacement valves can be ordered). If electronic monitoring equipment is to be used, prepare instructions and distribute.

2. Set out or ask students to bring watches with second hands. Provide each group with a meter stick, alcohol swabs, a felt-tipped pen, a small basin or large finger bowl, and a laboratory thermometer. Have ice available.

3. Set out one 0.4 meter (16-inch) high bench (for women) and one 0.5 meter (20-inch) high bench (for men). You may have to compromise with a 0.45 meter (18-inch) bench. Set up a cot, if available.

4. Set up the appropriate player for heart sounds.

5. Divide the class into small groups to collect data for Effect of Various Factors on Blood Pressure and Heart Rate. It may be hard to define *well-conditioned* and *poorly conditioned* subjects. A runner or a member of an athletic team might be compared to a more sedentary person (see Comments and Pitfalls, item 4).

6. Set out equipment and materials for conducting the BIOPAC® activity. Introduce your students to the basic features of the equipment prior to beginning the lab activity.

Comments and Pitfalls

1. Most students in the health sciences will have no trouble with this lab, and in fact enjoy bringing their own stethoscopes and sphygmomanometers to lab if they are given advance notice.

2. If students have trouble hearing the heart sounds with the bell stethoscope, have them try the diaphragm model. This will be particularly helpful when trying to hear the split sounds. The sounds are louder with the bell stethoscopes, but placement must be more precise.

3. Caution students against overtightening the valve on the sphygmomanometer. If the air in the cuff can't be released, it is very painful to the subject. If the valve does stick, most cuffs can be undone even when filled with air. To avoid problems once the cuff is inflated, have students practice first with the bulb valve.

4. Students performing the Harvard step test should be carefully monitored to be sure that they step completely up and completely down at the prescribed rate. This can be very fatiguing. If the student population is fairly uniform it may be difficult to detect major differences between the *well-conditioned* and *poorly conditioned* individuals. Try to compare people of the same general age and sex, and do not compare a smoker to a nonsmoker. Students who are aware that they have heart problems should be discouraged from acting as subjects.

5. Many fitness tests are designed for people in their early twenties. Some tests take age and gender into account (see the President's Challenge, Physical Fitness Test at www.presidentschallenge.org).

6. If a person with Raynaud's disease is used as the subject for the cold pressor test, he or she may experience temporary loss of feeling in the hand.

7. Students who are testing the effects of venous congestion should be reminded to keep both arms quietly on the lab bench for the full 5 minutes. Check to be sure pressure is maintained at 40 mm Hg.

Answers to Pre-Lab Quiz (pp. 495–496)

1. diastole
2. b, cardiac cycle
3. true
4. b, 75
5. murmurs
6. c, pulse
7. radial
8. sphygmomanometer
9. 90
10. d, sounds of Korotkoff

Answers to Activity Questions

Activity 1: Auscultating Heart Sounds (p. 498)

3. The interval is about 0.5 second. It is about twice as long as the interval between the first and second heart sounds.

Activity 2: Palpating Superficial Pulse Points (p. 499)

The carotid pulse point has the greatest amplitude, and the dorsalis pedis artery has the least. This is related to distance from the left ventricle of the heart.

Activity 6: Estimating Venous Pressure (p. 503)

4. During the Valsalva maneuver, peripheral venous pressure increases due to the increase in intrathoracic pressure.

Activity 7: Observing the Effect of Various Factors on Blood Pressure and Heart Rate (pp. 504–506)

Exercise

6. Greater elevation of blood pressure is generally noted just after completion of exercise. Increased cardiac output during exercise results in increased systolic pressure. A poorly conditioned individual usually has a higher systolic pressure at the end of exercise, and it usually takes a longer time for the pressure to return to normal. A well-conditioned individual usually has a larger stroke volume and thus can pump more blood with fewer beats per minute than a poorly conditioned individual. Diastolic pressure usually does not increase significantly, as it is the resting pressure of the vessels.

A Noxious Sensory Stimulus (Cold)

Blood pressure changes will be variable. The pulse rate will probably increase.

Activity 8: Examining the Effect of Local Chemical and Physical Factors on Skin Color (pp. 506–508)

Vasodilation and Flushing of the Skin Due to Local Metabolites

7. Stopping blood flow causes the hand to turn very pale. Weakness and a tingling sensation may be felt (variable). The skin flushes bright red immediately upon release of pressure and normal color is restored after several minutes or longer. There may be some lingering pain in the forearm region.

Effects of Venous Congestion

2. Slight pressure may be felt in the hand at the end of 5 minutes (variable). The veins are bulging and the hand has a mottled appearance, much darker in color than the control. Upon release of pressure, the veins deflate, and color and feeling return to normal.

3. Intensity of skin color (pink or blue) is related to the volume of blood in the area. The color is determined by the degree of oxygenation of the blood. In this experiment, venous blood gives a blue tint and arterial blood gives a pink tint.

Collateral Blood Flow

5. Results are variable. The hand usually turns intensely red and a warm tingling sensation may be felt. Redness may last for several minutes.

6. The hand does not become totally ischemic. The second test result is much less dramatic, with much less intense reactive hyperthermia.

7. With only the ulnar artery compressed, the results are intermediate between questions 5 and 6. The ulnar artery has a larger diameter than the radial artery, but they anastomose in the hand to serve the same areas.

Effect of Mechanical Stimulation of Blood Vessels of the Skin

Results will vary. A red streak develops with moderate pressure. With heavy pressure, a wider, darker, longer-lasting streak develops and may swell.

Human Cardiovascular Physiology: Blood Pressure and Pulse Determinations

Cardiac Cycle

1. Using the grouped sets of terms to the right of the diagram, correctly identify each trace, valve closings and openings, and each time period of the cardiac cycle.

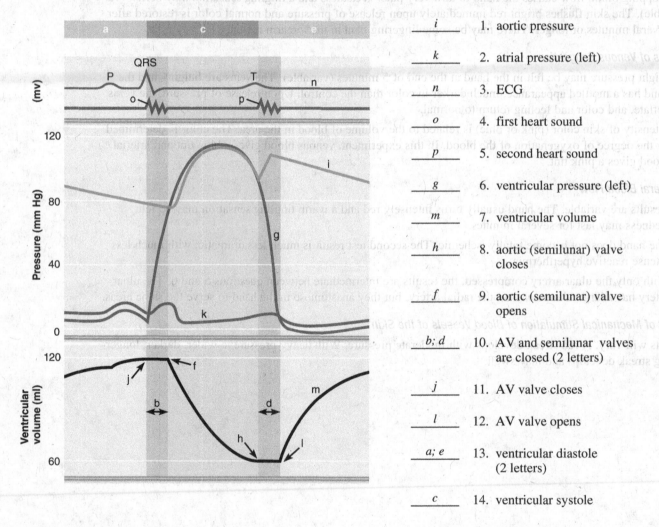

_i_	1. aortic pressure
_k_	2. atrial pressure (left)
_n_	3. ECG
_o_	4. first heart sound
_p_	5. second heart sound
_g_	6. ventricular pressure (left)
_m_	7. ventricular volume
_h_	8. aortic (semilunar) valve closes
_f_	9. aortic (semilunar) valve opens
_b; d_	10. AV and semilunar valves are closed (2 letters)
_j_	11. AV valve closes
_l_	12. AV valve opens
_a; e_	13. ventricular diastole (2 letters)
_c_	14. ventricular systole

2. Define the following terms.

systole: _Contraction of the ventricles (general usage)_ _____

diastole: _Ventricular relaxation (general usage)_ _____

cardiac cycle: _One complete heartbeat including atrial and ventricular contraction_ _____

3. Answer the following questions concerning events of the cardiac cycle.

When are the AV valves closed? *During ventricular systole and early diastole*

What event within the heart causes the AV valves to open? *Atrial pressure greater than ventricular pressure*

When are the semilunar valves closed? *During the period of relaxation of the heart as a whole and during atrial contraction*

What event causes the semilunar valves to open? *Ventricular pressure greater than pressure in great arteries*

Are both sets of valves closed during any part of the cycle? *Yes*

If so, when? *Momentarily after atrial contraction and ventricular systole*

Are both sets of valves open during any part of the cycle? *No*

At what point in the cardiac cycle is the pressure in the heart highest? *Ventricular systole*

Lowest? *Ventricular diastole*

What event results in the pressure deflection called the dicrotic notch? *The momentary increase in aortic pressure that occurs when its semilunar valves snap shut*

4. Using the key below, indicate the time interval occupied by the following events of the cardiac cycle.

Key: a. 0.8 sec   b. 0.4 sec   c. 0.3 sec   d. 0.1 sec

_a_____ 1. the length of the normal cardiac cycle   _b_____ 3. the quiescent period

_d_____ 2. the time interval of atrial contraction   _c_____ 4. the time interval of ventricular contraction

5. If an individual's heart rate is 80 beats/min, what is the length of the cardiac cycle? *0.75 sec* What portion of the cardiac cycle decreases with a more rapid heart rate? *Quiescent period (ventricular relaxation period)*

6. What two factors promote the movement of blood through the heart? *Alternate contraction and relaxation of the myocardium* and *opening and closing of the heart valves*

Heart Sounds

7. Complete the following statements.

The two monosyllables describing the heart sounds are 1 . The first heart sound is a result of closure of the 2 valves, whereas the second is a result of closure of the 3 valves. The heart chambers that have just been filled when you hear the first heart sound are the 4 , and the chambers that have just emptied are the 5 . Immediately after the second heart sound, both the 6 and 7 are filling with blood.

1. *lub-dup*

2. *atrioventricular*

3. *aortic and pulmonary (semilunar)*

4. *ventricles*

5. *atria*

6. *atria*

7. *ventricles*

8. As you listened to the heart sounds during the laboratory session, what differences in pitch, length, and amplitude (loudness) of the two sounds did you observe? _First heart sound is longer, louder, and lower in pitch than the second heart sound, which is short, sharp, and high-pitched._

9. In order to auscultate most accurately, indicate where you would place your stethoscope for the following sounds:

closure of the tricuspid valve: _Left or right sternal border of the 5th intercostal space_

closure of the aortic valve: _Right sternal border of the 2nd intercostal space_

apical heartbeat: _5th intercostal space in line with the middle of the left clavicle_

Which valve is heard most clearly when the apical heartbeat is auscultated? _Mitral_

10. No one expects you to be a full-fledged physician on such short notice, but on the basis of what you have learned about heart sounds, give an example of how abnormal sounds might be used to diagnose a heart problem?

Abnormal sounds such as swishing sounds after valvular closure or high-pitched sounds arising when blood is forced through constricted (valve) openings might indicate valvular problems.

The Pulse

11. Define *pulse.* _Pressure surges in an artery occurring during each contraction and relaxation of the left ventricle_

12. Describe the procedure used to take the pulse. _Place the first 2–3 fingertips of one hand over an arterial pressure point. Compress firmly and then release the pressure slightly to palpate the pulse._

13. Identify the artery palpated at each of the pressure points listed.

at the wrist: _Radial_   on the dorsum of the foot: _Dorsalis pedis_

in front of the ear: _Temporal_   at the side of the neck: _Carotid_

14. When you were palpating the various pulse or pressure points, which appeared to have the greatest amplitude or tension?

Carotid artery   Why do you think this was so? _The carotid arteries are the major arteries that deliver blood to the brain and they are closest to the heart._

15. Assume someone has been injured in an auto accident and is hemorrhaging badly. What pressure point would you compress to help stop bleeding from each of the following areas?

the thigh: _Femoral artery_   the calf: _Popliteal artery_

the forearm: _Brachial artery_   the thumb: _Radial artery_

16. How could you tell by simple observation whether bleeding is arterial or venous? _If it spurts, it is arterial. It will flow evenly if it is venous blood._

17. You may sometimes observe a slight difference between the value obtained from an apical pulse (beats/min) and that from an arterial pulse taken elsewhere on the body. What is this difference called?

Pulse deficit

Blood Pressure Determinations

18. Define *blood pressure*. _Pressure exerted by blood against the walls of the blood vessels_

19. Identify the phase of the cardiac cycle to which each of the following applies.

systolic pressure: _Systole (ventricular contraction)_   diastolic pressure: _Diastole (relaxation)_

20. What is the name of the instrument used to compress the artery and record pressures in the auscultatory method of determining blood pressure? _Sphygmomanometer_

21. What are the sounds of Korotkoff? _Sounds that can be auscultated over a partially occluded artery_

What causes the systolic sound? _Sound of turbulent blood flow as it first begins to move through the constricted artery_

What causes the disappearance of the sound? _Blood is flowing freely; the artery is no longer constricted_

22. Interpret the pressure reading for each of the numbers listed: 145/85. _145 = systolic pressure reported as the point when the sounds first appear; 85 = diastolic pressure reported as the point where the sounds muffle or disappear_

23. Define *pulse pressure*. _Systolic pressure minus diastolic pressure_

Why is this measurement important? _It indicates the actual working pressure (actual amount of blood forced out of the heart during systole)._

24. Explain why *pulse pressure* is different from *pulse rate*. _Pulse pressure is what generates the pulse felt calculated as the systolic pressure minus the diastolic pressure; pulse rate is the number of pulsations per minute._

25. How do venous pressures compare to arterial pressures? _Venous pressures are lower._

Why? _Veins are far removed from the pumping action of the heart._

26. What maneuver to increase the thoracic pressure illustrates the effect of external factors on venous pressure? _Valsalva maneuver_

How is it performed? _A person takes a deep breath, and mimics the motions of exhaling forcibly, but without actually exhaling. The glottis will close and the intrathoracic pressure will increase._

27. What might an abnormal increase in venous pressure indicate? (Think!) _Heart failure. With the heart unable to adequately pump blood, it pools in the lower extremities and increases venous pressure._

Observing the Effect of Various Factors
on Blood Pressure and Heart Rate

28. What effect do the following have on blood pressure? (Indicate increase by ↑ and decrease by ↓.)

↓_____ 1. increased diameter of the arterioles   ↓_____ 4. hemorrhage

↑_____ 2. increased blood viscosity   _____ 5. arteriosclerosis

↑_____ 3. increased cardiac output   ↑_____ 6. increased pulse rate

29. In which position (sitting, reclining, or standing) is the blood pressure normally the highest?

Standing _____ The lowest? _Reclining_ _____

What immediate changes in blood pressure did you observe when the subject stood up after being in the sitting or reclining

position? _It decreased initially and then increased._

What changes in the blood vessels might account for the change? _Upon standing, gravitational pull caused blood pooling in the_

lower part of the body, but then vasoconstriction initiated by the vasomotor center caused blood pressure to rise.

After the subject stood for 3 minutes, what changes in blood pressure did you observe? _It decreased once again._

How do you account for this change? _Decreased activity of the sympathetic nervous system_

30. What was the effect of exercise on blood pressure? _It increased the blood pressure._

On pulse rate? _It increased the pulse rate._ Do you think these effects reflect changes in cardiac output _or_ in peripheral

resistance? _Both; cardiac output increases, but peripheral resistance also changes (it decreases as vessels to skeletal muscles and_

the heart dilate, and increases as vessels to other organs [e.g., GI tract and kidneys] constrict). Overall, peripheral resistance often

decreases during exercise, but it decreases less than cardiac output increases. Therefore, blood pressure rises.

Why are there normally no significant increases in diastolic pressure after exercise? _Since diastolic pressure reflects the heart_

in relaxation, it would not be expected to increase in healthy individuals.

31. What effects of cold temperature did you observe on blood pressure in the laboratory? _Increased BP_

What do you think the effect of heat would be? _Decreased BP_

Why? _Vasodilation would occur._

32. Differentiate between a hypo- and a hyperreactor relative to the cold pressor test. _Hyperreactors exhibit a rise of 23 mm Hg or_

more in BP during the test. Hyporeactors exhibit a smaller increase or a decrease in BP.

Skin Color as an Indicator of Local Circulatory Dynamics

33. Describe normal skin color and the appearance of the veins in the subject's forearm before any testing was conducted.

Skin pink; veins flat and difficult to see

34. What changes occurred when the subject emptied the forearm of blood (by raising the arm and making a fist) and the flow was occluded with the cuff? *Skin becomes pale (cyanotic in some cases) and cool.*

What changes occurred during venous congestion? *Skin becomes pink (red) and warm, and veins are congested and very visible.*

35. What is the importance of collateral blood supplies? *Can maintain the blood supply to an organ or body part in case the major*

nutrient artery is occluded

36. Explain the mechanism by which mechanical stimulation of the skin produced a flare. *Local inflammatory response produced*

by the chemical mediators released by injured tissue cells

Frog Cardiovascular Physiology

 Time Allotment: 3 hours. (Allow additional time if students must learn to use equipment.)

 Multimedia Resources: See Appendix B for Guide to Multimedia Resource Distributors.

PhysioEx™ 9.0 Exercise 6 (PE: CD-ROM, website)

 Solutions:

Ringer's Solution, Frog

- 6.50 grams sodium chloride
- 0.14 gram potassium chloride
- 0.12 gram calcium chloride
- 0.20 gram sodium bicarbonate

Combine salts in flask and add distilled water to make 1 liter of solution.

Test Solutions:

Atropine Sulfate in Frog Ringer's Solution, 5%
Weigh out 5 grams of atropine sulfate. Add frog Ringer's solution to a final volume of 100 milliliters.
Caution! Atropine sulfate is toxic. Label TOXIC.

Calcium Chloride in Frog Ringer's Solution, 2%
Weigh out 2 grams of calcium chloride. Add frog Ringer's solution to a final volume of 100 milliliters.

Digitalis in Frog Ringer's Solution, 2%
Weigh out 2 grams of digitoxin. Add frog Ringer's solution to a final volume of 100 milliliters.

Epinephrine in Frog Ringer's Solution, 1%
Weigh out 1 gram of epinephrine (Carolina). Dissolve in 0.5 milliliter of 1 *N* HCl. Add frog Ringer's solution to a final volume of 100 milliliters. **Caution! Epinephrine is toxic. Label TOXIC.**

Histamine in Frog Ringer's Solution, 0.01%
Weigh out 0.01 gram histamine. Add frog Ringer's solution to a final volume of 100 milliliters.

Hydrochloric Acid (HCl) in Frog Ringer's Solution, 0.01 N
Add 0.8 milliliter concentrated HCl to 900 milliliters frog Ringer's solution. Add distilled water to make 1 liter of solution.

Pilocarpine in Frog Ringer's Solution, 2.5%
Weigh out 2.5 grams of pilocarpine chloride. Add frog Ringer's solution to a final volume of 100 milliliters.

Potassium Chloride in Frog Ringer's Solution, 5%
Weigh out 5 grams of potassium chloride. Add frog Ringer's solution to a final volume of 100 milliliters.

Sodium Chloride (NaCl) in Frog Ringer's Solution, 0.7%
Weigh out 0.7 gram of sodium chloride. Add frog Ringer's solution to a final volume of 100 milliliters.

Laboratory Materials

Ordering information is based on a lab size of 24 students, working in groups of 4. A list of supply house addresses appears in Appendix A.

6 frogs
Disposable gloves
Apparatus A or B:
A: physiograph (polygraph), paper, ink, myograph transducer, transducer cables, stimulator output extension cable, electrodes
B: BIOPAC® BSL PRO Software, MP36/35 data acquisition unit, PC or Mac computer, BIOPAC® HDW100A tension adjuster (or equivalent). BIOPAC® SS12LA force transducer with S-hook, small hook with thread, and transducer (or ring) stand

Disposable container for organic debris
Dissecting pins
18 bottles of Ringer's solution, frog
Water bath at 32°C and 5°C
12 petri dishes
6 medicine droppers
6 dissecting pans and dissecting kits
6 millimeter rulers
Thread
6 large rubber bands
Box of fine common pins
6 frog boards
Cotton balls
Paper towels

6 compound microscopes, lens paper, lens cleaning solution
6 dropper bottles of each of the following (using frog Ringer's solution as the solvent):
5% atropine sulfate
2% digitalis
1% epinephrine
2.5% pilocarpine
5% potassium chloride (KCl)
2% calcium chloride ($CaCl_2$)
0.7% sodium chloride (NaCl)
0.01% histamine
0.01 N HCl

Advance Preparation

1. Order frogs to be delivered close to the date of the lab (see the frog experiment in Exercise 14). Each group will need one double-pithed frog. If time (or student aversion) is a problem, frogs can be pithed just before the lab begins (see Exercise 14). Keep the frogs moist with *frog Ringer's solution.*

2. Set out data acquisition equipment (one per group of four). If the equipment has not been used in an earlier experiment, acquaint students with its setup and use (see Exercise 14).

   a. *BIOPAC®.* Set out equipment and materials for the conduction of the BIOPAC® activity, including a computer with BIOPAC® BSL Pro Software installed, tension adjuster, force transducer, and transducer (or ring) stand.

   b. *Physiograph.* For each physiograph, set out paper, ink, transducer stand, myograph transducer, transducer cables, stimulator output extension cable, and electrodes.

3. Put bottles of *frog Ringer's solution* in a water bath set at 32°C and in a refrigerator set at 5°C. Have a supply bottle of room temperature *frog Ringer's solution* available.

4. Each group should be provided with disposable gloves, a dissecting pan and instruments, a 250-milliliter bottle of *frog Ringer's solution*, two petri dishes, a medicine dropper, a millimeter ruler, thread, sturdy rubber bands, several fine common pins, a frog board with a hole in one end (biology supply company), cotton balls, paper towels, and dropper bottles of *test solutions.* Have supply bottles of the *test solutions* available.

5. Have microscopes, lens paper, and lens cleaning solution available.

6. Designate an appropriate disposal area for the frogs.

Comments and Pitfalls

1. Remind students to keep the tissue moist with *frog Ringer's solution* at all times.

2. Be sure the students have correctly located the vagus nerve and have not invented a nerve from connective tissue.

3. Do not overstretch the heart when attaching it to the recording equipment.

4. A Stannius ligature is a simple overhand knot in a loop of thread that can be tightened by pulling on both ends of the thread.

5. See Exercise 14 for additional comments on troubleshooting the recording equipment.

Answers to Pre-Lab Quiz (pp. 515–516)

1. true
2. b, rhythmicity
3. b, three
4. true
5. An extra beat that shows up on the ventricular contraction peak

6. b, digitalis
7. d, vagus
8. vagal escape
9. true
10. c, histamine

Answers to Activity Questions

Activity 1: Investigating the Automaticity and Rhythmicity of Heart Muscle (p. 516)

4. The heart is contracting rhythmically while the gastrocnemius muscle is not contracting at all.
5. The sinus venosus will continue to beat.
6. Each atrium should continue to beat, as well as the ventricle.
7. The sinus venosus usually displays the most automaticity (contracts at the fastest rate) and the ventricle the least.

Activity 3: Investigating the Refractory Period of Cardiac Muscle Using the Physiograph (p. 521)

3. Extrasystole can be induced during the first part of ventricular relaxation.
4. The heart does not go into tetanus. The heart would be of no value as a pump if it could go into tetanus as a result of rapid repeated stimulation.

Activity 4: Assessing Physical and Chemical Modifiers of Heart Rate (pp. 521–523)
Temperature

5. Cold Ringer's solution slows down the heart rate. Warm Ringer's solution speeds it up.

Chemical Agents: Pilocarpine

Pilocarpine slows the heart. Pilocarpine is an *agonist* of acetylcholine (cholinergic agonist).

Chemical Agents: Atropine Sulfate

The heart rate should increase. Atropine is *antagonistic* to acetylcholine (cholinergic antagonist).

Chemical Agents: Epinephrine

Epinephrine increases heart rate, imitating the sympathetic nervous system.

Chemical Agents: Digitalis

Digitalis slows and steadies heart contraction.

Various Ions

Ca^{2+} increases strength of contraction.

Na^+ decreases strength and rate of contraction.

K^+ weakens heart contractions and causes premature beats.

Yes. Students may observe arrhythmia with all three ions.

Vagus Nerve Stimulation

3. Vagal stimulation slows down and eventually stops the heart.

Intrinsic Conduction System Disturbance (Heart Block)

4. A normal AV rhythm should reestablish after removing the block.

Activity 5: Investigating the Effect of Various Factors on the Microcirculation (pp. 523–524)

5. RBCs move through capillaries in single file. They are flexible and they may appear "stacked" and slightly curved as they move through. White blood cells resembling monocytes may be seen.

6. Blood flow in the arterioles is rapid and pulsating, while it is slow and steady in the venules. Movement is very slow in the capillaries. The capillaries are much smaller in diameter than the arterioles.

Temperature

Arterioles respond most noticeably to the temperature change. Cold saline causes a reduction in diameter and warm saline an increase in diameter.

Inflammation

HCl causes vasodilation, increasing capillary blood flow. This is a local response to bring more inflammatory cells to the damaged area.

Histamine

1. Histamine also causes vasodilation and increased blood flow. The response to histamine is similar to the response to HCl.

2. Epinephrine causes vasoconstriction and reduced blood flow.

Frog Cardiovascular Physiology

Special Electrical Properties of Cardiac Muscle: Automaticity and Rhythmicity

1. Define the following terms.

   automaticity: *Ability to depolarize spontaneously in the absence of external stimulation*

   rhythmicity: *Depolarization/repolarization events occur in a regular and continuous manner*

2. Discuss the anatomical differences between frog and human hearts. *The frog heart has a single ventricle and two atria.*

   Dorsally there is an expanded area called the sinus venosus. The human heart has two atria and two ventricles. No sinus venosus

   is present.

3. Which region of the dissected frog heart had the highest intrinsic rate of contraction? *Sinus venosus*

   The greatest automaticity? *Sinus venosus*

   The greatest regularity or rhythmicity? *Sinus venosus* _____ How do these properties correlate with the

   duties of a pacemaker? *The human pacemaker (SA node) has automaticity, rhythmicity, and the highest depolarization rate in*

   the heart.

   Is this region the pacemaker of the frog heart? *Yes*

   Which region had the lowest intrinsic rate of contraction? *Ventricle*

Investigating the Refractory Period of Cardiac Muscle

4. Define *extrasystole*. *An extra beat occurring before the time a normal contraction would occur*

5. Respond to the following questions if you used a physiograph.

   What was the effect of stimulation of the heart during ventricular contraction? *No effect*

   During ventricular relaxation (first portion)? *Extrasystole*

   During the pause interval? *No effect*

   What does this indicate about the refractory period of cardiac muscle? *Much longer than that of skeletal muscle*

Assessing Physical and Chemical Modifiers of Heart Rate

6. Describe the effect of thermal factors on the frog heart.

cold: _Decreased heart rate_   heat: _increased heart rate_

7. Once again refer to your recordings. Did the administration of the following produce any changes in force of contraction (shown by peaks of increasing or decreasing height)? If so, explain the mechanism.

epinephrine: _Increases heart rate and force of contraction; acts on the SA and AV nodes and the myocardium to increase membrane permeability to NA^+ and Ca^{2+}_

pilocarpine: _Decreases heart rate; no effect on force of contraction_

calcium ions: _Increase force of contraction; effects in skeletal muscle (i.e., Ca^{2+} is the "trigger" for sliding of myofilaments)_

8. Excessive amounts of each of the following ions would most likely interfere with normal heart activity. Note the type of changes caused in each case.

K^+: _Heart block; cardiac arrest_

Ca^{2+}: _Increases force of contraction; causes arrythmias_

Na^+: _Decreases force of contraction; causes arrythmias_

9. Respond to the following questions if you used a physiograph. What was the effect of vagal stimulation on heart rate?

Decreased heart rate

Which of the following factors cause the same (or very similar) heart rate–reducing effects: epinephrine, acetylcholine, atropine sulfate, pilocarpine, sympathetic nervous system activity, digitalis, potassium ions?

Acetylcholine, pilocarpine, digitalis, potassium ions

Which of the factors listed above would reverse or antagonize vagal effects? _Epinephrine, atropine sulfate, sympathetic nervous system activity_

10. What is vagal escape? _Return to a normal heart rate after a period of rate depression by the vagus nerve_

Why is vagal escape valuable in maintaining homeostasis? _Continued vagal depression can completely stop the heart and lead to death; vagal escape allows the heart to begin beating again even though the vagus nerve continues to be stimulated._

11. How does the Stannius ligature used in the laboratory produce heart block? _It physically blocks transmission of impulses from the atria to the ventricle._

12. Define *partial heart block*, and describe how it was recognized in the laboratory. *Partial heart block occurs when the electrical signal is partially prevented from reaching the ventricles. The 1:1 contraction ratio of atrial to ventricular contractions is replaced by different whole number ratios (e.g., 2:1, 3:1).*

13. Define *total heart block*, and describe how it was recognized in the laboratory. *Total heart block occurs when the electrical signal from the SA node is prevented from reaching the ventricles. Atria and ventricles beat independently of each other, and you can no longer count a whole number ratio of atrial to ventricular contractions.*

14. What do your heart block experiment results indicate about the spread of impulses from the atria to the ventricles?

    In normal heart activity, the ventricles are depolarized by the depolarization wave spreading from the atria.

Observing the Microcirculation Under Various Conditions

15. In what way are the red blood cells of the frog different from those of the human? *Frog RBCs are nucleated; human RBCs are anucleate.*

    On the basis of this one factor, would you expect their life spans to be longer or shorter? *Longer*

16. The following statements refer to your observation of one or more of the vessel types observed in the microcirculation in the frog's web. Characterize each statement by choosing the best response from the key.

    Key: a. arterioles   b. venules   c. capillaries

    _c_   1. smallest vessels observed

    _a_   2. vessels in which blood flow is rapid, pulsating

    _c_   3. vessels in which blood flow is least rapid

    _c_   4. red blood cells pass through these vessels in single file

    _b_   5. blood flow is smooth and steady

    _c_   6. most numerous vessels

    _a_   7. vessels that deliver blood to the capillary bed

    _c_   8. vessels that serve the needs of the tissues via exchanges

    _b_   9. vessels that drain the capillary beds

17. Which of the vessel diameters changed most? *Arterioles*

    What division of the nervous system controls the vessels? *Autonomic nervous system, sympathetic division*

18. Discuss the effects of the following on blood vessel diameter (state specifically the blood vessels involved) and rate of blood flow. Then explain the importance of the reaction observed to the general well-being of the body.

local application of cold: *Vasoconstriction of arterioles; bypasses the skin capillaries and withdraws blood to deeper body tissues*

to prevent heat loss to the external environment

local application of heat: *Vasodilation of arterioles and flushing of capillary bed with blood; increases the local blood supply and*

allows heat radiation from the skin surface

inflammation (or application of HCl): *Vasodilation locally bringing in WBCs and more nutrients to help fight the inflammatory*

stimulus

histamine: *Same reaction as with inflammation*

35 EXERCISE

The Lymphatic System and Immune Response

Time Allotment: 1 hour.

Multimedia Resources: See Appendix B for Guide to Multimedia Resource Distributors.

The Human Immune System: The Fighting Edge (FHS: 44 minutes, DVD, 3-year streaming webcast)
Internal Defenses (FHS: 28 minutes, DVD, 3-year streaming webcast)
Practice Anatomy Lab™ 3.0 (PAL) (PE: DVD, website)
PhysioEx™ 9.1 Exercise 12 (PE: CD-ROM, website)
Interactive Physiology™ 10-System Suite: Immune System (PE: CD-ROM, website)

Solutions:

Simple Saline Agar

- 2 grams agar (Difco Bacto)
- 1 gram sodium chloride (NaCl)
- 100 milliliters distilled water
- 0.1 gram sodium azide (optional)

Prepare a clear solution by boiling the mixture gently. Pour while hot to a depth of 3 millimeters into 100-millimeter plastic petri dishes that have been divided into three compartments (7 milliliters per compartment). Leave open until the gel cools. To store, either steam sterilize the agar before pouring or add 0.1 gram sodium azide per 100 milliliters.

Laboratory Materials

Ordering information is based on a lab size of 24 students, working in groups of 4. A list of supply house addresses appears in Appendix A.

Anatomical chart of human lymphatic system or 3-D model of human lymphatic system
Disposable gloves
24 pairs of safety glasses
24 compound microscopes, lens paper, lens cleaning solution
24 prepared microscope slides of lymph nodes, spleens, and tonsils

wax marking pencils
6 petri plates with simple saline agar
6 medicine droppers
6 dropper bottles of red and green food coloring
Dropper bottles of goat antibody to horse serum albumin, goat antibody to bovine serum albumin, goat antibody to swine serum

albumin, horse serum albumin diluted to 20% with physiological saline, unknown albumin sample diluted to 20% (prepared from horse, swine, and/or bovine albumin)
Colored pencils

Advance Preparation

1. Set out anatomical charts of the lymphatic system; prepared slides of lymph nodes, spleen, and tonsil; lens paper; and lens cleaning solution. Have microscopes available.

2. Prepare saline agar petri dishes in advance.

3. Set out petri dishes with saline agar (one per group), dropper bottles of red and green food coloring, dropper bottles of goat antibody to bovine serum albumin, horse serum albumin and swine serum albumin, dropper bottles of horse serum albumin, dropper bottles of unknown serum albumin samples diluted to 20%, medicine droppers, and wax marking pencils.

Answers to Pre-Lab Quiz (p. 529)

1. true
2. b, excess tissue fluid that has leaked out of capillaries
3. true
4. b, lymph nodes
5. true

6. b, specificity
7. T cells
8. cellular
9. true
10. c, four

Answers to Activity Questions

Answers to Group Challenge: Compare and Contrast Lymphoid Organs and Tissues (p. 534)

Lymphoid pair	Similarities	Differences
Lymph node Spleen	Both have trabeculae, a capsule, and a hilum. Both have similar cell populations. Each is an active filter; lymph nodes filter lymph and the spleen filters the blood.	Humans have only one spleen but many lymph nodes. In their roles as filters, the lymph nodes and spleen filter different body fluids.
Lymph node Tonsil	Both have follicles and germinal centers. Both have similar cell populations.	The tonsil contains deep tonsillar crypts, and its capsule is incomplete.
Peyer's patches Tonsils	Both have germinal centers. Both are located in the digestive tract, and are considered to be a part of the mucosa-associated lymphoid tissues (MALT).	Tonsils are lymphoid organs and Peyer's patches are lymphoid tissue. The tonsils are located at the beginning of the digestive tract; Peyer's patches are in the distal ileum.
Tonsil Spleen	Both have similar cell populations (lymphocytes and macrophages).	The tonsil contains deep tonsillar crypts, and its capsule is incomplete. The spleen is a blood-rich organ that contains many erythrocytes. It stores iron, platelets, and monocytes.
Thymus Spleen	Both have a capsule. Both have similar cell populations.	The thymus is a primary lymphoid organ and the spleen is a secondary lymphoid organ. T cells become immunocompetent in the thymus but not in the spleen.

Activity 3: Using the Ouchterlony Technique to Identify Antigens (pp. 535–536)

Results

4. A color change occurred where the two colors met.
5. No evidence of a precipitate.
6. Horse serum albumin functioned as the antigen.
7. Goat anti-horse serum (goat antibody) reacts with the antigen in section II.

    A white precipitin line formed between wells 1 and 2.
8. The swine albumin in well 1 would have reacted with the anti-swine antibody in well 4.
9. No reaction. The antibodies are specific to horse, bovine, and swine albumins.

The Lymphatic System and Immune Response

The Lymphatic System

1. Match the terms below with the correct letters on the diagram.

   _k_ 1. axillary lymph nodes

   _b_ 2. cervical lymph nodes

   _j_ 3. cisterna chyli

   _g_ 4. inguinal lymph nodes

   _h_ 5. lymphatic vessels

   _f_ 6. Peyer's patches (in small intestine)

   _i_ 7. red bone marrow

   _l_ 8. right lymphatic duct

   _e_ 9. spleen

   _c_ 10. thoracic duct

   _d_ 11. thymus

   _a_ 12. tonsils

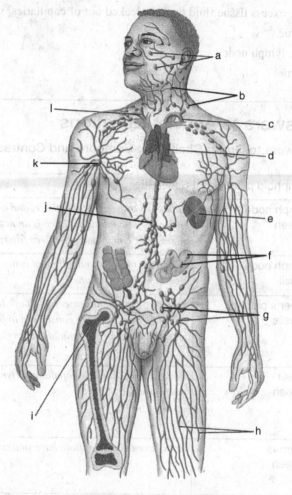

2. Explain why the lymphatic system is a one-way system, whereas the blood vascular system is a two-way system.

   Blood vessels form a complete circuit from and to the heart. The lymphatic system lacks arteries and begins with blind-ended lymphatic

   capillaries. Thus, it is a "return" system only.

3. How do lymphatic vessels resemble veins? *They are thin walled and have valves.*

   How do lymphatic capillaries differ from blood capillaries? *Lymphatic capillaries are more permeable and are blind ended; they*

   have no "feeder" arterioles.

4. What is the function of the lymphatic vessels? *To pick up and return excess tissue fluid (and leaked proteins) to the blood vascular system*

5. What is lymph? *Leaked plasma (but contains fewer proteins); tissue fluid that has entered lymphatic vessels*

6. What factors are involved in the flow of lymphatic fluid? *"Milking" action of skeletal muscles; pressure changes in the thorax.*

7. What name is given to the terminal duct draining most of the body? *Thoracic duct*

8. What is the cisterna chyli? *Enlarged terminus of the thoracic duct, which receives lymph from the digestive viscera*

How does the composition of lymph in the cisterna chyli differ from lymph composition in the general lymphatic stream? Use your textbook or other reference if necessary. *Same, except that the lymph in the cisterna chyli is very fat-rich*

9. Which portion of the body is drained by the right lymphatic duct? *Right half of upper torso and head; right arm*

10. Note three areas where lymph nodes are densely clustered: *axillary region*, *cervical region*, and *inguinal region (groin)*

11. What are the two major functions of the lymph nodes? *To remove debris from the lymph* and *to provide a site for cloning and multiplication of lymphocytes*

12. The radical mastectomy is an operation in which a cancerous breast, surrounding tissues, and the underlying muscles of the anterior thoracic wall, plus the axillary lymph nodes, are removed. After such an operation, the arm usually swells, or becomes edematous, and is very uncomfortable—sometimes for months. Why?

The lymphatic fluid is not being drained from the area due to a disruption of lymphatic vessels and nodes.

The Immune Response

13. What is the function of B cells in the immune response? *Upon antigen challenge, they clone to produce daughter cells, most of which are plasma cells that release antibodies to the blood (humoral response).*

14. What is the function of T cells in the immune response? *They mount cell-mediated immunity; attack virus-infected cells, tumor cells, bacteria, etc.; also activate B cells and enhance the migration of other WBCs into the area to help destroy antigens.*

15. Define the following terms related to the operation of the immune system.

immunological memory: *Response that recognizes and mounts an attack on antigens previously encountered*

specificity: *Ability to distinguish between closely related antigens*

self-tolerance: *Ability to recognize proteins on own tissue cells as "self" and not attack them*

autoimmune disease: *An inability of the immune system to recognize self, resulting in attack of self cells by the immune system*

Studying the Microscopic Anatomy of a Lymph Node, the Spleen, and a Tonsil

16. In the space below, make a rough drawing of the structure of a lymph node. Identify the cortex area, germinal centers, and medulla. For each identified area, note the cell type (T cell, B cell, or macrophage) most likely to be found there.

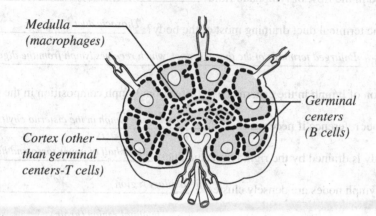

Medulla (macrophages)

Germinal centers (B cells)

Cortex (other than germinal centers-T cells)

17. What structural characteristic ensures a *slow* flow of lymph through a lymph node? _There are more afferent than efferent vessels._

Why is this desirable? _Allows time for the macrophages in the node to remove antigens and other debris, and for activation of_

immune cells

18. What similarities in structure and function are found in the lymph nodes, spleen, and tonsils? _All are lymphoid tissue containing_

macrophages and lymphocytes. They are all areas where exposure to antigen causes lymphocytes to proliferate and form clones.

Antibodies and Tests for Their Presence

19. Distinguish between antigen and antibody. _An antigen is a molecule capable of provoking an immune response. An antibody is a_

protein produced by plasma cells that interacts with a particular antigen to form a complex.

20. Describe the structure of the immunoglobulin monomer, and label the diagram with the choices given in the key. _Four_

polypeptide chains, two "heavy" and two "light," held together by disulfide bonds to form a Y-shaped molecule. Each chain has constant

(C) and variable (V) regions.

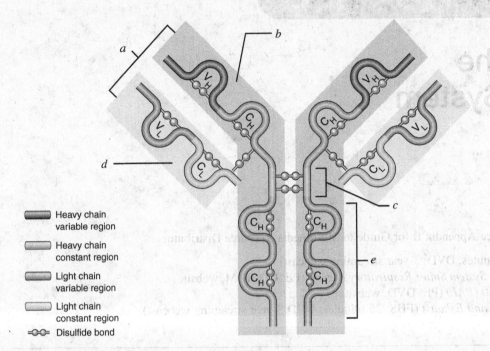

Key:

a. antigen-binding site

b. heavy chain

c. hinge region

d. light chain

e. stem region

Heavy chain
variable region

Heavy chain
constant region

Light chain
variable region

Light chain
constant region

Disulfide bond

21. Are the genes coding for one antibody entirely different from those coding for a different antibody? _No_

Explain your answer. _Only a few genes exist for coding antibody-constant regions; therefore many antibodies have identical constant_

regions. The variable (antigen-binding) regions differ for each antibody responding to a different antigen.

22. In the Ouchterlony test, what happened when the antibody to horse serum albumin mixed with horse serum albumin?

A white precipitate formed (between wells 1 and 2).

23. If the unknown antigen contained bovine and swine serum albumin, what would you expect to happen in the Ouchterlony

test, and why? _Antigen-antibody complexes would form a white precipitate between bovine serum albumin and the antibody to bovine serum_

albumin (between wells 1 and 3), and between swine serum albumin and antibody to swine serum albumin (between wells 1 and 4).

Anatomy of the Respiratory System

 Time Allotment: 1 hour.

 Multimedia Resources: See Appendix B for Guide to Multimedia Resource Distributors.

Breath of Life (FHS: 26 minutes, DVD, 3-year streaming webcast)
Interactive Physiology® *10-System Suite: Respiratory System* (PE: CD-ROM, website)
Practice Anatomy Lab™ *3.0 (PAL)* (PE: DVD, website)
Respiratory System: Intake and Exhaust (FHS: 25 minutes, DVD 3-year streaming webcast)

Laboratory Materials

Ordering information is based on a lab size of 24 students, working in groups of 4. A list of supply house addresses appears in Appendix A.

Human torso models
Respiratory system model and/or anatomical chart of the respiratory system
Larynx model (if available)
Resin cast of the respiratory tree (if available)
Preserved inflatable lung preparation (obtained from a biological supply house) or sheep pluck fresh from the slaughterhouse
Source of compressed air
24 prepared microscope slides of each of the following (if available): trachea (cross section), normal lung tissue, pathological lung tissues (e.g., with bronchitis, pneumonia, emphysema, or lung cancer)
24 compound and stereomicroscopes, lens paper, lens cleaning solution
6 dissecting trays
Disposable gloves
Disposable autoclave bags

Advance Preparation

1. Set out human torso models, respiratory organ system model, larynx model, and/or charts of the respiratory system.

2. Set out a sheep pluck (fresh if possible), or set up an inflatable swine lungs kit (Nasco), and disposable gloves.

3. Arrange for a source of compressed air.

4. Set out prepared slides of the trachea, normal lung tissue, and pathological lung tissue exhibiting conditions such as bronchitis, pneumonia, emphysema, or lung cancer; lens paper; and lens cleaning solution. Have compound microscopes and stereomicroscopes available.

Comments and Pitfalls

1. Many prepared slides of the trachea also include the esophagus. Remind the students that the trachea is held open by cartilaginous rings, while the esophagus is not. Showing an appropriate image of the microscopic section might be useful.

2. When using a preserved sheep pluck with a compressed air supply, be careful to avoid overinflation (leading to an explosion of preserved tissue)!

3. The inflatable swine lungs kit includes an inflation rack and tray, inflatable swine lungs, and a section of dried swine lung. The inflatable lungs will last for several years and give a much more dramatic response than that usually seen with the preserved lungs of the sheep pluck. An inflatable diseased lung is also available from Nasco and is excellent for comparison to a healthy lung.

Answers to Pre-Lab Quiz (p. 541)

1. d, supply the body with oxygen and dispose of carbon dioxide
2. true
3. c, pharynx
4. thyroid cartilage
5. true
6. b, left and right main bronchi
7. columnar epithelium
8. true
9. Alveoli
10. two

Anatomy of the Respiratory System

Upper and Lower Respiratory System Structures

1. Complete the labeling of the diagram of the upper respiratory structures (sagittal section).

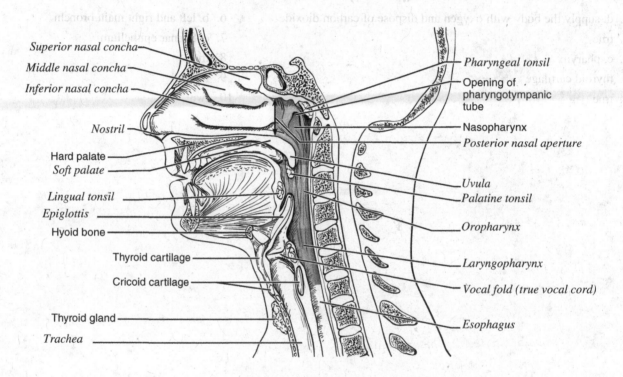

Superior nasal concha

Middle nasal concha

Inferior nasal concha

Nostril

Hard palate

Soft palate

Lingual tonsil

Epiglottis

Hyoid bone

Thyroid cartilage

Cricoid cartilage

Thyroid gland

Trachea

Pharyngeal tonsil

Opening of pharyngotympanic tube

Nasopharynx

Posterior nasal aperture

Uvula

Palatine tonsil

Oropharynx

Laryngopharynx

Vocal fold (true vocal cord)

Esophagus

2. Two pairs of vocal folds are found in the larynx. Which pair are the true vocal cords (superior or inferior)?

   Inferior

3. Name the specific cartilages in the larynx that correspond to the following descriptions.

   forms the Adam's apple: *thyroid*   shaped like a ring: *cricoid*

   a "lid" for the larynx: *epiglottis*   vocal cord attachment: *arytenoids*

4. Why is it important that the human trachea is reinforced with cartilaginous rings?

Prevents its collapse during pressure changes that occur during breathing

Why is it important that the rings are incomplete posteriorly? *Allows a food bolus traveling down the posterior esophagus to*

bulge anteriorly

5. What is the function of the pleural fluid? *A serous fluid that reduces friction during breathing movements and helps hold the lungs*

tightly to the thorax wall, which keeps the lungs inflated

6. Name two functions of the nasal conchae: *Enhances air turbulence* and *helps trap particles in the mucus*

7. The following questions refer to the main bronchi.

Which is longer? *Left* _____ Larger in diameter? *Right* _____ More horizontal? *Left* _____

Which more commonly traps a foreign object that has entered the respiratory passageways? *Right* _____

8. Appropriately label all structures provided with leader lines on the diagrams below.

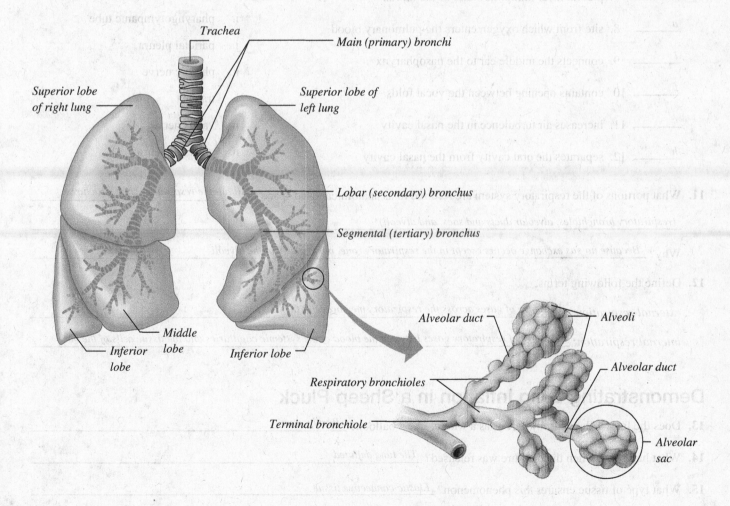

9. Trace a molecule of oxygen from the nostrils to the pulmonary capillaries of the lungs: Nostrils →

nasal cavity → pharynx → larynx → trachea → main (primary) bronchus → lobar/segmental bronchi (etc.) → bronchiole →

respiratory bronchiole → alveolar duct → alveolar sac → across alveolar/capillary walls → pulmonary blood

10. Match the terms in column B to the descriptions in column A.

Column A		Column B
_l_ 1. connects the larynx to the main bronchi		a. alveolus
_b_ 2. includes terminal and respiratory as subtypes		b. bronchiole
_e_ 3. food passageway posterior to the trachea		c. conchae
_d_ 4. covers the glottis during swallowing of food		d. epiglottis
_g_ 5. contains the vocal cords		e. esophagus
_k_ 6. nerve that activates the diaphragm during inspiration		f. glottis
_j_ 7. pleural layer lining the walls of the thorax		g. larynx
_a_ 8. site from which oxygen enters the pulmonary blood		h. palate
_i_ 9. connects the middle ear to the nasopharynx		i. pharyngotympanic tube
_f_ 10. contains opening between the vocal folds		j. parietal pleura
_c_ 11. increases air turbulence in the nasal cavity		k. phrenic nerve
_h_ 12. separates the oral cavity from the nasal cavity		l. trachea
		m. vagus nerve
		n. visceral pleura

11. What portions of the respiratory system are referred to as anatomical dead space? _All but the respiratory zone structures_

  (respiratory bronchioles, alveolar ducts and sacs, and alveoli)

Why? _Because no gas exchange occurs except in the respiratory zone, particularly in the alveoli_

12. Define the following terms.

external respiration: _Exchange of gases across the respiratory membrane in the lungs_

internal respiration: _Exchange of respiratory gases between the blood of the systemic capillaries and the tissue cells of the body_

Demonstrating Lung Inflation in a Sheep Pluck

13. Does the lung inflate part by part or as a whole, like a balloon? _Part by part_

14. What happened when the pressure was released? _The lung deflated_

15. What type of tissue ensures this phenomenon? _Elastic connective tissue_

Examining Prepared Slides of Trachea and Lung Tissue

16. What structural characteristics of the alveoli make them an ideal site for the diffusion of gases?

Thin walls, extremely large surface area

Why does oxygen move from the alveoli into the pulmonary capillary blood? *Because the partial pressure of oxygen is greater*

in the alveoli; therefore, it moves according to the laws of diffusion into the pulmonary blood.

17. If you observed pathological lung sections, record your observations. Also record how the tissue differed from normal lung tissue. Complete the table below using your answers.

Slide type	Observations	Comparison to normal lung tissue
(Student data)	(Student data)	

Respiratory System Physiology

Time Allotment: 2 hours (allow an additional half hour if students are unfamiliar with the recording apparatus).

Multimedia Resources: See Appendix B for Guide to Multimedia Resource Distributors.

Breath of Life (FHS: 26 minutes, DVD, 3-year streaming webcast)
Breathing (FHS: 20 minutes, DVD, 3-year streaming webcast)
Interactive Physiology® 10-System Suite: Respiratory System (PE: CD-ROM, website)
The Physiology of Exercise (FHS: 15 minutes, DVD)
Respiratory System: Intake and Exhaust (FHS: 25 minutes, DVD, 3-year streaming webcast)
PhysioEx™ 9.1 Exercise 7 (PE: DVD, website)

Solutions:

Hydrochloric Acid (HCl), 0.01 M
Add 0.8 milliliter concentrated HCl to 900 milliliters distilled water. Add distilled water to make 1 liter of solution; *or* add 10 milliliters of 1 *N* HCl to 900 milliliters of distilled water. Add distilled water to a final volume of 1 liter.

Sodium Hydroxide (NaOH), 0.05 M
Weigh out 2 grams of NaOH and add to distilled water to make 1 liter of solution.

Laboratory Materials

Ordering information is based on a lab size of 24 students, working in groups of 4. A list of supply house addresses appears in Appendix A.

Model of lung (bell jar demonstrator)
6 tape measures with centimeter divisions
6 100-milliliter beakers
6 dropper bottles of phenol red
50 milliliters of 0.05 *M* NaOH
Alcohol swabs
6 paper bags
6 stethoscopes
30 250-milliliter beakers
12 50-milliliter beakers
6 100-milliliter graduated cylinders
6 dropper bottles of concentrated HCl
6 dropper bottles of concentrated NaOH

6 pH meters standardized with buffer of pH 7
2 liters standard buffer solution (pH 7)
Animal plasma
6 wash bottles of distilled water
6 glass stirring rods
6 dropper bottles of 0.01 *M* HCl
Straws
Physiograph, pneumograph, and recording attachments for physiograph
Apparatus A or B:
A: Spirometer, disposable cardboard mouthpieces, nose clips, table (on chalkboard/whiteboard) for

recording class data, disposable autoclave bag, battery jar containing 70% ethanol solution
B: BIOPAC® BSL System for Windows with BSL software version 3.7.5 to 3.7.7, or BSL System for Mac OS X with BSL software version 3.7.4 to 3.7.7, MP36/35 or MP45 data acquisition unit, PC or Mac computer, BIOPAC® airflow transducer, BIOPAC® calibration syringe, disposable mouthpiece, nose clip, and bacteriological filter

238

Advance Preparation

1. Set out the model lung (bell jar demonstrator).

2. For each group set out a tape measure, nose clips, spirometer, disposable mouthpieces (enough for each member of the group), alcohol swabs, a paper bag, a physiograph with a pneumograph and recording attachments, respiratory belt transducer and cable, paper, and a stethoscope. See the frog experiment in Exercise 14 for further directions for the physiograph. If a wet spirometer is used, be sure it is filled with distilled water according to the manufacturer's instructions. Set out a battery jar of 70% ethanol.

3. Set out equipment and materials for the conduction of the BIOPAC® activity. Introduce your students to the basic features of the equipment prior to beginning the lab activity.

4. For each group set out a pH meter standardized with a buffer of pH 7, five 250-milliliter beakers, two 50-milliliter beakers, a 100-milliliter graduated cylinder, a dropper bottle of concentrated HCl, a dropper bottle of concentrated NaOH, 300 milliliters of standard buffer solution (pH 7), 500 milliliters of distilled water, a wash bottle of distilled water, a dropper bottle of *0.01 M HCl*, a glass stirring rod, and animal plasma.

5. Set up a disposable autoclave bag.

6. Draw a class data chart on the chalkboard or whiteboard to record TV (V_t), IRV, ERV, and VC.

7. Set out bottles of *0.05 M NaOH*, dropper bottles of phenol red, distilled water, 100-milliliter beakers, and straws for each group.

Comments and Pitfalls

1. If a dry spirometer is used, the tidal volume readings are not very accurate. Somewhat better readings are obtained if the student exhales three times into the spirometer and divides the result by three.

2. Students will have to adjust the pneumograph until a good recording can be made. Be sure that it fits comfortably around the chest. Check all connections for a good fit, and if a tambour is used, be sure the rubber is intact. (This can be easily replaced using rubber sheeting. Use a good adhesive to reattach the clip.)

3. When using the pneumograph, be sure that students can correctly interpret the tracings. On some equipment, inspiration results in a downward deflection of the pointer (opposite the direction noted on the spirometer tracing in Figure 37.2).

4. Students may be confused about hyperventilation. The forced hyperventilation here results in a decreased breathing rate. Hyperventilation during psychological stress can produce a positive feedback situation, resulting in further hyperventilation. As hypocapnia increases, cerebral vessels constrict and increasingly acidotic conditions in the brain stimulate the medullary respiratory centers. Rebreathing air in the latter case raises blood PCO_2, reverses the cerebral vessel constriction, and stops the hyperventilation.

5. For the experiment in Observing the Operation of Standard Buffers, Activity 8, if you wish to avoid using concentrated acid and base and conserve pH buffer, you can scale down the experiment by using 1 *M* NaOH, 1 *M* HCl, and 50 milliliters of pH 7 buffer.

Answers to Pre-Lab Quiz (pp. 553–554)

1. expiration
2. c, inspiratory muscles relax
3. false
4. b, 500
5. vital capacity

6. false
7. aortic and carotid bodies
8. c, 7.4 ± 0.02
9. acids
10. false

Answers to Activity Questions

Activity 1: Operating the Model Lung (pp. 554–555)

3. They deflate.

4. The walls of the human thorax expand and collapse, bringing about changes in thoracic volume. In the model, the bottle walls are rigid. All changes in thoracic volume are realized only by the diaphragm. In real lungs, the intrapleural cavity is a fluid-filled space with pleural fluid maintaining the lungs expanded against the rib cage. In the model, this cavity is air filled though sealed. Consequently, the simulation of a pneumothorax is not as significant as would occur in the biologic system.

Activity 5: Measuring Respiratory Volumes Using BIOPAC® (pp. 563–567)

Data Analysis

11. Generally, the taller and larger a subject is, the larger will be the vital capacity. This is because a larger person requires more oxygen for cellular respiration. Other factors that can affect vital capacity include aerobic conditioning of the subject, chronic obstructive pulmonary diseases, smoking, etc.

Activity 6: Visualizing Respiratory Variations (pp. 567–568)

3. During breath holding, the subject has the desire to expire. After a deep and forceful exhalation, the urge is to inspire. This may be explained by the Hering-Breuer reflex. Stretch receptors in the lungs are sensitive to extreme inflation and extreme deflation of the lungs. Impulses to the medulla oblongata initiate expiration or inspiration, respectively.

4. After hyperventilation, the breathing rate slows down.

5. Breath-holding time increases after hyperventilation.

6. After 3 minutes of rebreathing breathed air, the ventilation rate increases. It is much faster than the breathing rate after hyperventilating.

8. Forced expiration results in dilation of the neck and face veins. Increased intrathoracic pressure reduces blood flow back to the heart, decreasing cardiac output. This results in increased cardiac rate (seen here as increased pulse rate).

Activity 7: Demonstrating the Reaction Between Carbon Dioxide (in Exhaled Air) and Water (p. 569)

3. Carbon dioxide in the exhaled air combines with water to form carbonic acid, lowering the pH of the solution. The phenol red in the water changes from red to yellow.

Activity 8: Observing the Operation of Standard Buffers (p. 570)

4. The buffer system should resist change in pH. The contrast between the pH change with water alone and the pH change with buffer should be clear.

Activity 9: Exploring the Operation of the Carbonic Acid–Bicarbonate Buffer System (p. 570)

4. When testing the plasma carbonic acid–bicarbonate buffer system, it is the bicarbonate that counteracts the change in pH.

NAME _____

LAB TIME/DATE _____

Respiratory System Physiology

Mechanics of Respiration

1. For each of the following cases, check the column appropriate to your observations on the operation of the model lung.

Change	Diaphragm pushed up		Diaphragm pulled down	
	Increased	Decreased	Increased	Decreased
In internal volume of the bell jar (thoracic cage)		✓	✓	
In internal pressure	✓			✓
In the size of the balloons (lungs)		✓	✓	

2. Base your answers to the following on your observations in question 1.

Under what internal conditions does air tend to flow into the lungs? _↑ thoracic volume, and ↓ pressure_

Under what internal conditions does air tend to flow out of the lungs? Explain why this is so. _↓ thoracic volume, ↑ pressure._

Gases move in the direction that tends to equalize pressure inside and outside the "container."

3. Activation of the diaphragm and the external intercostal muscles begins the inspiratory process. What effect does contraction

of these muscles have on thoracic volume, and how is this accomplished? _↑ thoracic volume. The diaphragm moves inferiorly,_

increasing the superior/inferior dimension; the ribs swing up and out, increasing the lateral and anterior/posterior dimensions.

4. What was the approximate increase in diameter of chest circumference during a quiet inspiration? _(student data)_

_____ centimeter(s)

During forced inspiration? _(student data)_ _____ centimeter(s)

What temporary physiological advantage is created by the substantial increase in chest circumference during forced

inspiration? _Increases the thoracic volume more; therefore, creates a greater negative internal pressure, causing the gases to rush in_

quickly. Also, more "fresh" air reaches the alveoli.

5. The presence of a partial vacuum between the pleural membranes is integral to normal breathing movements. What would happen if an opening were made into the chest cavity, as with a puncture wound?

Destroys the partial vacuum in the pleural space and the lung on the affected side collapses

What must be done to treat this condition medically? _Air is withdrawn (chest tube) and the chest is closed_

241

Respiratory Sounds

6. Which of the respiratory sounds is heard during both inspiration and expiration? *Bronchial*

Which is heard primarily during inspiration? *Vesicular*

7. Where did you best hear the vesicular respiratory sounds? *Heard over most of the lung area*

Respiratory Volumes and Capacities—Spirometry or BIOPAC®

8. Write the respiratory volume term and the normal value that is described by the following statements.

Volume of air present in the lungs after a forceful expiration: *Residual volume, 1100–1200 milliliters*

Volume of air that can be expired forcibly after a normal expiration: *Expiratory reserve, 700–1200 milliliters*

Volume of air that is breathed in and out during a normal respiration: *Tidal volume, 500 milliliters*

Volume of air that can be inspired forcibly after a normal inspiration: *Inspiratory reserve, 1900–3100 milliliters*

Volume of air corresponding to TV + IRV + ERV: *Vital capacity, 3100–4800 milliliters*

9. For the spirometer activities, record experimental respiratory volumes as determined in the laboratory. (Corrected values and FEV_1 are for the recording spirometer only.)

Average TV: *(student data)* milliliters   Corrected value for ERV: *(student data)* milliliters

Corrected value for TV: *(student data)* milliliters   Average VC: *(student data)* milliliters

Average IRV: *(student data)* milliliters   Corrected value for VC: *(student data)* milliliters

Corrected value for IRV: *(student data)* milliliters   % predicted VC: *(student data)* percent

MRV: *(student data)* milliliters/minute FEV_1: *(student data)* percent FVC

Average ERV: *(student data)* milliliters

For the BIOPAC® activity, record the following experimental respiratory volumes as determined in the laboratory.

TV: *(student data)* liters   IRV: *(student data)* liters

ERV: *(student data)* liters   VC: *(student data)* liters

Why This Matters

10. With incentive spirometry, the patient is instructed to take a normal quiet breath and then inhale from the mouthpiece of the incentive spirometer as slowly and completely as possible. What respiratory volume/capacity measurement do you think this maneuver approximates? *Inspiratory capacity (IC)*

11. Explain how you would obtain the respiratory volume/capacity value (from question 10) when using the nonrecording dry spirometer. _The inspiratory capacity (IC) must be calculated from the measured vital capacity, tidal volume, and expiratory reserve volume using the equation: IC = IRV + TV where IRV = VC − (TV + ERV)_

12. Which respiratory ailments can respiratory volume tests be used to detect?

Chronic bronchitis and emphysema (often associated). Chronic bronchitis ↓ the volume of air that can be inhaled due to excessive mucus production; emphysema ↓ the amount of air that can be exhaled (check-valve effect).

Factors Influencing Rate and Depth of Respiration

13. Where are the neural control centers of respiratory rhythm? _Medulla oblongata_ and _pons_

For questions 14–21, use your Activity 6 data.

14. In your data, what was the rate of quiet breathing?

Initial testing _(student data)_ breaths/minute

Test performed	Observations (breaths per minute)
Talking	_Respiratory rate becomes irregular during talking._
Yawning	_Yawning is reflected by extremely deep prolonged inspiration._
Laughing	_Respiratory rate becomes irregular. Respiratory depth may be ↑ or ↓ depending on the nature of the laugh._
Standing	_Regular rhythm and rate._
Concentrating	_Respiratory rate is regular unless punctuated by intervals of apnea in individuals who hold their breath when concentrating._
Swallowing water	_Respiration ceases during the period of swallowing._
Coughing	_Respiration rate becomes irregular and marked by ↑ depth of expirations during coughing._
Lying down	_Regular rhythm and regular (or slightly depressed) rate. Depth decreases._
Running in place	_Increased rate and depth of breathing._

15. Record student data below.

Breath-holding interval after a deep inhalation: _(student data)_ seconds length of recovery period: _(student data)_ seconds

Breath-holding interval after a forceful expiration: _(student data)_ seconds length of recovery period: _(student data)_ seconds

After breathing quietly and taking a deep breath (which you held), was your urge to inspire _or_ expire? _Expiration_

After exhaling and then holding one's breath, was the desire for inspiration _or_ expiration? _Inspiration_

Explain these results. (_Hint:_ What reflex is involved here?) _Hering-Breuer reflex. Both extreme deflation and inflation of the lungs excite receptors there. Impulses are transmitted to the medulla oblongata, which then initiates inspiration or expiration (respectively)._

16. Observations after hyperventilation: *(student data)* _____

17. Breath-holding interval after hyperventilation: *(student data)* _____ seconds

Why does hyperventilation produce apnea or a reduced respiratory rate? *Hyperventilation washes CO_2 out of the blood. Since*

CO_2 is the major chemical stimulus for inspiration, the desire or drive to breathe is decreased.

18. Observations for rebreathing air: *(student data)* _____

Why does rebreathing air produce an increased respiratory rate? *CO_2 (exhaled) accumulates in the bag; this stimulates increased*

force/rate of respiration.

19. What was the effect of running in place (exercise) on the duration of breath holding? *↓ the duration*

Explain this effect. *The body's need to get rid of CO_2 and obtain oxygen is increased by exercise.*

20. Record student data from the test illustrating the effect of respiration on circulation.

Radial pulse before beginning test: _____ /minute   Radial pulse after testing: _____ /minute

Relative pulse force before beginning test: _____   Relative force of radial pulse after testing: _____

Condition of neck and facial veins after testing: _____

Explain these data. *Forced expiration increases intrathoracic pressure, reducing blood flow back to the heart, resulting in dilation of*

the neck and facial veins. Decreased cardiac output results in increased cardiac rate (seen here as increased pulse rate).

21. Do the following factors generally increase (indicate ↑) or decrease (indicate ↓) the respiratory rate and depth?

increase in blood CO_2: _____↑_____   increase in blood pH: _____↓_____

decrease in blood O_2: _____↑_____   decrease in blood pH: _____↑_____

Did it appear that CO_2 or O_2 had a more marked effect on modifying the respiratory rate? *CO_2*

22. Where are sensory receptors sensitive to changes in blood pressure located? *Aortic arch and carotid sinus*

23. Where are sensory receptors sensitive to changes in O_2 levels in the blood located? *Aortic bodies in the aortic arch and*

carotid bodies at the bifurcation of the common carotid artery

24. What is the primary factor that initiates breathing in a newborn infant? *↑ levels of CO_2 in the blood*

25. Which, if any, of the measurable respiratory volumes would likely be increased in a person who is cardiovascularly fit, such

as a runner or a swimmer? *VC, IRV, ERV, FEV would all be increased.*

Which, if any, of the measurable respiratory volumes would likely be decreased in a person who has smoked a lot for over

20 years? *VC, IRV, ERV, FEV would all be reduced.*

26. Blood CO_2 levels and blood pH are related. When blood CO_2 levels increase, does the pH increase or decrease?

Decrease _____ Explain why. *CO_2 combines with water (H_2O) to*

produce carbonic acid (H_2CO_3), which dissociates and liberates a hydrogen ion (H^+).

Role of the Respiratory System in Acid-Base Balance of Blood

27. Define *buffer*. *A molecule or molecular system that resists changes in pH* _____

28. How successful was the laboratory buffer (pH 7) in resisting changes in pH when the acid was added? *(student data)*

(Anticipated response: very successful) _____

When the base was added? *(student data) (Anticipated response: very successful)* _____

How successful was the buffer in resisting changes in pH when the additional drops of the acid and base were added to the

original samples? *Successful; only slight pH changes are seen.* _____

29. What buffer system operates in blood plasma? *Carbonic acid–bicarbonate system* _____

Which component of the buffer system resists a *drop* in pH? *HCO_3^-* _____ which resists a *rise* in pH? *H_2CO_3*

30. Explain how the carbonic acid–bicarbonate buffer system of the blood operates. *H_2CO_3, a weak acid, remains undissociated at*

physiologic pH or acid pH. However, if the pH starts to rise, H_2CO_3 dissociates and liberates H^+, which ↓ the pH. HCO_3^- (bicarbonate ion)

is the "alkaline reserve"; it ties up excess H^+ into H_2CO_3 when the environment becomes too acidic. Since it is a weak base, it does not

function under physiologic or alkaline conditions. _____

31. What happened when the carbon dioxide in exhaled air mixed with water? *Phenol red turned yellow as CO_2 mixed with water to*

form carbonic acid. _____

What role does exhalation of carbon dioxide play in maintaining relatively constant blood pH? *CO_2 leaves the blood during*

exhalation. This prevents an accumulation of carbonic acid. _____

38 EXERCISE

Anatomy of the Digestive System

Time Allotment: 2 hours.

Multimedia Resources: See Appendix B for Guide to Multimedia Resource Distributors.

Digestive System: Your Personal Power Plant (FHS: 34 minutes, DVD, 3-year streaming webcast)
The Human Digestive System (DE: 18 minutes, DVD, CD-ROM)
Interactive Physiology® 10-System Suite: Digestive System (PE: CD-ROM, website)
Practice Anatomy Lab™ 3.0 (PAL) (PE: DVD, website)

Laboratory Materials

Ordering information is based on a lab size of 24 students, working in groups of 4. A list of supply house addresses appears in Appendix A.

24 prepared microscope slides of each of the following: mixed salivary glands, liver, longitudinal sections of the gastroesophageal junction and a tooth, and cross sections of the stomach, duodenum, ileum, and large intestine

24 compound microscopes and/or hand lenses, lens paper, lens cleaning solution
Anatomical charts of the human digestive system

Jaw model and/or human skull
Dissectible torso model
3-D model of a villus (if available)
3-D model of liver lobules (if available)

Advance Preparation

1. Set out the dissectible torso model and anatomical charts of the human digestive system.

2. Set out models of a villus and the liver, if available; a jaw model; and/or a human skull.

3. Set out slides of liver, mixed salivary glands, longitudinal sections of the gastroesophageal junction and a tooth; cross sections of the stomach, duodenum, ileum, and large intestine; lens paper and lens cleaning solution. Have compound microscopes and/or hand lenses available.

Answers to Pre-Lab Quiz (pp. 577–578)

1. d, all of the above
2. absorption
3. a, mucosa
4. esophagus
5. d, peristalsis
6. d, stomach
7. true
8. descending colon
9. d, root
10. b, liver

Answers to Activity Questions

Activity 2: Studying the Histologic Structure of the Stomach and the Gastroesophageal Junction (pp. 583–584)

1. Stomach

The extra layer of smooth muscle produces the churning movement because of the additional planes in which contraction can take place.

2. Gastroesophageal Junction

The esophagus is lined with stratified squamous epithelium, while the stomach is lined with simple columnar epithelium. The esophagus is designed to handle abrasion. The stomach lining has secretory and some absorptive functions. The stomach is designed to resist acid and the esophagus is not.

Activity 3: Observing the Histologic Structure of the Small Intestine (pp. 586–587)

1. Duodenum

Simple columnar epithelium lines the duodenum.

2. Ileum

Peyer's patches are lymphatic tissue.

Activity 4: Examining the Histologic Structure of the Large Intestine (p. 588)

Mucus in the large intestine helps the contents pass along the tract more easily.

Anatomy of the Digestive System

General Histological Plan of the Alimentary Canal

1. The general anatomical features of the alimentary canal are listed below. Fill in the table to complete the information.

Wall layer	Subdivisions of the layer (if applicable)	Major functions
mucosa	1) epithelium; 2) lamina propria; 3) muscularis mucosa	absorption secretion
submucosa	(not applicable)	vascular supply for mucosa; protection
muscularis externa	1) circular layer 2) longitudinal layer	churning; mixing; propulsion of food along the tract
serosa or adventitia	(not applicable)	protection and anchoring for adventitia; reduction of friction for abdominal organs by serosa

Organs of the Alimentary Canal

2. The tubelike digestive system canal that extends from the mouth to the anus is known as the *alimentary*

   canal or the *gastrointestinal (GI)* tract.

3. How is the muscularis externa of the stomach modified? *It has a third (obliquely oriented) muscle layer.*

   How does this modification relate to the function of the stomach? *Vigorous churning activity occurs here.*

4. What transition in epithelial type exists at the gastroesophageal junction? *Changes from stratified squamous (esophagus) to*

   simple columnar (stomach)

   How do the epithelia of these two organs relate to their specific functions? *The esophagus is subjected to constant abrasion*

   (stratified squamous is well adapted for this). The stomach has secretory (and some absorptive) functions and is better protected

   from acid.

5. Differentiate the colon from the large intestine. *The large intestine includes the colon, but also includes the cecum, appendix,*

   rectum, and anal canal.

6. Match the items in column B with the descriptive statements in column A.

	Column A	Column B
_l_	1. structure that suspends the small intestine from the posterior body wall	a. anus
_w_	2. fingerlike extensions of the intestinal mucosa that increase the surface area for absorption	b. appendix
_o_	3. large collections of lymphoid tissue found in the submucosa of the small intestine	c. circular folds
_c_	4. deep folds of the mucosa and submucosa that extend completely or partially around the circumference of the small intestine	d. esophagus
_v_	5. mobile organ that manipulates food in the mouth and initiates swallowing	e. frenulum
_p_	6. conduit for both air and food	f. greater omentum
_d_	7. the "gullet"; no digestive/absorptive function	g. hard palate
_r_	8. folds of the gastric mucosa	h. haustra
_h_	9. pocketlike sacs of the large intestine	i. ileocecal valve
_m_	10. projections of the plasma membrane of a mucosal epithelial cell	j. large intestine
_i_	11. valve at the junction of the small and large intestines	k. lesser omentum
_s_	12. primary region of food and water absorption	l. mesentery
_e_	13. membrane securing the tongue to the floor of the mouth	m. microvilli
_j_	14. absorbs water and forms feces	n. oral vestibule
_n_	15. area between the teeth and lips/cheeks	o. Peyer's patches
_b_	16. wormlike sac that outpockets from the cecum	p. pharynx
_u_	17. initiates protein digestion	q. pyloric valve
_k_	18. structure attached to the lesser curvature of the stomach	r. rugae
_f_	19. covers most of the abdominal organs like an apron	s. small intestine
_q_	20. valve controlling food movement from the stomach into the duodenum	t. soft palate
_t_	21. posterosuperior boundary of the oral cavity	u. stomach
_a_	22. region containing two sphincters through which feces are expelled from the body	v. tongue
_g_	23. bone-supported anterosuperior boundary of the oral cavity	w. villi

7. Correctly identify all organs depicted in the diagram below.

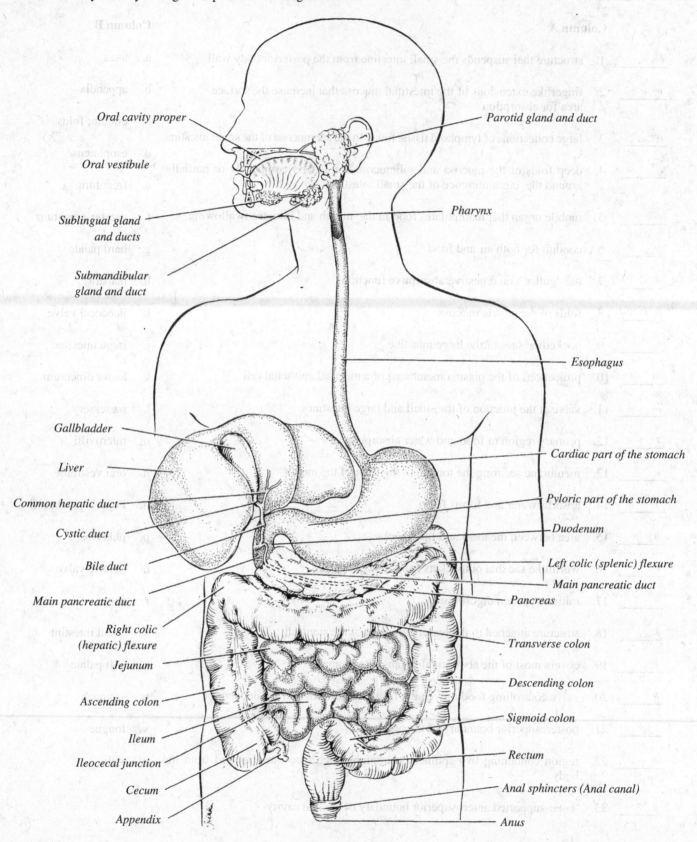

Oral cavity proper

Oral vestibule

Sublingual gland and ducts

Submandibular gland and duct

Parotid gland and duct

Pharynx

Esophagus

Gallbladder

Liver

Common hepatic duct

Cystic duct

Bile duct

Main pancreatic duct

Right colic (hepatic) flexure

Jejunum

Ascending colon

Ileum

Ileocecal junction

Cecum

Appendix

Cardiac part of the stomach

Pyloric part of the stomach

Duodenum

Left colic (splenic) flexure

Main pancreatic duct

Pancreas

Transverse colon

Descending colon

Sigmoid colon

Rectum

Anal sphincters (Anal canal)

Anus

8. You have studied the histologic structure of a number of organs in this laboratory. Three of these are diagrammed below. Identify and correctly label each.

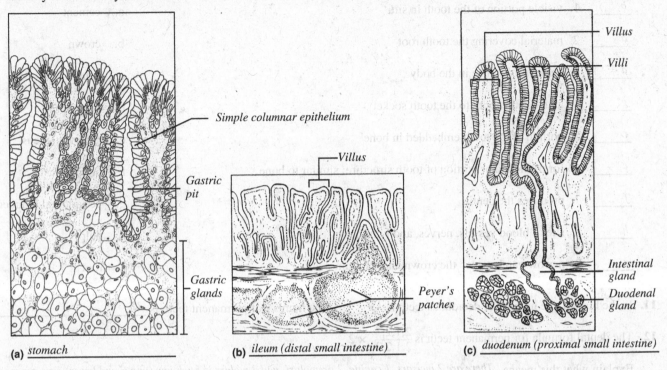

(a) stomach

(b) ileum (distal small intestine)

(c) duodenum (proximal small intestine)

Accessory Digestive Organs

9. Correctly label all structures provided with leader lines in the diagram of a molar below. (*Note:* Some of the terms in the key for question 10 may be helpful in this task.)

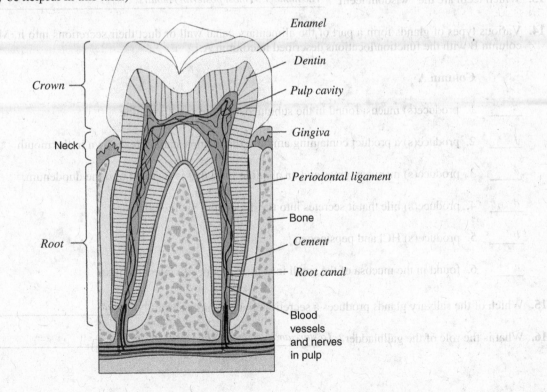

10. Use the key to identify each tooth area described below.

<u>b</u>   1. visible portion of the tooth in situ

<u>a</u>   2. material covering the tooth root

<u>d</u>   3. hardest substance in the body

<u>g</u>   4. attaches the tooth to the tooth socket

<u>i</u>   5. portion of the tooth embedded in bone

<u>c</u>   6. forms the major portion of tooth structure; similar to bone

<u>f</u>   7. produces the dentin

<u>h</u>   8. site of blood vessels, nerves, and lymphatics

<u>e</u>   9. narrow gap between the crown and the gum

Key:

a. cement

b. crown

c. dentin

d. enamel

e. gingival sulcus

f. odontoblast

g. periodontal ligament

h. pulp

i. root

11. In the human, the number of deciduous teeth is <u>20</u>; the number of permanent teeth is <u>32</u>

12. The dental formula for permanent teeth is $\frac{2,1,2,3}{2,1,2,3} \times 2$

Explain what this means. *There are 2 incisors, 1 canine, 2 premolars, and 3 molars in each jaw (upper and lower) from the median line posteriorly.*

What is the dental formula for the deciduous teeth? $\frac{2,1,0,2}{2,1,0,2} \times 2 = 20$ *(deciduous teeth)*

13. Which teeth are the "wisdom teeth"? *The number 3 (most posterior) molars*

14. Various types of glands form a part of the alimentary canal wall or duct their secretions into it. Match the glands listed in column B with the function/locations described in column A.

Column A

<u>a</u>   1. produce(s) mucus; found in the submucosa of the small intestine

<u>f</u>   2. produce(s) a product containing amylase that begins starch breakdown in the mouth

<u>e</u>   3. produce(s) many enzymes and an alkaline fluid that is secreted into the duodenum

<u>d</u>   4. produce(s) bile that it secretes into the duodenum via the bile duct

<u>b</u>   5. produce(s) HCl and pepsinogen

<u>c</u>   6. found in the mucosa of the small intestine; produce(s) intestinal juice

Column B

a. duodenal glands

b. gastric glands

c. intestinal crypts

d. liver

e. pancreas

f. salivary glands

15. Which of the salivary glands produces a secretion that is mainly serous? *Parotid*

16. What is the role of the gallbladder? *To store and concentrate bile made by the liver*

17. Name three structures always found in the portal triad regions of the liver. *Branch of the bile duct,* _____,

branch of hepatic artery _____, and *branch of hepatic portal vein* _____

18. Where would you expect to find the stellate macrophages of the liver? *Lining the sinusoids* _____

What is their function? *Phagocytosis of debris and worn-out blood cells* _____

19. Why is the liver so dark red in the living animal? *Because it is a blood reservoir* _____

20. The pancreas has two major populations of secretory cells—those in the islets and the acinar cells. Which population serves

the digestive process? *Acinar cells* _____

Digestive System Processes: Chemical and Physical

Time Allotment: 3 hours. (Two parts of the exercise require 2-hour incubations.)

Multimedia Resources: See Appendix B for Guide to Multimedia Resource Distributors.

Breakdown (FHS: 28 minutes, DVD, 3-year streaming webcast)
Digestion: Eating to Live (FHS: 27 minutes, DVD, 3-year streaming webcast)
The Human Digestive System (DE: 18 minutes, DVD, CD-ROM)
Interactive Physiology® 10-System Suite: Digestive System (PE: CD-ROM, website)
PhysioEx™ 9.1 Exercise 8 (PE: CD-ROM, website)

Solutions:

Alpha-Amylase, 1%
Weigh out 1 gram of alpha-amylase. Add distilled water to a final volume of 100 milliliters. For best results, be sure that the enzyme is not standardized with maltose.

BAPNA, 0.01%
Weigh out 0.01 gram BAPNA. Add distilled water to a final volume of 100 milliliters.

Benedict's Solution

- 173.0 grams sodium citrate
- 100.0 grams sodium carbonate, anhydrous
- 17.3 grams cupric sulfate (pure crystalline)

Add the citrate and carbonate salts to 700–800 milliliters distilled water. Heat to dissolve. Add the cupric sulfate to 100 milliliters distilled water and heat to dissolve. Cool the solutions and then combine. Add distilled water to make 1 liter of solution.

Hydrochloric Acid (HCl), 0.1 N
Add 8 milliliters concentrated HCl to 900 milliliters distilled water. Add distilled water to a final volume of 1 liter; *or* add 100 milliliters of 1 *N* HCl to 850 milliliters of distilled water. Add distilled water to a final volume of 1 liter.

Litmus Cream
Add powdered litmus to fresh cream to achieve a blue color.

Lugol's Iodine (IKI)

- 20 grams potassium iodide
- 4 grams iodine crystals

Dissolve potassium iodide in 1 liter distilled water. Add the iodine crystals and stir to dissolve. Store in dark bottles.

Maltose, 1%
Weigh out 1 gram maltose. Add distilled water to a final volume of 100 milliliters.

Pancreatin, 1%
Weigh out 1 gram pancreatin. Dissolve in distilled water to a final volume of 100 milliliters.

Starch Solution, Boiled, 1%
Add 1 gram of starch to 100 milliliters distilled water. Boil just until it changes from cloudy to translucent. Cool and filter. Add a pinch of NaCl. Prepare fresh daily. For best results, use potato starch from a biological supply house.

Trypsin, 1%
Weigh out 1 gram trypsin. Add distilled water to a final volume of 100 milliliters.

Laboratory Materials

Ordering information is based on a lab size of 24 students, working in groups of 4. A list of supply house addresses appears in Appendix A.

Part I: Enzyme Action

General Supply Area

144 test tubes
6 test tube racks
6 wax markers
6 test tube holders
6 250-milliliter beakers
Ice water bath
Water bath at 37°C
Boiling chips
6 hot plates
Chart (or chalkboard/whiteboard) for
    recording class data

Activity 1: Starch Digestion

6 dropper bottles of distilled water
6 dropper bottles of 1% boiled starch
    solution, freshly prepared
6 dropper bottles of 1% alpha-amylase
    solution

6 dropper bottles of 1% maltose
    solution
6 dropper bottles of Benedict's
    solution
6 dropper bottles of Lugol's solution
    (IKI)
6 spot plates

Activity 2: Protein Digestion

6 dropper bottles of 1% trypsin
6 dropper bottles of 0.01% BAPNA

Activity 3: Bile Action and Fat Digestion

6 dropper bottles of 1% pancreatin
6 dropper bottles of 0.1 N HCl
6 dropper bottles of vegetable oil
6 dropper bottles of litmus cream
Bile salts (sodium taurocholate)
Parafilm (small squares to cover test
    tubes)

Part II: Physical Processes

Activity 5: Observing Digestion

Water pitcher
24 paper cups
12 stethoscopes
Alcohol swabs
Disposable autoclave bag
Watch, clock, or timer

Activity 6: Videotape

Television and VCR or DVD player
    for independent viewing

Advance Preparation

1. Put a chart on the board for recording class results.
2. Decide how to divide the class into groups to do the experiments.
3. Set up five supply areas.

   General supply area (for a class of 24, divided into six groups of four each):

   144 test tubes, 6 test tube racks, 6 test tube holders, and 6 wax marking pencils, hot plates, 250-milliliter beakers, ice water bath, 37°C water bath, boiling chips (biological supply company), and dropper bottles of distilled water

   Supply area 1 (for each group of four students):

   Dropper bottles of distilled water, *1% boiled starch solution*, freshly prepared, *1% amylase solution, 1% maltose solution, Lugol's solution* (biological supply company), *Benedict's solution* (biological supply company), and spot plates

   Supply area 2 (for each group of four students):

   Dropper bottles of *1% trypsin* (Sigma) and *0.01% BAPNA* (Sigma).

   Supply area 3 (for each group of four students):

   Bile salts, parafilm, and dropper bottles of *1% pancreatin solution, 0.1 N HCl*, vegetable oil, and *litmus cream* (litmus powder—biological supply company)

Supply area 4 (for each group of four students):

Pitcher of water, four paper cups, a stethoscope, disposable autoclave bag, and alcohol swabs.

4. Set up a viewing area with a VCR or DVD on the digestive system.

Comments and Pitfalls

1. This lab requires a great deal of organization and coordination on the part of the students. Emphasize the need for careful labeling and record keeping.

2. If a 37°C water bath is not available, incubate the tubes at room temperature and double the incubation time.

3. Enzyme activity can vary. Enzyme solutions should be prepared just before the lab and adjusted for appropriate activity.

4. An alternative to having each group perform each activity is to assign each activity to a different group. At the end of the lab period, have each group present their data along with an explanation of their activity to all of the students.

Answers to Pre-Lab Quiz (p. 599)

1. catalysts
2. true
3. b, control
4. salivary amylase
5. true
6. b, green to orange
7. d, trypsin
8. pancreatic lipase
9. true
10. d, segmental

Answers to Activity Questions

Activity 3: Demonstrating the Emulsification Action of Bile and Assessing Fat Digestion by Lipase (p. 604)

2. Emulsification occurs in the tubes containing bile salts.

Answers to Group Challenge: Odd Enzyme Out (p. 605)

1. Which is the "odd enzyme"?	Why is it the odd one out?
Trypsin Carboxypeptidase (Pepsin) Chymotrypsin	*Pepsin is the odd enzyme out because it is produced in the stomach, not the pancreas. Pepsin is optimally active at a very acidic pH whereas the pancreatic proteases are most active at a slightly alkaline pH.*
2. Which is the "odd enzyme"?	Why is it the odd one out?
(Lactase) Pepsin Aminopeptidase Trypsin	*Lactase is the odd enzyme out because it digests carbohydrates, not protein.*

3. Which is the "odd enzyme"?	Why is it the odd one out?
Maltase (Pancreatic lipase) Nucleosidase Dipeptidase	*Pancreatic lipase is the odd enzyme out because it is not a brush border enzyme.*
4. Which is the "odd enzyme"?	Why is it the odd one out?
Sucrase Dextrinase Glucoamylase (Chymotrypsin)	*Chymotrypsin is the odd enzyme out because it digests protein, not carbohydrates.*

Activity 5: Observing Movements and Sounds of Digestion (pp. 606–607)

2. Before swallowing, the tongue rises to touch the hard palate, remains raised during swallowing, then relaxes after swallowing.

3. Superior movement of the larynx ensures that its passageway is covered by the epiglottis.

Digestive System Processes: Chemical and Physical

Digestion of Foodstuffs: Enzymatic Action

1. Match the following definitions with the proper choices from the key.

Key: a. catalyst   b. control   c. enzyme   d. substrate

d; substrate _____ 1. substance on which a catalyst works

c; enzyme _____ 2. biologic catalyst; protein in nature

a; catalyst (also c; enzyme) _____ 3. increases the rate of a chemical reaction without becoming part of the product

b; control _____ 4. provides a standard of comparison for test results

2. List the three characteristics of enzymes. *Specificity (act on one or a small number of substrates); temperature specific;*

pH specific _____

3. The enzymes of the digestive system are classified as hydrolases. What does this mean?

Hydrolases break down organic food molecules by adding water to the molecular bonds, thus cleaving the bonds between the

subunits or monomers.

4. Fill in the following chart about the various digestive system enzymes encountered in this exercise.

Enzyme	Organ producing it	Site of action	Substrate(s)	Optimal pH
Salivary amylase	*Salivary glands*	*Oral cavity*	*Starch*	6.7–7.0
Trypsin	*Pancreas*	*Small intestine*	*Proteins*	8.0
Lipase (pancreatic)	*Pancreas*	*Small intestine*	*Fats*	7.4–8.0

5. Name the end products of digestion for the following types of foods.

proteins: *amino acids* _____ carbohydrates: *simple sugars* _____

fats: *fatty acids* _____ and *monoglycerides* _____

Why This Matters

6. How does the substrate for amylase differ from the substrate for lactase? *The substrate for amylase is starch, which is a* *complex carbohydrate. The substrate for lactase is lactose, a disaccharide.*

How are the substrates similar? *Both substrates are carbohydrates.*

7. Where does lactose hydrolysis occur for lactase-persistent individuals? *In the small intestine, where the lactase is secreted*

Where does lactose hydrolysis occur for lactose-intolerant individuals who have consumed probiotic bacterial microflora? *In the colon, where the probiotic bacteria reside*

8. You used several indicators or tests in the laboratory to determine the presence or absence of certain substances. Choose the correct test or indicator from the key to correspond to the condition described below.

Key: a. Lugol's iodine (IKI) b. Benedict's solution c. litmus d. BAPNA

_d_ 1. used to test for protein hydrolysis, which was indicated by a yellow color

_a_ 2. used to test for the presence of starch, which was indicated by a blue-black color

_c_ 3. used to test for the presence of fatty acids, which was evidenced by a color change from blue to pink

_b_ 4. used to test for the presence of reducing sugars (maltose, sucrose, glucose) as indicated by a blue to green or orange color change

9. What conclusions can you draw when an experimental sample gives both a positive starch test and a positive maltose test after incubation? *Starch digestion is partial (incomplete).*

Why was 37°C the optimal incubation temperature? *It is body temperature.*

Why did very little, if any, starch digestion occur in test tube 4A? *The enzyme was destroyed by boiling.*

When starch was incubated with amylase at 0°C, did you see any starch digestion? *No*

Why or why not? *Amylase has an optimal temperature closer to that of the human body. At 0°C, the rate of enzyme activity and* *diffusion of enzymes and substrate has slowed to near zero.*

Assume you have said to a group of your peers that amylase is capable of starch hydrolysis to maltose. If you had not done control tube 1A, what objection to your statement could be raised? *A positive maltose test could also result from maltose* *contamination of the starting amylase solution.*

What if you had not done tube 2A? *A negative Benedict's test indicates starch was not contaminated with maltose. (And that* *starch did not break down in the absence of amylase.)*

10. In the exercise concerning trypsin function, why was an enzyme assay such as Benedict's or Lugol's iodine (IKI), which test for the presence of a reaction product, not necessary? *The enzyme assay is "built in" to the substrate BAPNA. Peptide bond cleavage results in a yellow color.*

Why was tube 1T necessary? *Tube 1T was a control to prove that trypsin did not turn yellow by itself.*

Why was tube 2T necessary? *Tube 2T proved that BAPNA did not turn yellow by itself.*

Trypsin is a protease similar to pepsin, the protein-digesting enzyme in the stomach. Would trypsin work well in the stomach? *No* Why? *The pH optimum for trypsin is slightly basic; the pH optimum for pepsin is acidic (stomach is acidic).*

11. In the procedure concerning pancreatic lipase digestion of fats and the action of bile salts, how did the appearance of tubes 1E and 2E differ? *1E—2 layers; oil over water. 2E—fat droplets dispersed*

Explain the reason for the difference. *Bile, present in tube 2E, acted to emulsify the fat.*

Why did the litmus indicator change from blue to pink during fat hydrolysis? *Fatty acids decreased the pH. Litmus in the cream is an indicator that changes from blue to red as the pH changes from alkaline to acidic conditions.*

Why is bile not considered an enzyme? *Bile only physically separates the fat droplets. It does not break the molecular bonds as do the digestive enzymes.*

How did the tubes containing bile compare with those not containing bile? *The tubes containing bile showed more hydrolysis than those not containing bile.*

What role does bile play in fat digestion? *Emulsification of fat by bile increases the surface area for lipase activity.*

12. The three-dimensional structure of a functional protein is altered by intense heat or nonphysiological pH even though peptide bonds may not break. Such inactivation is called denaturation, and denatured enzymes are nonfunctional. Explain why.

Their three-dimensional structures and active sites are necessary for their activity. If their structures are changed, the active sites change, thus inactivating the enzyme.

What specific experimental conditions resulted in denatured enzymes? *Boiling the enzyme solution in all experiments denatured the enzymes.*

13. Pancreatic and intestinal enzymes operate optimally at a pH that is slightly alkaline, yet the chyme entering the duodenum from the stomach is very acid. How is the proper pH for the functioning of the pancreatic-intestinal enzymes ensured?

The pancreas delivers its enzymes to the small intestine in an alkaline-rich (HCO_3^-) fluid.

14. Assume you have been chewing a piece of bread for 5 or 6 minutes. How would you expect its taste to change during this interval? _The bread would begin to taste sweet._

Why? _Starch is broken down to maltose by amylase._

15. Note the mechanism of absorption (passive or active transport) of the following food breakdown products, and indicate by a check mark (✓) whether the absorption would result in their movement into the blood capillaries or the lymphatic capillaries (lacteals).

Substance	Mechanism of absorption	Blood	Lymph
Monosaccharides	*Most by active transport*	✓	
Fatty acids and monoglycerides	*Diffusion*	*Some*	*Most*
Amino acids	*Active transport*	✓	
Water	*Osmosis*	✓	
Na^+, Cl^-, Ca^{2+}	*Na^+, Ca^{2+} active transport; Cl^- diffusion*	✓	

16. People on a strict diet to lose weight begin to metabolize stored fats at an accelerated rate. How does this condition affect

blood pH? _It would become acidic (decreased pH)._

17. Using a flowchart, trace the pathway of a ham sandwich (ham = protein and fat; bread = starch) from the mouth to the site of absorption of its breakdown products, noting where digestion occurs and what specific enzymes are involved.

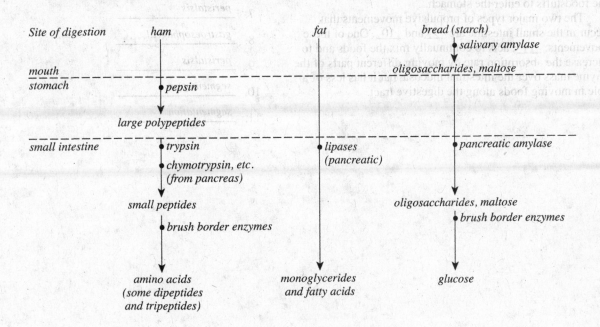

18. Some of the digestive organs have groups of secretory cells that liberate hormones into the blood. These exert an effect on the digestive process by acting on other cells or structures and causing them to release digestive enzymes, expel bile, or increase the motility of the digestive tract. For each hormone below, note the organ producing the hormone and its effects on the digestive process. Include the target organs affected.

Hormone	Produced by	Target organ(s) and effects
Secretin	*Intestinal mucosa*	*It stimulates (1) the pancreas and liver to release bicarbonate-rich fluid, and (2) the liver to secrete bile. Inhibits gastric activity.*
Gastrin	*Stomach mucosa*	*Gastrin acts on the stomach glands to increase their secretory activity (particularly of HCl).*
Cholecystokinin	*Intestinal mucosa*	*It stimulates release of enzymes from the pancreas, and causes gallbladder contraction.*

Physical Processes: Mechanisms of Food Propulsion and Mixing

19. Complete the following statements.

Swallowing, or _1_, occurs in two phases—the _2_ and _3_. One of these phases, the _4_ phase, is voluntary. During the voluntary phase, the _5_ is used to push the food into the back of the throat. During swallowing, the _6_ rises to ensure that its passageway is covered by the epiglottis so that the ingested substances don't enter the respiratory passageways. It is possible to swallow water while standing on your head because the water is carried along the esophagus involuntarily by the process of _7_. The pressure exerted by the foodstuffs on the _8_ sphincter causes it to open, allowing the foodstuffs to enter the stomach.

The two major types of propulsive movements that occur in the small intestine are _9_ and _10_. One of these movements, _11_, acts to continually mix the foods and to increase the absorption rate by moving different parts of the chyme mass over the intestinal mucosa, but it has less of a role in moving foods along the digestive tract.

1. *deglutition*
2. *buccal*
3. *pharyngeal-esophageal*
4. *buccal*
5. *tongue*
6. *larynx*
7. *peristalsis*
8. *gastroesophageal*
9. *peristalsis*
10. *segmentation*
11. *segmentation*

Anatomy of the Urinary System

Time Allotment: 1 hour.

Multimedia Resources: See Appendix B for Guide to Multimedia Resource Distributors.

Interactive Physiology® 10-System Suite: Urinary System and *Fluids and Electrolytes* (PE: CD-ROM, website)
Practice Anatomy Lab™ 3.0 (PAL) (PE: DVD, website)
The Urinary Tract: Water! (FHS: 28 minutes, DVD, 3-year streaming webcast)

Laboratory Materials

Ordering information is based on a lab size of 24 students, working in groups of 4. A list of supply house addresses appears in Appendix A.

6–12 pig or sheep kidneys (doubly or triply injected)

24 prepared microscope slides of each of the following: kidney (longitudinal section), bladder (cross section)

24 compound microscopes, lens paper, lens cleaning solution

Dissectible human torso model

3-D model or anatomical chart of the human urinary system

3-D models of the kidney and nephron (if available)

6–12 dissecting pans
6–12 dissecting kits
Disposable gloves
24 pairs of safety glasses
Soap, sponges, disinfectant

Advance Preparation

1. Make arrangements for appropriate storage, disposal, and cleanup of dissection materials. Check with the Department of Health, the Department of Environmental Protection, or their counterparts for state regulations.

2. Set out disposable gloves and safety glasses.

3. Set out dissecting kits, dissecting pans, and pig or sheep kidneys.

4. Set out slides of longitudinal sections of the kidney and cross sections of the bladder; lens paper; and lens cleaning solution. Have compound microscopes available.

5. Set out the dissectible human torso and/or any anatomical charts and models of the urinary system, kidney, and nephron.

Answers to Pre-Lab Quiz (p. 613)

1. nitrogenous
2. a, kidneys
3. medulla
4. segmental arteries
5. nephrons
6. b, glomerulus
7. d, proximal convoluted tubule
8. efferent
9. false
10. external

Answers to Activity Questions

Activity 3: Studying Bladder Structure (p. 621)

5. Both organs have an internal mucosa, a layer of smooth muscle, and an external adventitia. The ureter has only two layers of smooth muscle.

Answers to Group Challenge: Urinary System Sequencing (p. 622)

1. renal pelvis, minor calyx, renal papilla, urinary bladder, ureter, major calyx, and urethra. *renal papilla, minor calyx, major calyx, renal pelvis, ureter, urinary bladder, and urethra*

2. distal convoluted tubule, ascending limb of the nephron loop, glomerulus, collecting duct, descending limb of the nephron loop, proximal convoluted tubule, and glomerular capsule. *glomerulus, glomerular capsule, proximal convoluted tubule, descending limb of the nephron loop, ascending limb of the nephron loop, distal convoluted tubule, and collecting duct*

3. segmental artery, afferent arteriole, cortical radiate artery, glomerulus, renal artery, interlobar artery, and arcuate artery. *renal artery, segmental artery, interlobar artery, arcuate artery, cortical radiate artery, afferent arteriole, and glomerulus*

4. arcuate vein, inferior vena cava, peritubular capillaries, renal vein, interlobar vein, cortical radiate vein, and efferent arteriole. *efferent arteriole, peritubular capillaries, cortical radiate vein, arcuate vein, interlobar vein, renal vein, and inferior vena cava*

Anatomy of the Urinary System

Gross Anatomy of the Human Urinary System

1. Complete the following statements.

The kidney is referred to as an excretory organ because it excretes __1__ wastes. It is also a major homeostatic organ because it maintains the electrolyte, __2__, and __3__ balance of the blood.

Urine is continuously formed by the structural and functional units of the kidneys, the __4__, and is routed down the __5__ by the mechanism of __6__ to a storage organ called the __7__. Eventually, the urine is conducted to the body __8__ by the urethra. In the male, the urethra is __9__ centimeters long and transports both urine and __10__. The female urethra is __11__ centimeters long and transports only urine.

Voiding or emptying the bladder is called __12__. Voiding has both voluntary and involuntary components. The voluntary sphincter is the __13__ sphincter. An inability to control this sphincter is referred to as __14__.

1. *nitrogenous* _____

2. *water/fluid* _____

3. *acid-base* _____

4. *nephrons* _____

5. *ureters* _____

6. *peristalsis* _____

7. *urinary bladder* _____

8. *exterior* _____

9. *20 (8 inches)* _____

10. *semen* _____

11. *4 (1.5 inches)* _____

12. *micturition* _____

13. *external urethral* _____

14. *incontinence* _____

2. What is the function of the fat cushion that surrounds the kidneys in life? *Helps anchor the kidneys to the dorsal body wall and cushions them against blows*

3. Define *ptosis*. *Dropping of the kidney(s) to a more inferior position in the abdominal cavity*

4. Complete the labeling of the diagram to correctly identify the urinary system organs.

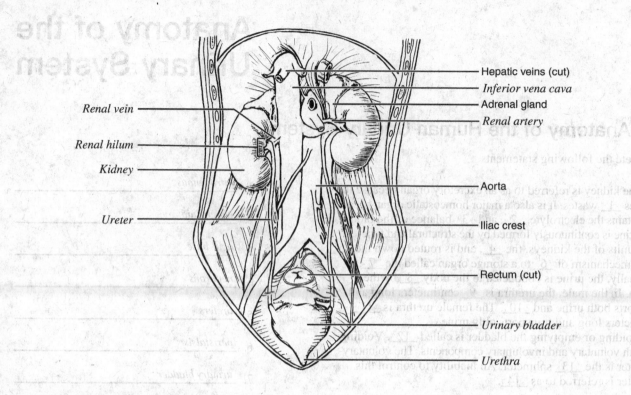

Renal vein

Renal hilum

Kidney

Ureter

Hepatic veins (cut)

Inferior vena cava

Adrenal gland

Renal artery

Aorta

Iliac crest

Rectum (cut)

Urinary bladder

Urethra

Gross Internal Anatomy of the Pig or Sheep Kidney

5. Match the appropriate structure in column B to its description in column A. The items in column B may be used more than once.

Column A	Column B
_b_ 1. smooth membrane, tightly adherent to the kidney surface	a. cortex
_c_ 2. portion of the kidney containing mostly collecting ducts	b. fibrous capsule
_a_ 3. portion of the kidney containing the bulk of the nephron structures	c. medulla
_a_ 4. superficial region of kidney tissue	d. minor calyx
_f_ 5. basinlike area of the kidney, continuous with the ureter	e. renal column
_d_ 6. a cup-shaped extension of the pelvis that encircles the apex of a pyramid	f. renal pelvis
_e_ 7. area of cortical tissue running between the medullary pyramids	

Functional Microscopic Anatomy of the Kidney and Bladder

6. Label the blood vessels and parts of the nephron by selecting the letter for the correct structure from the key below. The items in the key may be used more than once.

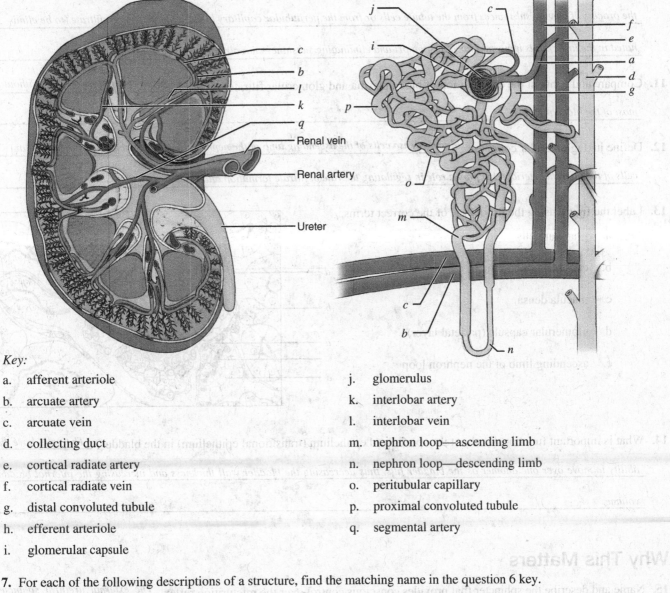

Key:

a. afferent arteriole
b. arcuate artery
c. arcuate vein
d. collecting duct
e. cortical radiate artery
f. cortical radiate vein
g. distal convoluted tubule
h. efferent arteriole
i. glomerular capsule

j. glomerulus
k. interlobar artery
l. interlobar vein
m. nephron loop—ascending limb
n. nephron loop—descending limb
o. peritubular capillary
p. proximal convoluted tubule
q. segmental artery

7. For each of the following descriptions of a structure, find the matching name in the question 6 key.

__j__ 1. capillary specialized for filtration

__o__ 2. capillary specialized for reabsorption

__i__ 3. cuplike part of the renal corpuscle

__m__ 4. location of macula densa

__p__ 5. primary site of tubular reabsorption

__d__ 6. receives urine from many nephrons

8. Explain *why* the glomerulus is such a high-pressure capillary bed. *It is both fed and drained by arterioles (which are high-pressure vessels compared to venules), and the afferent arteriole has a larger diameter than the efferent arteriole.*

How does its high-pressure condition aid its function of filtrate formation? *The higher the capillary pressure, the more filtrate will be formed.*

9. What structural modification of certain tubule cells enhances their ability to reabsorb substances from the filtrate?

Their possession of dense microvilli (especially the PCT cells)

10. Explain the mechanism of tubular secretion, and explain its importance in the urine-formation process. *Tubular secretion is*

the process of moving substances from the tubule cells or from the peritubular capillary blood into the nephron filtrate (to be elimi-

nated in the urine). It is important for adjusting pH and eliminating substances not already in the filtrate.

11. Compare and contrast the composition of blood plasma and glomerular filtrate. *Glomerular filtrate = blood plasma without*

most of the blood proteins.

12. Define juxtaglomerular complex. *Macula densa cells of the ascending limb of the nephron loop and granular (juxtaglomerular)*

cells of the afferent arteriole that play a role in regulating the rate of filtrate formation and systemic blood pressure

13. Label the figure using the key letters of the correct terms.

Key: a. granular cells

b. cuboidal epithelium

c. macula densa

d. glomerular capsule (parietal layer)

e. ascending limb of the nephron loop

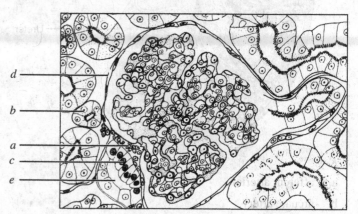

14. What is important functionally about the specialized epithelium (transitional epithelium) in the bladder? *The cells have the*

ability to move over one another as the bladder fills, thus decreasing the bladder wall thickness and increasing the internal bladder

volume.

Why This Matters

15. Name and describe the sphincter that provides conscious control over the micturition reflex. *The external urethral sphincter*

composed of skeletal muscle controls the micturition reflex.

16. The practice of elimination communication seems to indicate that babies can gain the ability to inhibit the micturition reflex.

Hypothesize how this control might be achieved and which nervous system (central, autonomic, or somatic) is most likely

involved. *The inhibition most likely involves higher brain centers. Higher brain centers would be found in the central nervous system.*

Urinalysis

Time Allotment: 1 hour.

Solutions:

Barium Chloride (BaCl), 10%
Weigh out 10 grams of barium chloride. Add water to a final volume of 100 milliliters.

Bleach Solution, 10%
Measure out 100 milliliters of household bleach. Add water to a final volume of 1 liter.

Hydrochloric Acid (HCl), Dilute, 3 N
Add 250 milliliters of concentrated (approximately 12 *N*) HCl to 700 milliliters distilled water. Add distilled water to a final volume of 1 liter.

Nitric Acid (HNO$_3$), Dilute, 3 N
Add 189 milliliters of concentrated (approximately 16 *N*) HNO$_3$ to 700 milliliters distilled water. Add distilled water to a final volume of 1 liter.

Silver Nitrate (AgNO$_3$), 3%
Weigh out 3 grams of silver nitrate. **Use caution: This is an oxidizing substance.** Add distilled water to make 100 milliliters of solution. Store in light-resistant bottles. Make fresh for each use.

Urine, Artificial Normal Human*

• 36.4 grams urea
• 15 grams sodium chloride
• 9.0 grams potassium chloride
• 9.6 grams sodium phosphate
• 4.0 grams creatinine
• 100 milligrams albumin

Add urea to 1.5 liters of distilled water. Mix until crystals dissolve. Add sodium chloride, potassium chloride, and sodium phosphate. Mix until solution is clear. The pH should be within the 5 to 7 pH range for normal human urine. Adjust pH, if necessary, with 1 *N* HCl or 1 *N* NaOH. Place a urine hydrometer in the solution and dilute with water to a specific gravity within the range of 1.015 to 1.025. This stock solution may be refrigerated for several weeks or frozen for months. Before use, warm to room temperature and add 4.0 grams creatinine and 100 milligrams of albumin for each 2 liters of solution.

Urine, Glycosuria*
For a minimally detectable level of glucose, add a minimum of 600 milligrams of glucose to 1 liter of "normal" urine solution. For moderate to high glycosuria, add 2.5 to 5.0 grams of glucose to each liter of solution.

Urine, Hematuria*
Add 1 milliliter of heparinized or defibrinated sheep blood to 1 liter of "normal" urine solution.

Urine, Hemoglobinuria*
Add 2 milligrams of bovine hemoglobin to 1 liter of "normal" urine solution.

Urine, Hyposthenuria*
Add distilled water to a sample of "normal" urine until the specific gravity approaches 1.005.

Urine, Ketonuria*

Add a minimum of 100 milligrams of acetoacetic acid or at least 1 milliliter of acetone to 1 liter of "normal" urine solution.

Urine, Leukocyte Presence*

Add 100 to 200 units of pork or rabbit liver esterase to 100 milliliters of the "normal" urine solution. This test must be performed immediately after adding the enzyme.

Urine, pH Imbalance*

Adjust "normal" urine to a pH of 4.0 to 4.5 with 1 N HCl for acid urine. Adjust "normal" urine to a pH of 8 to 9 with 1 *N* NaOH for alkaline urine.

Urine, Proteinuria*

Add 300 milligrams or more of albumin per liter of "normal" urine solution. For severe renal damage, add 1 gram of albumin to each liter of solution.

Urine, Whole Spectrum Pathological Artificial Human*

Mix appropriate amounts of abnormal condition reagents to 1 liter of "normal" urine solution.
Diabetes mellitus: glycosuria and ketonuria
Glomerular damage: proteinuria, hemoglobinuria, and hematuria

* From B. R. Shmaefsky, "Artificial Urine for Laboratory Testing," *American Biology Teacher* 52 (3), March 1990, pp. 170–172 (Reston, VA: National Association of Biology Teachers). Reprinted with permission.

Laboratory Materials

Ordering information is based on a lab size of 24 students, working in groups of 4. A list of supply house addresses appears in Appendix A.

Disposable gloves
Student urine samples collected at the beginning of the lab, or "normal" artificial urine provided by the instructor
Numbered "pathological" urine specimens provided by the instructor
6 packages of wide-range pH paper
24 of each of the following dipsticks: Clinistix, Ketostix, Albustix, Hemastix *or* 24 combination dipsticks (Chemstrip or Multistix)
Urinometer
24 urinometer cylinders and floats
120 test tubes and test tube holders

24 test tube racks
24 glass stirring rods
6 hot plates
24 10-cc graduated cylinders
24 medicine droppers
6 dropper bottles of each of the following: dilute HCl, dilute HNO_3, 3.0% silver nitrate, concentrated HNO_3
6 dropper bottles containing 100 milliliters of 10% barium chloride
6 dropper bottles containing 100 milliliters of dilute ammonium molybdate
24 500-milliliter beakers

24 microscope slides and coverslips
24 compound microscopes, lens paper, lens cleaning solution
6 Clinitest color charts
24 Clinitest tablets
24 Ictotest reagent tablets and mats
Timer (watch or clock with a second hand)
2 laboratory buckets of 10% bleach
6 flasks of 10% bleach
Disposable autoclave bags
Instructor-prepared specimen of urine sediment set up for microscopic analysis

Advance Preparation

1. Prepare *"normal" artificial urine* (about 1 liter for a class of 30 students) and *"pathological" artificial urine* samples and number them.

2. Set out two laboratory buckets containing *10% bleach solution*, and a disposable autoclave bag. Put a flask of *10% bleach solution* and a sponge at each lab bench.

3. For each student in the class set out disposable gloves, five test tubes, a glass stirring rod, a test tube rack, a medicine dropper, a urinometer cylinder and float, microscope slides, coverslips, individual reagent strips

(Clinistix, Ketostix, and Hemastix, and Albustix—available online), or combination strips (Chemstrip—available from Carolina, Multistix—available from Fisher), Clinitest tablets (Fisher), a 10-milliliter graduated cylinder, a wax marking pencil, Ictotest reagent tablet, and mat (available online). Have compound microscopes, lens paper, and lens cleaning solution available.

4. For each group set out wide-range pH paper, a bottle containing 100 milliliters of *10% barium chloride*, a bottle containing 100 milliliters of dilute ammonium molybdate (LabChem), a hot plate, a 500-milliliter beaker, and dropper bottles of *dilute HCl, dilute HNO₃*, freshly prepared *3.0% silver nitrate*, and concentrated HNO_3.

5. Set up a demonstration slide of urine sediment stained with Sedi-stain (Fisher). To prepare the slide, centrifuge a 5-milliliter sample of urine at 2000 to 2500 rpm for 5 to 6 minutes. Decant the supernatant and add one or two drops of Sedi-stain to the pellet. Put stained material onto a slide and cover with a coverslip.

Comments and Pitfalls

1. When preparing pathological samples, do not substitute sucrose for glucose. Vitamin C contamination will give false-positive glucose tests. The artificial urine is suitable for test strips, but not for use with clinical analyzers (Shmaefsky, 1990).

2. Urge students to use extreme caution when using the concentrated HCl and HNO_3 solutions.

3. Because students are usually very interested in the crystals, cells, and casts in urine, have additional references available for them.

Answers to Pre-Lab Quiz (p. 627)

1. c, urochrome
2. 6.0
3. false
4. a, albumin
5. hematuria
6. b, bilirubinuria
7. pyuria
8. casts
9. false
10. A precipitate is an insoluble compound that is no longer in solution.

Urinalysis

Characteristics of Urine

1. What is the normal volume of urine excreted in a 24-hour period? _0.8–2.0 liters_

2. Assuming normal conditions, note whether each of the following substances would be (a) in greater relative concentration in the urine than in the glomerular filtrate, (b) in lesser concentration in the urine than in the glomerular filtrate, or (c) absent from both the urine and the glomerular filtrate. Use an appropriate reference as needed.

   _b_ 1. water   _b_ 6. amino acids   _a_ 11. uric acid

   _a_ 2. phosphate ions   _b_ 7. glucose   _a_ 12. creatinine

   _a_ 3. sulfate ions   _c_ 8. protein   _c_ 13. white blood cells

   _a_ 4. potassium ions   _c_ 9. red blood cells   _c_ 14. nitrites

   _b_ 5. sodium ions   _a_ 10. urea

3. Explain why urinalysis is a routine part of any good physical examination. _Finding "abnormal" constituents in the urine may_ _indicate pathology._

4. What substance is responsible for the normal yellow color of urine? _Urochrome_

5. Which has a greater specific gravity: 1 ml of urine or 1 ml of distilled water? _1 ml of urine_ Explain your answer. _Urine_ _contains dissolved solutes, which are not found in distilled water and add to the density of the sample._

6. Explain the relationship between the color, specific gravity, and volume of urine. _Generally, the smaller the volume, the_ _greater the specific gravity (more solutes/volume) and the deeper the color._

Abnormal Urinary Constituents

7. A microscopic examination of urine may reveal the presence of certain abnormal urinary constituents.

   Name three constituents that might be present if a urinary tract infection exists. _WBCs (pus)_ ,

   RBCs , and _casts_

8. How does a urinary tract infection influence urine pH? _Becomes alkaline_

   How does starvation influence urine pH? _Becomes acidic_

9. All urine specimens become alkaline and cloudy on standing at room temperature. Explain why. _This is a result of bacterial_ _metabolism of urinary components._

10. Several specific terms have been used to indicate the presence of abnormal urine constituents. Identify each of the abnormalities described below by inserting a term from the key that names the condition.

b; hematuria   1. presence of erythrocytes in the urine

c; hemoglobinuria   2. presence of hemoglobin in the urine

a; glycosuria   3. presence of glucose in the urine

e; proteinuria   4. presence of protein in the urine

d; ketonuria   5. presence of ketone bodies in the urine

f; pyuria   6. presence of white blood cells in the urine

Key:
a. glycosuria
b. hematuria
c. hemoglobinuria
d. ketonuria
e. proteinuria
f. pyuria

11. What are renal calculi, and what conditions favor their formation? *Kidney stones; urinary retention, urinary tract infection,*

alkaline urine

12. Glucose and protein are both normally absent in the urine, but the reason for their exclusion differs. Explain the reason for

the absence of glucose. *Unless it is present in the blood in excessive levels, glucose is completely reabsorbed.*

Explain the reason for the absence of protein. *Albumin is too large to pass through the filtration membrane.*

13. The presence of abnormal constituents or conditions in urine may be associated with diseases, disorders, or other causes listed in the key. Select and list all conditions associated with each numbered item. Some choices will be used more than once.

b   1. low specific gravity

c, f, k   2. high specific gravity

c, d   3. glucose

e, j   4. protein

e, f, i, k   5. blood cells

g   6. hemoglobin

a, h   7. bile pigments

c, l   8. ketone bodies

e, k   9. casts

f, k   10. pus

Key:
a. cirrhosis of the liver
b. diabetes insipidus (uncontrolled)
c. diabetes mellitus (uncontrolled)
d. eating a 2-pound box of sweets for lunch
e. glomerulonephritis
f. gonorrhea
g. hemolytic anemias
h. hepatitis
i. kidney stones
j. pregnancy, exertion
k. pyelonephritis
l. starvation

14. Name the three major nitrogenous wastes found in the urine. *Urea*,

uric acid , and *creatinine*

15. Explain the difference between organized and unorganized sediments. *Unorganized sediments (such as certain salts and uric*

acid) crystallize or precipitate out of solution, whereas organized sediments contain cellular elements (WBCs, epithelial cells, etc.).

42 EXERCISE

Anatomy of the Reproductive System

 Time Allotment: 1 hour.

 Multimedia Resources: See Appendix B for Guide to Multimedia Resource Distributors. See Exercise 6 for histology listings.

Biologix: The Human Female Reproductive System (DE: 29 minutes, VHS, DVD)
Human Biology (FHS: 58 minutes, DVD)
Human Reproductive Biology (FHS: 35 minutes, DVD, 3-year streaming webcast)
Practice Anatomy Lab™ 3.0 (PAL) (PE: DVD, website)
Reproduction: Shares in the Future (FHS: 26 minutes, DVD, 3-year streaming webcast)

Laboratory Materials

Ordering information is based on a lab size of 24 students, working in groups of 4. A list of supply house addresses appears in Appendix A.

3-D models and/or large lab charts of the male and female reproductive tracts

24 prepared slides of cross sections of the penis, seminal glands, epididymis, uterus showing endometrium (secretory phase), and uterine tube

24 compound microscopes, lens paper, lens cleaning solution

Advance Preparation

1. Set out slides of the penis, epididymis, seminal glands, uterine tube, and uterus showing endometrium (secretory phase). Set out lens paper and lens cleaning solution, and have compound microscopes available.

2. Set out models and anatomical charts of the male and female reproductive systems.

Comments and Pitfalls

1. If you are not planning to do Exercise 43, you may wish to include the microscopic studies of the testis and ovary described there in this laboratory session.

Answers to Pre-Lab Quiz (pp. 635–636)

1. b, gonads
2. scrotum
3. c, epididymis
4. a, seminal fluid
5. interstitial endocrine cells

6. b, progesterone
7. clitoris
8. c, uterus
9. endometrium
10. ovulation

Answers to Activity Questions

Activity 2: Penis (p. 639)

The epithelium is stratified columnar epithelium. Its basic function is protection of underlying tissues.

Activity 4: Epididymis (p. 640)

The smooth muscle rhythmically contracts under sympathetic stimulation during emission and ejaculation. The peristaltic movements propel sperm/seminal fluid from the epididymis through the ductus (vas) deferens, ejaculatory duct, and urethra.

Activity 6: Wall of the Uterus (p. 643)

During the birth process the myometrium contracts, pushing the baby toward the cervical canal, and exerting pressure on the amniotic sac.

Anatomy of the Reproductive System

Gross Anatomy of the Human Male Reproductive System

1. List the two principal functions of the testis. *Sperm production*

   and *testosterone production*

2. Identify all indicated structures or portions of structures on the diagrammatic view of the male reproductive system below.

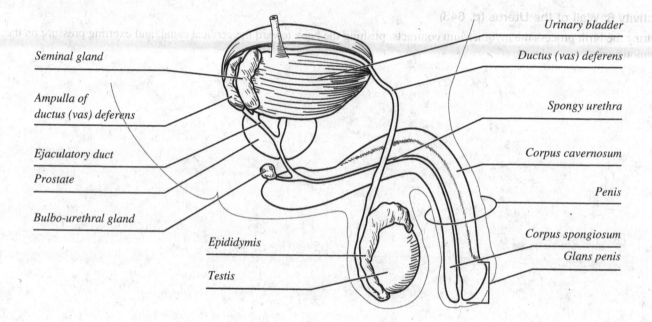

Seminal gland

Ampulla of
ductus (vas) deferens

Ejaculatory duct

Prostate

Bulbo-urethral gland

Epididymis

Testis

Urinary bladder

Ductus (vas) deferens

Spongy urethra

Corpus cavernosum

Penis

Corpus spongiosum

Glans penis

3. Why are the testes located in the scrotum rather than inside the ventral body cavity?

   Testes are located in the scrotum to provide a slightly cooler temperature necessary for sperm production.

Why This Matters

4. A screening tool for benign prostatic hyperplasia and prostate cancer includes palpation of the prostate. Explain how this is accomplished. *The prostate can be palpated through the anterior wall of the rectum.*

5. Would you expect a male with benign prostatic hyperplasia to have difficulty with ejaculation? Why or why not?

   Yes, this would be expected because an enlarged prostate could constrict the ducts that run through the prostate, the ejaculatory duct,

   and the urethra, preventing the passage of semen and urine.

6. Match the terms in column B to the descriptive statements in column A.

Column A	Column B
e; penis 1. copulatory organ/penetrating device	a. bulbo-urethral glands
b; ductus (vas) deferens 2. muscular passageway conveying sperm to the ejaculatory duct; in the spermatic cord	b. ductus (vas) deferens
k; spongy urethra 3. distal urethra that transports both sperm and urine	c. epididymis
c; epididymis 4. sperm maturation site	d. intermediate part of the urethra
i; scrotum 5. location of the testis in adult males	e. penis
f; prepuce 6. loose fold of skin encircling the glans penis	f. prepuce
d; intermediate part of the urethra 7. portion of the urethra that is located in the urogenital diaphragm	g. prostate
g; prostate 8. empties a secretion into the prostatic urethra	h. prostatic urethra
a; bulbo-urethral glands 9. empties a secretion into the intermediate part of the urethra	i. scrotum
	j. seminal gland
	k. spongy urethra

7. Describe the composition of semen, and name all structures contributing to its formation. *Sperm and the secretions of the prostate, the seminal glands (also containing fructose), and the bulbo-urethral glands*

8. Of what importance is the fact that seminal fluid is alkaline? *It buffers the sperm against the acidic environment of the female reproductive tract.*

9. What structures compose the spermatic cord? *Connective tissue sheath (extension of abdominal fascia), ductus deferens, blood vessels, nerves, and lymph vessels*

Where is it located? *Passes from the scrotal sac through the inguinal canal into the abdominal cavity*

10. Using the following terms, trace the pathway of sperm from the testes to the urethra: rete testis, epididymis, seminiferous tubule, ductus deferens. *seminiferous tubule* → *rete testis* → *epididymis* → *ductus deferens*

Gross Anatomy of the Human Female Reproductive System

11. Name the structures composing the external genitalia, or vulva, of the female. *Mons pubis, labia majora and minora, clitoris,*

vaginal and urethral openings, hymen, and greater vestibular glands

12. On the diagram below of a frontal section of a portion of the female reproductive system, identify all indicated structures.

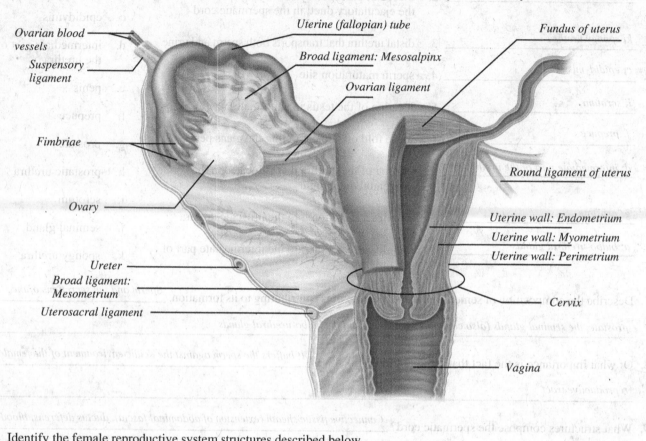

Ovarian blood vessels

Suspensory ligament

Fimbriae

Ovary

Ureter

Broad ligament: Mesometrium

Uterosacral ligament

Uterine (fallopian) tube

Broad ligament: Mesosalpinx

Ovarian ligament

Fundus of uterus

Round ligament of uterus

Uterine wall: Endometrium

Uterine wall: Myometrium

Uterine wall: Perimetrium

Cervix

Vagina

13. Identify the female reproductive system structures described below.

uterus	1.	site of fetal development
vagina	2.	copulatory canal
uterine tube	3.	egg typically fertilized here
clitoris	4.	becomes erect during sexual excitement
uterine tube	5.	duct extending from ovaries to the uterus
hymen	6.	partially closes the vaginal opening; a membrane
ovary	7.	produces oocytes, estrogens, and progesterone
fimbriae	8.	fingerlike ends of the uterine tube

14. Do any sperm enter the pelvic cavity of the female? Why or why not? _Yes. The uterine tube opens to the pelvic cavity._

15. What is an ectopic pregnancy, and how can it happen? _Implantation of the embryo in a site other than the uterus. It most often_ _occurs in a uterine tube, especially if the tube is partially blocked; it may also occur in the peritoneal cavity if an egg is fertilized there._

16. Put the following vestibular-perineal structures in their proper order from the anterior to the posterior aspect: vaginal orifice, anus, external urethral opening, and clitoris. Anterior limit: _clitoris_ → _urethral opening_ → _vaginal orifice_ → _anus_

17. Assume that a couple has just consummated the sex act and that the sperm have been deposited in the vagina. Trace the pathway of the sperm through the female reproductive tract. _vagina → cervix → uterus → uterine tube → peritoneal cavity_

18. Define *ovulation*. _Ejection of an egg (actually an oocyte) from the ovary_

Microscopic Anatomy of Selected Male and Female Reproductive Organs

19. The testis is divided into a number of lobes by connective tissue. Each of these lobes contains one to four _seminiferous_ _tubules_, which converge to empty sperm into another set of tubules called the _rete testis_.

20. What is the function of the cavernous bodies seen in the penis? _This tissue can become engorged with blood, thus making_ _the penis stiff and more effective as a penetrating device._

21. Name the three layers of the uterine wall from the inside out.

Endometrium, _Myometrium_, _Perimetrium_

Which of these is sloughed during menses? _Endometrium_

Which contracts during childbirth? _Myometrium_

22. Describe the epithelium found in the uterine tube. _A ciliated secretory epithelium lines the uterine tube_

23. Describe the arrangement of the layers of smooth muscle in the seminal gland. _Two layers of smooth muscle surround the_ _seminal gland, an inner circular layer and an outer longitudinal layer._

24. What is the function of the stereocilia exhibited by the epithelial cells of the mucosa of the epididymis? _They absorb excess_ _fluid and provide nutrients to the maturing sperm._

25. On the diagram showing the sagittal section of the human testis, correctly identify all structures provided with leader lines.

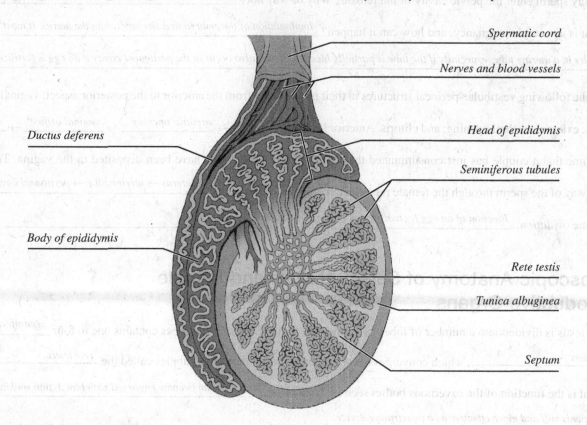

Spermatic cord

Nerves and blood vessels

Head of epididymis

Seminiferous tubules

Ductus deferens

Body of epididymis

Rete testis

Tunica albuginea

Septum

The Mammary Glands

26. Match the key term with the correct description.

		Key:
a; alveoli	glands that produce milk during lactation	a. alveoli
e; lobule	subdivision of mammary lobes that contains alveoli	b. areola
d; lactiferous sinus	enlarged storage chamber for milk	c. lactiferous duct
c; lactiferous duct	duct connecting alveoli to the storage chambers	d. lactiferous sinus
b; areola	pigmented area surrounding the nipple	e. lobule
f; nipple	releases milk to the outside	f. nipple

27. Using the key terms, correctly identify breast structures.

Key:
  a. adipose tissue

      b. areola

      c. lactiferous duct

      d. lactiferous sinus

      e. lobule containing alveoli

      f. nipple

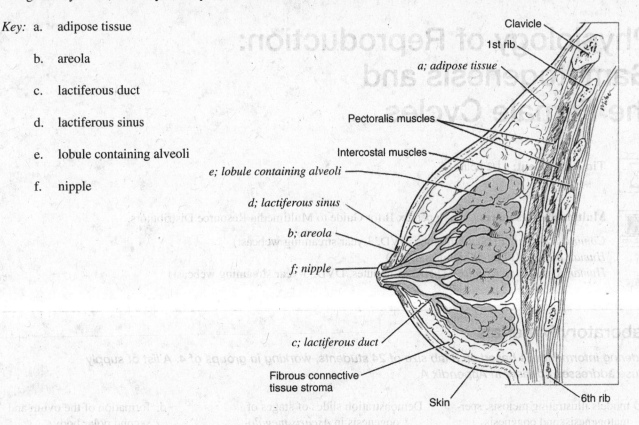

Clavicle
1st rib
a; adipose tissue
Pectoralis muscles
Intercostal muscles
e; lobule containing alveoli
d; lactiferous sinus
b; areola
f; nipple
c; lactiferous duct
Fibrous connective tissue stroma
Skin
6th rib

28. Describe the procedure for self-examination of the breasts. (Men are not exempt from breast cancer, you know!)

While lying down, place one arm behind your head and with the three middle fingers of the other arm palpate the breast in a circular

motion, pressing first lightly, then with increasing pressure. Check the entire breast systematically using a vertical pattern from superior

lateral to inferior medial regions.

43 EXERCISE

Physiology of Reproduction: Gametogenesis and the Female Cycles

Time Allotment: $1^{1}/2$ hours.

Multimedia Resources: See Appendix B for Guide to Multimedia Resource Distributors.

Coming Together (FHS: 28 minutes, DVD, 3-year streaming webcast)
Human Biology (FHS: 58 minutes, DVD)
Human Reproductive Biology (FHS: 35 minutes, DVD, 3-year streaming webcast)

Laboratory Materials

Ordering information is based on a lab size of 24 students, working in groups of 4. A list of supply house addresses appears in Appendix A.

3-D models illustrating meiosis, spermatogenesis, and oogenesis

12 sets of "pop-it" beads in two colors with magnetic centromeres

24 compound microscopes, lens paper, lens cleaning solution

24 prepared slides of testis, ovary, human sperm, uterine endometrium (showing menses, proliferative, and secretory stages)

Demonstration slides of stages of oogenesis in *Ascaris megalocephala* set up on microscopes to show:

a. primary oocyte with fertilization membrane, sperm nucleus, and aligned tetrads apparent
b. formation of first polar body
c. secondary oocyte with dyads aligned

d. formation of the ovum and second polar body
e. fusion of the male and female pronuclei to form the fertilized egg

Advance Preparation

1. Set out models illustrating meiosis, spermatogenesis, and oogenesis.

2. Set out prepared slides of testis, ovary, human sperm, and uterine endometrium (showing menses, proliferative, and secretory stages). Set out lens paper and immersion oil. Have compound microscopes available.

3. Set up five microscopes in a demonstration area with the following slides of stages of oogenesis in *Ascaris megalocephala* (*Parascaris equorum*—Triarch): (1) primary oocyte with fertilization membrane, sperm nucleus, and aligned tetrads apparent; (2) formation of first polar body; (3) secondary oocyte with dyads aligned; (4) formation of ovum and second polar body; and (5) fusion of the male and female pronuclei to form the fertilized egg.

4. Set out sets of colored "pop-it" beads (two colors) and magnetic centromeres (in Chromosome Simulation Lab Activity from WARD'S).

Comments and Pitfalls

1. If students have trouble counting chromosomes, have them count centromeres.

2. Note that in *Ascaris*, meiosis does not begin until the sperm has penetrated the primary ooctye, whereas in humans, meiosis I occurs before sperm penetration. See the section Demonstration of Oogenesis in *Ascaris* (Optional) in the lab manual.

Answers to Pre-Lab Quiz (pp. 651–652)

1. b, 23
2. d, four haploid daughter cells
3. tetrad, meiosis
4. c, sustenocytes
5. acrosome
6. follicle
7. c, primary follicle
8. true
9. corpus luteum
10. b, menstrual

Answers to Activity Questions

Activity 2: Examining Events of Spermatogenesis (pp. 653–654)

3. Tetrads may be visible. Evidence of crossing over may be difficult to see, but the tetrads may appear to have chromatids wrapped around each other. Tetrads are in primary spermatocytes, which are closer to the spermatogonia than to the lumen.

Physiology of Reproduction: Gametogenesis and the Female Cycles

Meiosis

1. The following statements refer to events occurring during mitosis and/or meiosis. For each statement, decide whether the event occurs in (a) mitosis only, (b) meiosis only, or (c) both mitosis and meiosis.

   _c_   1. dyads are visible

   _b_   2. tetrads are visible

   _a_   3. product is two diploid daughter cells genetically identical to the mother cell

   _b_   4. product is four haploid daughter cells quantitatively and qualitatively different from the mother cell

   _c_   5. involves the phases prophase, metaphase, anaphase, and telophase

   _a_   6. occurs throughout the body

   _b_   7. occurs only in the ovaries and testes

   _a_   8. provides cells for growth and repair

   _b_   9. homologues synapse; crossovers are seen

   _c_   10. chromosomes are replicated before the division process begins

   _b_   11. provides cells for perpetuation of the species

   _b_   12. consists of two consecutive nuclear divisions, without chromosomal replication occurring before the second division

2. Describe the process of synapsis. _The homologous chromosomes become closely aligned along their entire length._

3. How does crossover introduce variability in the daughter cells? _Where crossovers occur, chromosome breakage occurs and parts are exchanged. This results in chromosomes with different parental contributions._

4. Define homologous chromosomes. _Chromosomes that carry genes for the same traits (one = paternal chromosome; the other = maternal chromosome)_

Spermatogenesis

5. The cell types seen in the seminiferous tubules are listed in the key. Match the correct cell type or types with the descriptions given below.

Key: a. primary spermatocyte   c. spermatogonium   e. spermatid
     b. secondary spermatocyte   d. sustentocyte   f. sperm

<u> *c* </u> 1. primitive stem cell   <u> *e* </u> 4. products of meiosis II

<u>*b, e, f*</u> 2. haploid (3 responses)   <u> *f* </u> 5. product of spermiogenesis

<u> *d* </u> 3. provides nutrients to   <u> *b* </u> 6. product of meiosis I
            developing sperm

6. Why are spermatids not considered functional gametes? *They have too much superfluous cytoplasm and are nonmotile.*

7. Differentiate *spermatogenesis* from *spermiogenesis*. *Spermatogenesis is the formation of haploid gametes by the male. During*

spermiogenesis, excessive spermatid cytoplasm is sloughed off to form a motile functional sperm.

8. Draw a sperm below, and identify the acrosome, head, midpiece, and tail. Then beside each label, note the composition and function of each of these sperm structures.

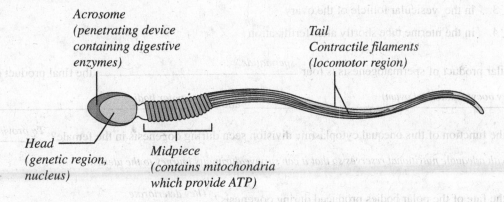

Acrosome
*(penetrating device
containing digestive
enzymes)*

Tail
*Contractile filaments
(locomotor region)*

Head
*(genetic region,
nucleus)*

Midpiece
*(contains mitochondria
which provide ATP)*

9. The life span of a sperm is very short. What anatomical characteristics might lead you to suspect this even if you don't know

its life span? *The sperm has little or no cytoplasm in which to store nutrients.*

Oogenesis, the Ovarian Cycle, and the Menstrual Cycle

10. The sequence of events leading to germ cell formation in the female begins during fetal development. By the time the child

is born, all viable oogonia have been converted to *primary oocytes*.

In view of this fact, how does the total germ cell potential of the female compare to that of the male? *Females produce fewer*

germ cells than males, and the total number produced is believed to be predetermined.

11. The female gametes develop in structures called *follicles*. What is a follicle? _A structure consisting of a capsule of follicle (or granulosa) cells that encloses a developing gamete (oocyte)_

How are primary and vesicular follicles anatomically different? _The primary follicle has one or a small number of layers of follicle cells surrounding the oocyte; the vesicular follicle has a large antrum containing fluid produced by the granulosa cells, and the developing oocyte, surrounded by several layers of granulosa cells, is pushed to one side._

What is a corpus luteum? _Glandular ovarian structure that produces progesterone. The ruptured vesicular follicle is converted to a corpus luteum._

12. What are the hormones produced by the corpus luteum? _Progesterone and estrogen_

13. Use the key to identify the cell type you would expect to find in the following structures. The items in the key may be used more than once.

Key: a. oogonium   b. primary oocyte   c. secondary oocyte   d. ovum

_b_ 1. forming part of the primary follicle in the ovary

_c_ 2. in the uterine tube before fertilization

_c_ 3. in the vesicular follicle of the ovary

_d_ 4. in the uterine tube shortly after fertilization

14. The cellular product of spermatogenesis is four _spermatids_; the final product of oogenesis is one _secondary oocyte (potential ovum)_ and three _polar bodies_.

What is the function of this unequal cytoplasmic division seen during oogenesis in the female? _To provide the functional gamete with adequate nutritional reserves so that it can survive during its journey to the uterus_

What is the fate of the polar bodies produced during oogenesis? _They deteriorate._

Why? _They lack sustaining cytoplasm with nutrient reserves._

Why This Matters

15. Which layer of the endometrium, the functional or basal layer, would you expect to be displaced with endometriosis?

Why? _The functional layer would be displaced since this is the layer that is shed with menstruation._

16. Explain the path that endometrial cells would travel to reach the peritoneum when retrograde menstruation occurs.

The endometrium would travel from the uterus through the uterine tube which is open to the pelvic cavity and would therefore reach the peritoneum.

17. For each statement below dealing with plasma hormone levels during the female ovarian and menstrual cycles, decide whether the condition in column A is usually (a) greater than, (b) less than, or (c) essentially equal to the condition in column B.

	Column A	Column B
_b_ 1.	amount of LH in the blood during menstruation	amount of LH in the blood at ovulation
_a_ 2.	amount of FSH in the blood on day 6 of the cycle	amount of FSH in the blood on day 20 of the cycle
_b_ 3.	amount of estrogen in the blood during menstruation	amount of estrogen in the blood at ovulation
_b_ 4.	amount of progesterone in the blood on day 14	amount of progesterone in the blood on day 23
_a_ 5.	amount of estrogen in the blood on day 10	amount of progesterone in the blood on day 10

18. What uterine tissue undergoes dramatic changes during the menstrual cycle? _Endometrium_

19. When during the female menstrual cycle would fertilization be unlikely? Explain why. _Any time but the three-day interval_

   (days 14–16) around ovulation. (Twenty-eight-day cycle is assumed.)

20. Assume that a woman could be an "on demand" ovulator like the rabbit, in which copulation stimulates the hypothalamic-pituitary-gonadal axis and causes LH release, and that an oocyte was ovulated and fertilized on day 26 of her 28-day cycle. Why would a successful pregnancy be unlikely at this time?

   The hormonal production of the ovary has ceased; the endometrium is beyond the receptive stage and is ready to slough off in menses.

21. The menstrual cycle depends on events within the female ovary. The stages of the menstrual cycle are listed below. For each, note its approximate time span and the related events in the uterus; and then to the right, record the ovarian events occurring simultaneously. Pay particular attention to hormonal events.

Menstrual cycle stage	Uterine events	Ovarian events
Menstruation	Days 1–5. Endometrium is sloughing off.	Primary follicle begins to grow.
Proliferative	Days 6–14. Endometrium repaired, glands and blood vessels proliferate. Endometrium thickens.	Follicular growth continues and vesicular follicle(s) produced. Estrogen secreted and peaks at day 14. Ovulation occurs on the 14th day.
Secretory	Days 15–28. Vascular supply increases and glands begin secretory activity.	Ruptured follicle is converted to a corpus luteum, which begins to produce progesterone (and some estrogen). Peaks at day 23 and then begins to decline.

Survey of Embryonic Development

 Time Allotment: 2 hours.

 Multimedia Resources: See Appendix B for Guide to Multimedia Resource Distributors.

A Human Life Emerges (FHS: 33 minutes, DVD, 3-year streaming webcast)
A New Life (FHS: 28 minutes, DVD)
Human Reproductive Biology (FHS: 35 minutes, DVD, 3-year streaming webcast)
Into the World (FHS: 28 minutes, DVD)
Life's Greatest Miracle (CBS: 60 minutes, DVD)

Laboratory Materials

Ordering information is based on a lab size of 24 students, working in groups of 4. A list of supply house addresses appears in Appendix A.

24 compound microscopes, lens paper, lens cleaning solution	Disposable gloves	*Life Before Birth: Normal Fetal Development*, Second Edition,
3-D models of human development	Fresh or formalin-preserved placenta	by Marjorie A. England, 1996,
3-D model of pregnant human torso	24 prepared slides of placenta tissue	Mosby-Wolfe
Dissected pregnant cat, pig, or rat uterus	24 prepared slides of sea urchin de-	
1–2 dissecting kits	velopment (zygote through larval stages)	

Advance Preparation

1. Order *Life Before Birth: Normal Fetal Development,* Second Edition (by Marjorie A. England, 1996, Mosby-Wolfe).

2. Set out lens paper, lens cleaning solution, and slides of sea urchin development (zygote to larval stages) and of a placenta tissue. Have compound microscopes available.

3. Set out models of human development and pregnant human torso.

4. Obtain a fresh or formalin-preserved human placenta from a clinical agency.

5. Set out a pregnant cat, rat, or pig uterus, disposable gloves, safety glasses, and dissecting equipment.

Comments and Pitfalls

1. Students may have difficulty with the questions in the text. Additional reference material (developmental biology or embryology books) might be helpful.

Answers to Pre-Lab Quiz (p. 665)

1. zygote
2. b, fertilization
3. true
4. three
5. c, blastocyst
6. a, ectoderm

7. c, fetus
8. false
9. amnion
10. It provides nutrients and oxygen to the embryo and fetus and removes carbon dioxide.

Answers to Activity Questions

Activity 2: Examining the Stages of Human Development (pp. 666–669)

2. The cleavage process results in large numbers of smaller cells that collectively retain the size of the original zygote.

5. Areas of the brain and the heart appear very early in development.

   Development is rostral to caudal and proximal to distal.

   The vernix caseosa covers the fetus and consists mainly of sebaceous secretions and dead epidermal cells. It may act as a lubricant and protect the growing fetus from chafing injuries.

   Lanugo is a downy coat of fetal hairs that appears at about the fifth month of development and is usually lost at birth or shortly thereafter.

Activity 3: Identifying Fetal Structures (p. 669)

1. The placenta of the pig is diffuse with villi distributed over the surface of the chorion. In the cat, the villi form a belt around the fetus (zonary placenta). The rat has a discoidal placenta similar to the human placenta.

   The umbilical cord connects the placenta to the fetus.

   Amniotic fluid is usually clear and watery.

   Fetal skin is relatively thin. If it is a very young fetus, the skin may be almost transparent.

2. The human placenta is discoidal in shape.

   Implantation usually occurs in the upper part of the uterus.

   One problem that may occur with lower implantation is placenta previa. The placenta may irritate the cervix, resulting in contractions and spontaneous abortion.

Activity 4: Studying Placental Structure (p. 670)

1. The fetal side is the smooth side. The ragged side was united with maternal tissue.

   The umbilical vein delivers relatively oxygen-rich blood to the fetus from the placenta.

   The umbilical arteries carry blood from the fetus to the placenta. If any fetal membranes are still attached, one may be the amnion.

Survey of Embryonic Development

Developmental Stages of Sea Urchins and Humans

1. Define *zygote*. <u>Fertilized egg</u>

2. Describe how you were able to tell by observation when a sea urchin egg was fertilized. <u>*A fertilization membrane is present*</u> <u>*beneath the outer jelly coat.*</u>

3. Use the key choices to identify the embryonic stage or process described below.

Key: a. blastocyst (blastula in sea urchins)   c. fertilization   e. morula

      b. cleavage   d. gastrulation   f. zygote

   <u>c</u>   1. process of male and female pronuclei fusion

   <u>e</u>   2. solid ball of embryonic cells

   <u>b</u>   3. process of rapid mitotic cell division without intervening growth periods

   <u>f</u>   4. cell resulting from combination of egg and sperm

   <u>d</u>   5. process involving cell rearrangements to form the three primary germ layers

   <u>a</u>   6. embryonic stage in which the embryo consists of a hollow ball of cells

4. What is the importance of cleavage in embryonic development? <u>*It provides a large number of smaller cells for morphogenesis.*</u>

How is cleavage different from mitotic cell division, which occurs later in life? <u>*During cleavage there are no intervening*</u> <u>*growth periods between the successive divisions. Therefore the cells get smaller and smaller, but the embryonic mass remains essentially*</u> <u>*the same size.*</u>

5. The cells of the human blastocyst have various fates. Which blastocyst derivatives have the following fates?

<u>*embryonic disc*</u>   1. forms the embryo proper

<u>*trophoblast*</u>   2. becomes the extraembryonic membrane called the chorion and cooperates with uterine tissues to form the placenta

<u>*inner cell mass*</u>   3. produces the amnion, yolk sac, and allantois

<u>*yolk sac*</u>   4. produces the primordial germ cells

<u>*allantois*</u>   5. an embryonic membrane that provides the structural basis for the umbilical cord

6. Using the letters on the diagram, correctly identify each of the following maternal or embryonic structures.

_j_ amnion   _a_ decidua capsularis   _e_ mesoderm

_g_ chorion   _d_ ectoderm   _c_ uterine cavity

_h_ chorionic villi   _f_ endoderm

_b_ decidua basalis   _i_ forming umbilical cord

Embryo

7. Explain the process and importance of gastrulation. _During gastrulation the embryonic cells move, migrate, and rearrange, forming the three primary germ layers of the embryo._

8. What is the function of the amnion and the amniotic fluid? _The amnion is a fluid-filled sac that surrounds the embryo. The fluid buffers or protects the embryo from physical trauma and prevents adhesion formation during rapid growth._

9. Describe the process of implantation, noting the role of the trophoblast cells. _The trophoblast cells overlying the inner cell mass adhere to the endometrium. The trophoblast cells then secrete enzymes that erode the endometrial lining to reach the vascular supply beneath it._

10. How many days after fertilization is implantation generally completed? _12–14_ What event in the female menstrual cycle ordinarily occurs just about this time if implantation does *not* occur? _Menstruation, because this is usually the 14th day after ovulation_

11. Referring to the illustrations and text of *Life Before Birth: Normal Fetal Development*, answer the following:

Which two organ systems are extensively developed in the *very young* embryo?

Nervous system and *circulatory system*

Describe the direction of development by circling the correct descriptions below:

(proximal-distal)   distal-proximal   caudal-rostral   (rostral-caudal)

Does body control during infancy develop in the same directions? Think! Can an infant pick up a common pin (pincer grasp) or wave his arms earlier? Is arm-hand or leg-foot control achieved earlier?

Yes. In the limbs, muscle control follows the proximal-distal pattern; arm muscle control (waving) develops before fine finger movements

(picking up small objects). Arm-hand control also occurs before leg-foot control, mimicking the rostral-caudal developmental pattern.

12. Note whether each of the following organs or organ systems develops from the (a) ectoderm, (b) endoderm, or (c) mesoderm.

c 1. skeletal muscle	*b* 4. respiratory mucosa	*a* 7. nervous system
c 2. skeleton	*c* 5. circulatory system	*c* 8. serous membrane
b 3. lining of the GI tract	*a* 6. epidermis of skin	*b* 9. liver, pancreas

In Utero Development

13. Make the following comparisons between a human and the dissected structures of another pregnant mammal.

Comparison object	Human	Dissected animal
Shape of the placenta	*Disc-shaped*	*(depends on animal)*
Shape of the uterus	*Pear-shaped*	*Y-shaped*

14. Where in the human uterus do implantation and placentation ordinarily occur? *High in the uterus*

15. Describe the function(s) of the placenta. *The placenta provides nutrients and oxygen to the fetus, removes fetal wastes, and produces*

the hormones of pregnancy.

16. Which two embryonic membranes has the placenta more or less "put out of business"? *Yolk sac and allantois*

17. When does the human embryo come to be called a fetus? *Ninth week of development*

18. What is the usual and most desirable fetal position in utero? *Head down*

Why is this the most desirable position? *The largest fetal dimension is the skull. Therefore, if the skull is used as a wedge, the rest*

of the body is delivered easily. Also, if difficulties are encountered, the baby can be suctioned and given oxygen even before delivery is

completed.

Gross and Microscopic Anatomy of the Placenta

19. Describe fully the gross structure of the human placenta as observed in the laboratory. *It is a blood-rich organ that is smooth on*

the side from which the umbilical cord issues and torn, rough, and bloody on the side that was united with maternal tissues.

20. What is the tissue origin of the placenta: fetal, maternal, or both? *Both*

21. What placental barriers must be crossed to exchange materials? *The membranes of the villi and capillary walls of the fetal*

vascular supply

45 EXERCISE

Principles of Heredity

Time Allotment: 2 hours+ with gel electrophoresis and if Punnett squares are done outside of lab.

Multimedia Resources: See Appendix B for Guide to Multimedia Resource Distributors.

Genetics (FHS: 23 minutes, DVD)
Genetics: A Popular Guide to the Principles of Human Heredity (FHS: DVD, 3-year streaming webcast)
Genetic Discoveries, Disorders, and Mutations (26 minutes)
Practical Applications and the Risks of Genetic Science (24 minutes)
Understanding the Basic Concepts of Genetics (30 minutes)
Reproduction: Shares in the Future (FHS: 26 minutes, DVD, 3-year streaming webcast)

Solutions:

Agarose gel, 1.2%
Weigh out 0.9 gram of agarose and add 1X Tris-Borate/EDTA buffer (ICN) to a volume of 75 milliliters. Boil on a hot plate or in a microwave oven until the agarose melts, stirring periodically.

Bleach Solution, 10%
Measure out 100 milliliters of household bleach. Add water to a final volume of 1 liter.

Laboratory Materials

Ordering information is based on a lab size of 24 students, working in groups of 4. A list of supply house addresses appears in Appendix A.

12 pennies
24 PTC (phenylthiocarbamide) taste strips
24 sodium benzoate taste strips
Chart drawn on chalkboard or white-board for tabulation of class results

Activity 5: Blood Typing

Anti-A and anti-B blood typing sera
Sterile lancets
Cotton
Alcohol swabs
24 clean microscope slides
Toothpicks

24 wax markers
2 large beakers of 10% bleach
Disposable autoclave bag

Activity 6: Hemoglobin Phenotyping

Disposable gloves
6 plastic baggies
Hemoglobin samples dissolved in TBE solubilizing buffer with bromophenol blue: HbA, HbS, HbA-HbS mixed solution, and unknown samples of each
6 electrophoresis units and power supplies

6 metric rulers
6 1.2% agarose gels
1X TBE (Tris-Borate/EDTA) buffer pH 8.4
Coomassie blue protein stain solution
Coomassie blue destaining solution
Staining tray
6 100-milliliter graduated cylinders
Micropipettes or variable automicropi-pette with tips
Distilled water
6 marking pens
Safety goggles (student-provided)

Advance Preparation

1. For each student set out PTC taste strips (Carolina), sodium benzoate taste strips (Carolina), pennies, wax markers, lancets, cotton, alcohol swabs, and toothpicks and clean microscope slides, or blood mixing sticks and test cards (Carolina).

2. Set out anti-A and anti-B blood typing sera, beakers of *10% bleach solution*, and a disposable autoclave bag.

3. Prepare a chart on the board for tabulation of class data.

4. Preparations for agarose gel electrophoresis:

    a. Prepare the casting tray. Place a clean glass slide into the gel casting tray and seal both ends of the tray with duct tape. Be sure the tray is tightly sealed.

    b. Prepare four gels. Pour 15 milliliters of the melted *1.2% agarose solution* onto the glass slide in the casting tray. Insert the well comb into the slots on the casting tray, and press down. Cool the gel for about 15 minutes and then carefully remove the tape and lift the comb straight up out of the gel. To store for later use, leave the comb in place, wrap the gel with comb in plastic wrap or a baggie, and refrigerate.

    c. Prepare the sample buffer. The hemoglobin samples should be prepared as 10%–20% solutions in TBE solubilization buffer with bromophenol blue (ICN). HbA and HbS can be purchased from Sigma. Solutions can be mixed to make a heterozygous sample. Label the samples: HbA as A, HBS as S, and HbA +HbS as AS. Provide unknown samples of each of the above.

5. Set out gel electrophoresis equipment, power supplies, micropipettes, or variable automatic micropipettes (2–20 microliters) with tips, and 1.2% agarose gels.

6. Set out Coomassie blue stain (Carolina), staining tray, destaining solution (Carolina), and plastic baggies.

7. Set out hemoglobin samples, TBE buffer pH 8.4, 100-milliliter graduated cylinders, millimeter rulers, goggles, and disposable gloves.

Comments and Pitfalls

1. Some students will have difficulty with the Punnett squares. It might be best to have these as an out-of-class assignment, and go over the solutions with the class.

2. Using Phenotype to Determine Genotype (Activity 5) is usually fun for the students and provides material for them to construct a genetic family tree.

3. Practice using micropipettes to fill wells in the agarose gel.

Answers to Pre-Lab Quiz (p. 675)

1. alleles
2. false
3. d, recessive
4. phenotype
5. c, Punnett square
6. a, incomplete dominance
7. Y
8. true
9. false
10. true

Answers to Activity Questions

Activity 1: Working Out Crosses Involving Dominant and Recessive Genes (pp. 676–677)

1. 50% *Tt*, 50% *tt*; 50% tall, 50% dwarf
2. 25% *TT*, 50% *Tt*, 25% *tt*; 75% tall, 25% dwarf
3. 50% *TT*, 50% *Tt*; 100% tall, 0% dwarf

Activity 2: Working Out Crosses Involving Incomplete Dominance (p. 677)

1. a. 100% *Rr*; 100% pink

   b. 50% *Rr*, 50% rr; 50% pink, 50% white

   c. 25% *RR*, 50% *Rr*, 25% *rr*; 25% red, 50% pink, 25% white

2. a. 100% *Ss*; 100% sickle cell trait

   b. 25% *SS*, 50% *Ss*, 25% *ss*; 25% normal hemoglobin, 50% sickle cell trait, 25% sickle cell anemia

   c. 50% *Ss*, 50% *ss*; 50% sickle cell trait, 50% sickle cell anemia

Activity 3: Working Out Crosses Involving Sex-Linked Inheritance (p. 678)

1. 50% will be color-blind.

   50% of the females and 50% of the males will be color-blind.

   25% of the individuals (50% of the females) will be carriers.

   The carriers are females.

2. 50% of the males, 0% of the females.

   50% neither exhibit nor carry the allele for hemophilia.

   25% of the individuals (50% of the females) will be carriers. The carriers are female.

Activity 4: Exploring Probability (p. 679)

1. b. The tosses are independent and do not influence each other.

   c. The probability of two heads is 25%; one head and one tail, 50%; and two tails, 25%.

2. The probability of a male is 50%; the probability of a female is 50%.

3. Dad's chances are 1/512 or 0.19%.

Answers to Group Challenge: Odd Phenotype Out (p. 682)

1. Which is the "odd phenotype"?	Why is it the odd one out?
Freckles Widow's peak (Sickle cell trait) Sodium benzoate "taster"	Sickle cell trait is the odd one out because it is not due to dominant-recessive inheritance. It is a result of incomplete dominance. An individual with sickle cell trait could not be homozygous. The other three phenotypes could be heterozygous or homozygous dominant.
2. Which is the "odd phenotype"?	Why is it the odd one out?
Blaze (Type AB blood) PTC "taster" Widow's peak	Type AB blood is the odd one out because the other phenotypes have only one allele expressed. Type AB blood has two alleles expressed in the same phenotype.
3. Which is the "odd phenotype"?	Why is it the odd one out?
No proximal finger hair Straight hairline (Color blindness) Sodium benzoate "nontaster"	Color blindness is the odd one out because the other phenotypes have two recessive alleles. Also, the other phenotypes are somatic characteristics carried on autosomes, not X-linked.
4. Which is the "odd phenotype"?	Why is it the odd one out?
Dimpled cheek (Straight hairline) Freckles Blaze	Straight hairline is the odd one out because it does not have at least one dominant allele. It has two recessive alleles.

Principles of Heredity

Introduction to the Language of Genetics

1. Match the key choices with the definitions given below.

Key:

a. alleles
b. autosomes
c. dominant
d. genotype
e. heterozygous
f. homozygous
g. phenotype
h. recessive
i. sex chromosomes

d; genotype	1.	actual genetic makeup
i; sex chromosomes	2.	chromosomes determining maleness/femaleness
f; homozygous	3.	situation in which an individual has identical alleles for a particular trait
h; recessive	4.	genes not expressed unless they are present in homozygous condition
g; phenotype	5.	expression of a genetic trait
e; heterozygous	6.	situation in which an individual has different alleles making up his or her genotype for a particular trait
a; alleles	7.	genes for the same trait that may have different expressions
b; autosomes	8.	chromosomes regulating most body characteristics
c; dominant	9.	the more potent gene allele; masks the expression of the less potent allele

Dominant-Recessive Inheritance

2. In humans, farsightedness is inherited by possession of a dominant allele *(A)*. If a man who is homozygous for normal vision *(aa)* marries a woman who is heterozygous for farsightedness *(Aa)*, what percentage of their children would be expected to be farsighted? _50_ %

3. A metabolic disorder called phenylketonuria (PKU) is due to an abnormal recessive gene *(p)*. Only homozygous recessive individuals exhibit this disorder. What percentage of the offspring will be anticipated to have PKU if the parents are *Pp* and *pp*? _50_ %

4. A man obtained 32 spotted and 10 solid-color rabbits from a mating of two spotted rabbits.

Which trait is dominant? _Spotted_____ Recessive?

_Solid-color_____

If the dominant allele is *S,* what is the probable genotype of the rabbit parents? _Ss_ × _Ss_

5. Assume that the allele controlling brown eyes (B) is dominant over that controlling blue eyes (b) in human beings. (In actuality, eye color in humans is an example of polygenic inheritance, which is much more complex than this.) A blue-eyed man marries a brown-eyed woman, and they have six children, all brown-eyed. What is the most likely genotype of the father?

_bb_____ Of the mother? _BB_____ If the seventh child had *blue* eyes, given this new information what could you conclude about the parents' genotypes?

Female is Bb; male is bb.
_____

Incomplete Dominance

6. Tail length on a bobcat is controlled by incomplete dominance. The alleles are *T* for normal tail length and *t* for tail-less.

   What name could/would you give to the tails of heterozygous *(Tt)* bobcats? *Bobtail*_____

   How would their tail length compare with that of *TT* or *tt* bobcats? *Intermediate in length*_____

7. If curly-haired individuals are genotypically *CC*, straight-haired individuals are *cc*, and wavy-haired individuals are heterozygotes *(Cc)*, what percentage of the various phenotypes would be anticipated from a cross between a *CC* woman and a *cc* man?

   _0_____ % curly   _100_____ % wavy   _0_____ % straight

Sex-Linked Inheritance

8. What does it mean when someone says a particular characteristic is sex-linked? *It is carried on the female X (sex)*

   *chromosome.*_____

9. You are a male, and you have been told that hemophilia "runs in your genes." Whose ancestors, your mother's or your

   father's, should you investigate? *Mother's*_____ Why? *Males can receive the X*

   *chromosome only from their mothers; the father's contribution is always Y.*_____

10. An $X^C X^C$ female marries an $X^c Y$ man. Do a Punnett square for this match.

    What is the probability of producing a color-blind son? _25%_____

    A color-blind daughter? _0%_____

    A daughter who is a carrier for the color-blind allele? _25%_____

	X^C	X^c
X^C	$X^C X^C$	$X^C X^c$
Y	$X^C Y$	$X^c Y$

11. Why are consanguineous marriages (marriages between blood relatives) prohibited in most cultures?

Blood relatives have similar gene pools. Thus, the likelihood of receiving a double dose of recessive genes (many of which are detrimental)

is dramatically increased.

Probability

12. What is the probability of having three daughters in a row? $(1/2 \times 1/2 \times 1/2) = 1/8$ or 12.5%

13. A man and a woman, each of seemingly normal intellect, marry. Although neither is aware of the fact, each is a heterozygote

for the allele for mental retardation. Is the allele for mental retardation dominant or recessive? *Recessive*

What is the probability of their having one mentally retarded child? 25% ($1/4$)

What is the probability that all their children (they plan a family of four) will be mentally retarded? $(1/4 \times 1/4 \times 1/4 \times 1/4) = 1/256$

or 0.39%

Genetic Determination of Selected Human Characteristics

14. Look back at your data to complete this section. For each of the situations described here, determine if an offspring with the
characteristics noted is possible with the parental genotypes listed. Check (✓) the appropriate column.

Parental genotypes	Phenotype of child	Possibility	
		Yes	No
$Ff \times ff$	Freckles	✓	
$dd \times dd$	Dimples		✓
$HH \times Hh$	Proximal finger hair	✓	
$I^A i \times I^B i$	Type O blood	✓	
$I^A I^B \times ii$	Type O blood		✓

15. You have dimples, and you would like to know whether you are homozygous or heterozygous for this trait. You have six brothers
and sisters. By observing your siblings, how could you tell, with some degree of certainty, that you are a heterozygote?

Absence of dimples indicates the homozygous recessive condition. If one or more of your siblings do not have dimples, there was a 50%

chance at your conception that you would be heterozygous for this trait.

Using Agarose Gel Electrophoresis to Identify Hemoglobin Phenotypes

16. Draw the banding patterns you obtained on the figure below.

Sample	Well	Banding pattern
1. A	1.	
2. AS	2.	
3. S	3.	
4. Unknown	4. (student data)	
5. A	5.	
6. AS	6.	
7. S	7.	
8. Unknown	8. (student data)	

17. What is the genotype of sickle cell anemia? _S_   Sickle cell trait? _AS_

18. Why does sickle cell hemoglobin behave differently from normal hemoglobin during agarose gel electrophoresis?

HbS has fewer negative charges than HbA, due to the base substitution of valine for glutamic acid in HbS.

Surface Anatomy Roundup

 Time Allotment: 2 hours for a thorough review.

Laboratory Materials

Ordering information is based on a lab size of 24 students, working in groups of 4. A list of supply house addresses appears in Appendix A.

Articulated skeletons	Washable markers	Stethoscopes
3-D charts and/or models of skeletal muscles	Hand mirrors	Alcohol swabs

Advance Preparation

1. Have articulated skeletons and skeletal muscle charts and models available.
2. Set out washable markers, hand mirrors, stethoscopes, and alcohol swabs.

Comments and Pitfalls

1. Muscles and other landmarks on the posterior aspect of the body trunk are difficult for students to palpate on themselves. If necessary, ask for volunteers (you may wish to select males) to act as subjects.

Answers to Pre-Lab Quiz (pp. 687–688)

1. b, You can relate external surface landmarks to the location of internal organs.
2. palpation
3. c, true scalp
4. d, sternocleidomastoid
5. b, triangle of auscultation
6. true
7. true
8. b, dorsal venous network
9. true
10. a, femoral triangle

Answers to Activity Questions

Activity 1: Palpating Landmarks of the Head (pp. 688–690)

Cranium

3. Scalp wounds bleed profusely. However, because the scalp is so well vascularized, these wounds heal quickly.

301

Activity 2: Palpating Landmarks of the Neck (pp. 690–691)

Triangles of the Neck

2. They result from damage to the cervical plexus and accessory nerve, which supply these skin regions and muscles.

Activity 3: Palpating Landmarks of the Trunk (pp. 692–694)

The Back: Muscles

2. This action draws the scapula anteriorly and enlarges the triangle of auscultation as much as possible.

Activity 5: Palpating Landmarks of the Upper Limb (pp. 696–699)

Forearm and Hand

2. In this fracture, the physician can feel that the styloid process of the radius has moved proximally from its normal position.

NAME _____

LAB TIME/DATE _____

Surface Anatomy Roundup

c _____ 1. A blow to the cheek is most likely to break what superficial bone or bone part? (a) superciliary arches, (b) mastoid process, (c) zygomatic arch, (d) ramus of the mandible

a _____ 2. Rebound tenderness (a) occurs in appendicitis, (b) is whiplash of the neck, (c) is a sore foot from playing basketball, (d) occurs when the larynx falls back into place after swallowing.

b _____ 3. The anatomical snuff box (a) is in the nose, (b) contains the radial styloid process, (c) is defined by tendons of the flexor carpi radialis and palmaris longus, (d) cannot really hold snuff.

d _____ 4. Some landmarks on the body surface can be seen or felt, but others are abstractions that you must construct by drawing imaginary lines. Which of the following pairs of structures is abstract and invisible? (a) umbilicus and costal margin, (b) anterior superior iliac spine and natal cleft, (c) linea alba and linea semilunaris, (d) McBurney's point and midaxillary line, (e) lacrimal fossa and sternocleidomastoid

c _____ 5. Many pelvic organs can be palpated by placing a finger in the rectum or the vagina, but only one pelvic organ is readily palpated through the skin. This is the (a) nonpregnant uterus, (b) prostate, (c) full bladder, (d) ovaries, (e) rectum.

b _____ 6. Contributing to the posterior axillary fold is/are (a) pectoralis major, (b) latissimus dorsi, (c) trapezius, (d) infraspinatus, (e) pectoralis minor, (f) a and e.

c _____ 7. Which of the following is *not* a pulse point? (a) anatomical snuff box, (b) inferior margin of mandible anterior to masseter muscle, (c) center of distal forearm at palmaris longus tendon, (d) medial bicipital furrow on arm, (e) dorsum of foot between the first two metatarsals

b _____ 8. Which pair of ribs inserts on the sternum at the sternal angle? (a) first, (b) second, (c) third, (d) fourth, (e) fifth

d _____ 9. The inferior angle of the scapula is at the same level as the spinous process of which vertebra? (a) C_5, (b) C_7, (c) T_3, (d) T_7, (e) L_4

a _____ 10. An important bony landmark that can be recognized by a distinct dimple in the skin is the (a) posterior superior iliac spine, (b) ulnar styloid process, (c) shaft of the radius, (d) acromion.

a _____ 11. A nurse missed a patient's median cubital vein while trying to withdraw blood and then inserted the needle far too deeply into the cubital fossa. This error could cause any of the following problems, *except* this one: (a) paralysis of the ulnar nerve, (b) paralysis of the median nerve, (c) bruising the insertion tendon of the biceps brachii muscle, (d) blood spurting from the brachial artery.

c _____ 12. Which of these organs is almost impossible to study with surface anatomy techniques? (a) heart, (b) lungs, (c) brain, (d) nose

c _____ 13. A preferred site for inserting an intravenous medication line into a blood vessel is the (a) medial bicipital furrow on arm, (b) external carotid artery, (c) dorsal venous network of hand, (d) popliteal fossa.

a _____ 14. One listens for bowel sounds with a stethoscope placed (a) on the four quadrants of the abdominal wall; (b) in the triangle of auscultation; (c) in the right and left midaxillary line, just superior to the iliac crests; (d) inside the patient's bowels (intestines), on the tip of an endoscope.

d _____ 15. A stab wound in the posterior triangle of the neck could damage any of the following structures *except* the (a) accessory nerve, (b) phrenic nerve, (c) external jugular vein, (d) external carotid artery.

303

Dissection and Identification of Cat Muscles

 Time Allotment: Skin removal: 1 hour. Muscle dissection: 4–6+ hours (depending on detail required).

 Multimedia Resources: See Appendix B for Guide to Multimedia Resource Distributors.

The Anatomy of the Cat (CBS: 85 minutes, DVD)
Cat Dissection (WNS: 46 minutes, DVD)
Practice Anatomy Lab™ 3.0 (PAL) (PE: DVD, website)

 Solutions:

Carboglycerine solution
30 grams fungicide (Benomyl, Sigma-Aldrich)
250 milliliters glycerine
1 liter water
Mix together and store in a closed container.

Laboratory Materials

Ordering information is based on a lab size of 24 students, working in groups of 4. A list of supply house addresses appears in Appendix A.

6–12 preserved double- or triple-injected cats	6–12 name tags and large plastic storage bags	Disposable gloves or protective skin cream
6–12 dissection trays	Paper towels	Embalming fluid
6–12 dissection kits with metric rulers	Safety glasses	Organic debris container

Advance Preparation

1. Order cats well in advance, as they may be in short supply.

2. Make arrangements for appropriate storage, disposal, and cleanup of dissection materials. Check with the Department of Health or the Department of Environmental Protection, or their counterparts, for state regulations. Designate a disposal container for organic debris, set up a dishwashing area with hot soapy water and sponges, and provide lab disinfectant such as Wavicide-01 (Carolina) or 10% bleach solution for washing down the lab benches.

3. Set out disposable gloves (or protective skin cream), safety glasses, dissecting kits, dissection trays, plastic storage bags, paper towels, and name tags.

4. Set out dissection animals (one per group of two to four students).

5. Set out *carboglycerine solution* or small plastic bags to hold embalming fluid.

Comments and Pitfalls

1. Be sure that students understand that the skin is to be removed in one piece.
2. Emphasize the use of the blunt probe as a dissecting instrument, rather than the scalpel. Cut only when everyone in the group agrees that a cut should be made!
3. Cat fur tends to clog the sink drains. Emphasize correct disposal of organic debris.
4. Students often "invent" muscles by tearing tissue apart. Emphasize that they should be separating muscles by breaking through the surrounding connective tissue.
5. Sometimes the dissection animal is in very poor condition, in which case the student should exchange it for a different specimen.
6. To prevent damage to muscles during skinning, separate skin from underlying tissues by inserting a blunt probe into the skin incision in the neck. Continue to use the probe to separate skin from underlying tissues before cutting the skin.

Answers to Activity Questions

Activity 2: Dissecting Neck and Trunk Muscles
Muscles of the Abdominal Wall (p. 709)

2. The external oblique muscles run medially and downward, while the internal oblique muscle fibers run upward and medially. They are not quite perpendicular to each other.

Superficial Muscles of the Shoulder and the Dorsal Trunk and Neck (pp. 709–711)

1. The clavotrapezius appears to originate on the occipital bone. This is similar to a part of the origin of the trapezius muscle in humans. The three cat muscles seem to have the same functions as the human trapezius muscle.
2. In humans the levator scapulae elevates the scapula and bends the neck laterally if the scapula is fixed.
3. The clavodeltoid inserts on the proximal end of the ulna. This muscle is used to flex the lower forelimb in walking.

Activity 3: Dissecting Forelimb Muscles
Muscles of the Lateral Surface (pp. 713–714)

1. The triceps muscle has a similar function in cats and humans.

Muscles of the Medial Surface (pp. 714–715)

1. The biceps brachii has only one head in the cat.

Activity 4: Dissecting Hindlimb Muscles
Posterolateral Hindlimb Muscles (pp. 715–718)

5. In humans the semimembranosus is also medial to and partially obscured by the semitendinosus. The human semimembranosus inserts on the tibia, but not on the femur.

Anteromedial Hindlimb Muscles (pp. 718–721)

2. The origin of the rectus femoris in humans is the anterior inferior iliac spine and just above the acetabulum.
3. The human gracilis muscle has a very similar origin and insertion.

Dissection Review

Many human muscles are modified from those of the cat (or any quadruped) . The following questions refer to these differences.

1. How does the human trapezius muscle differ from the cat's?

   Cat's trapezius is tripartite (clavo-, acromio-, and spino- portions); the human trapezius is a single muscle.

2. How does the deltoid differ?

   Cat has three deltoid muscles, the clavodeltoid, acromiodeltoid, and spinodeltoid. The human has a single deltoid muscle.

3. How does the biceps brachii differ?

   The biceps in the cat has only one head.

4. How do the size and orientation of the human gluteus maximus muscle differ from that in the cat?

   The human gluteus maximus muscle originates on the dorsal ilium, sacrum, and coccyx and inserts on the proximal

   femur and iliotibial tract as it runs inferior laterally; it forms the bulk of buttock mass. The cat gluteus maximus muscle

   originates on the sacrum and inserts on the proximal femur; it is a smaller triangular muscle that runs laterally.

5. Explain these differences between cat and human gluteus maximus muscles in terms of differences in function.

   The large human gluteus maximus muscle is the major extensor of the thigh, most powerful when the thigh is flexed.

   It is generally inactive during standing and walking. It also laterally rotates and abducts the thigh. The cat gluteus

   maximus muscle is much smaller in relation to the size of the cat. Its function is to abduct the thigh.

6. The human rectus abdominis is definitely divided by four transverse tendons (tendinous intersections). These tendons are absent or difficult to identify in the cat. How do these tendons help facilitate the human upright posture?

   These tendons support the abdominal muscular wall so that the viscera are not allowed to become pendulous in the

   upright posture of humans.

7. Match each term in column B to its description in column A.

	Column A	Column B
_a_	1. to separate muscles	a. dissect
_c_	2. to fold back a muscle	b. embalm
_d_	3. to cut through a muscle	c. reflect
_b_	4. to preserve tissue	d. transect

Dissection of Cat Spinal Nerves

 Time Allotment: 1 hour.

 Multimedia Resources: See Appendix B for Guide to Multimedia Resource Distributors.

The Anatomy of the Cat (CBS: 85 minutes, DVD)
Cat Dissection (WNS: 46 minutes, DVD)
Practice Anatomy Lab™ 3.0 (PAL) (PE: DVD, website)

Laboratory Materials

Ordering information is based on a lab size of 24 students, working in groups of 4. A list of supply house addresses appears in Appendix A.

6–12 preserved double- or triple-injected cats	6–12 dissection kits with metric rulers	Disposable gloves
6–12 dissection trays	Paper towels	Embalming fluid
	Safety glasses	Organic debris container

Advance Preparation

1. See Dissection Exercise 1 for setup instructions.
2. If cats were not skinned previously, see instructions in Dissection Exercise 1. Allow extra time for skinning: 1/2 hour to skin 1 forelimb and 1 hindlimb.

Dissection Review

1. From anterior to posterior, put in their proper order the nerves issuing from the brachial plexus (i.e., the median, musculocutaneous, radial, and ulnar nerves).

   Musculocutaneous, radial, median, ulnar

2. Which of the nerves named above serves the cat's forearm extensor muscles? *The radial nerve*

   Which serves the forearm flexors? *The median nerve*

3. Just superior to the gastrocnemius muscle, the sciatic nerve divides into its two main branches, the *tibial* and *common fibular* nerves.

4. What name is given to the cutaneous nerve of the cat's thigh? *The saphenous nerve*

307

Identification of Selected Endocrine Organs of the Cat

 Time Allotment: 1 hour.

 Multimedia Resources: See Appendix B for Guide to Multimedia Resource Distributors.

The Anatomy of the Cat (CBS: 85 minutes, DVD)
Cat Dissection (WNS: 46 minutes, DVD)
Practice Anatomy Lab™ 3.0 (PAL) (PE: DVD, website)

Laboratory Materials

Ordering information is based on a lab size of 24 students, working in groups of 4. A list of supply house addresses appears in Appendix A.

6–12 preserved double- or triple-
    injected cats
6–12 dissection trays
6–12 dissection kits with metric rulers

Paper towels
Disposable gloves
Safety glasses
Embalming fluid

Organic debris container
Bone cutters

Advance Preparation

1. See Dissection Exercise 1 for setup instructions.
2. If cats were not skinned previously, see instructions in Dissection Exercise 1. Allow extra time for skinning. (*Note:* It is not absolutely necessary to skin the cats to do dissection of internal structures.)
3. The thymus gland varies in size from very large, sometimes extending from the superior trachea onto the heart, to almost absent.

Comments and Pitfalls

1. It is possible to leave identification of glands in the dissection animal until later dissections.

Dissection Review

1. How do the locations of the endocrine organs in the cat compare with those in the human?

   They are similar, but in the cat the pancreas is more diffuse and the adrenal glands are medial and separate from,

   rather than superior and attached to, the kidneys.

2. Name two endocrine organs located in the neck region: *Thyroid gland* and *thymus gland*

3. Name three endocrine organs located in the abdominal cavity.

Pancreas, adrenal glands, ovaries in female

4. Given the assumption (not necessarily true) that human beings have more stress than cats, which endocrine organs would you expect to be relatively larger in humans? *The adrenal glands*

5. Cats are smaller animals than humans. Which would you expect to have a (relatively speaking) more active thyroid gland—cats or humans? *Cats* Why? (We know we are asking a lot with this one, but give it a whirl.) *It is a general rule of thumb that basal metabolic rate increases as body size decreases. The effect of an increased surface-to-volume relationship in maintaining internal temperature may be one of several factors explaining this phenomenon.*

Dissection of the Blood Vessels of the Cat

 Time Allotment: 1 1/2–2 hours (depending on detail required in dissection).

 Multimedia Resources: See Appendix B for Guide to Multimedia Resource Distributors.

The Anatomy of the Cat (CBS: 85 minutes, DVD)
Cat Dissection (WNS: 46 minutes, DVD)
Practice Anatomy Lab™ 3.0 (PAL) (PE: DVD, website)

Laboratory Materials

Ordering information is based on a lab size of 24 students, working in groups of 4. A list of supply house addresses appears in Appendix A.

6–12 preserved double- or triple-
   injected cats
6–12 dissection trays
6–12 dissection kits with metric rulers

Paper towels
Disposable gloves
Safety glasses
Embalming fluid

Organic debris container
Bone cutters
Scissors

Advance Preparation

1. See Dissection Exercise 1 for setup instructions.
2. If cats were not skinned previously, see instructions in Dissection Exercise 1. Allow extra time for skinning. (*Note:* It is not absolutely necessary to skin the cats to do dissection of internal structures.) Allow 1/2 hour to skin 1 forelimb and 1 hindlimb.

Comments and Pitfalls

1. As students dissect out the arteries and veins, caution them to avoid damaging other organs that will be studied in later exercises. *Especially caution them against cutting away the greater omentum.*
2. Students may want to forge ahead and do the entire dissection once the ventral body cavity has been opened. Remind them that the individual systems will be studied in detail at a later date.
3. If time is limited, the circulatory system may be studied in conjunction with the study of individual systems rather than as a separate exercise.
4. If desired by the instructor, a previously dissected animal may be put on demonstration.
5. If the specimen has been injected, frequently the right common carotid artery is damaged; therefore, tracing the common carotid artery to find the external and internal carotid arteries is more easily done by following the left common carotid artery.

310

Dissection Review

1. What differences did you observe between the origins of the left common carotid arteries in the cat and in the human?

   In the cat, both the R. and L. common carotid arteries branch off the R. brachiocephalic artery. In humans, the L. common carotid branches directly off the aortic arch; only the R. common carotid branches off the brachiocephalic artery.

   Between the origins of the internal and external iliac arteries?

   In the cat, the aorta gives off the two external iliac arteries, then persists briefly before dividing into the two internal iliac arteries and the median sacral artery; there are no common iliac arteries. In humans, the external and internal iliac arteries arise by branching off the common iliac arteries.

2. How do the relative sizes of the external and internal jugular veins differ in the human and the cat?

   In the cat, the external jugular vein is larger. In humans, the internal jugular vein is larger.

3. In the cat the inferior vena cava is also called the _*postcava*_, and the superior vena cava is also referred to as the _*precava*_.

4. Define the following terms:

   ascending aorta: _*The aorta as it emerges from the heart and travels toward the head*_

   aortic arch: _*The aorta as it arches to the left*_

   Descending thoracic aorta: _*The aorta as it passes through the thoracic cavity*_

   Descending abdominal aorta: _*The aorta as it passes through the abdominal cavity*_

The Main Lymphatic Ducts of the Cat

 Time Allotment: 1/2 hour (may be easily included with Dissection Exercise 4).

 Multimedia Resources: See Appendix B for Guide to Multimedia Resource Distributors.

The Anatomy of the Cat (CBS: 85 minutes, DVD)
Cat Dissection (WNS: 46 minutes, DVD)

Laboratory Materials

Ordering information is based on a lab size of 24 students, working in groups of 4. A list of supply house addresses appears in Appendix A.

6–12 preserved double- or triple-injected cats

6–12 dissection trays

6–12 dissection kits with metric rulers
Paper towels
Safety glasses

Disposable gloves
Embalming fluid
Organic debris container

Advance Preparation

1. See Dissection Exercise 1 for setup instructions.
2. If cats were not skinned previously, see instructions in Dissection Exercise 1. Allow extra time for skinning. (*Note:* It is not absolutely necessary to skin the cats to do dissection of internal structures.)

Comments and Pitfalls

1. If the student cats are double injected, it might be of value to order one triple-injected cat for demonstration of the lymphatic system. Before ordering, make sure that triple injected means that the lymphatic system has been injected. Often, triple injection means that the hepatic portal venous system has been injected separately from the vascular system injections.

Dissection Review

1. How does the cat's lymphatic drainage pattern compare to that of humans? *It is basically the same.*

2. What is the role of the following?

   a. thoracic duct *It returns lymph from the lower body and upper left quadrant of the body to the left subclavian vein.*

   b. right lymphatic duct *It returns lymph to the right subclavian vein from the upper right quadrant of the body.*

   c. cisterna chyli *It receives fat-rich lymph from the intestines.*

Dissection of the Respiratory System of the Cat

Time Allotment: 1 hour.

Multimedia Resources: See Appendix B for Guide to Multimedia Resource Distributors.

The Anatomy of the Cat (CBS: 85 minutes, DVD)
Cat Dissection (WNS: 46 minutes, DVD)
Practice Anatomy Lab™ 3.0 (PAL) (PE: DVD, website)

Laboratory Materials

Ordering information is based on a lab size of 24 students, working in groups of 4. A list of supply house addresses appears in Appendix A.

6–12 preserved double- or triple-
    injected cats
6–12 dissection trays
6–12 dissection kits with metric rulers

Paper towels
Disposable gloves
Safety glasses
Embalming fluid

Organic debris container
6–12 dissecting microscopes

Advance Preparation

1. See Dissection Exercise 1 for setup instructions.
2. If cats were not skinned previously, see instructions in Dissection Exercise 1. Allow extra time for skinning. (*Note:* It is not absolutely necessary to skin the cats to do dissection of internal structures.)
3. Set out dissecting microscopes.

Answers to Activity Questions

Activity 1: Identifying Organs of the Respiratory System (pp. 745–747)

5. The cat has four lobes in the right lung and three lobes in the left lung.

Dissection Review

1. Are the cartilaginous rings in the cat trachea complete or incomplete? *Incomplete*

2. Describe the appearance of the bronchial tree in the cat lung. *The bronchial tree is a series of branching tubing.*

   The main (primary) bronchi are large; subsequent branches are smaller and smaller in diameter.

3. Describe the appearance of lung tissue under the dissecting microscope. *Spongy-looking with small, irregular*

   openings

Dissection of the Digestive System of the Cat

Time Allotment: 1–1$^{1}/_{2}$ hours.

Multimedia Resources: See Appendix B for Guide to Multimedia Resource Distributors.

The Anatomy of the Cat (CBS: 85 minutes, DVD)
Cat Dissection (WNS: 46 minutes, DVD)
Practice Anatomy Lab™ 3.0 (PAL) (PE: DVD, website)

Laboratory Materials

Ordering information is based on a lab size of 24 students, working in groups of 4. A list of supply house addresses appears in Appendix A.

6–12 preserved double- or triple-injected cats	Paper towels	Organic debris container
6–12 dissection trays	Disposable gloves	Bone cutters
6–12 dissection kits with metric rulers	Safety glasses	6–12 hand lenses
	Embalming fluid	

Advance Preparation

1. See Dissection Exercise 1 for setup instructions.
2. Set out bone cutters, water bottles for flushing the intestines, and hand lenses.

Comments and Pitfalls

1. Warn students that they will probably encounter roundworms in the cat's stomach and intestines.

Answers to Activity Questions

Activity 1: Identifying Alimentary Canal Organs (pp. 750–752)

2. The cat liver has five lobes; the human liver has four lobes.
4. The stomach is a curved sac.
6. Blood vessels, lymphatics, and nerves are present in the mesenteries. The mesenteries provide a route for blood and lymphatic vessels and nerves to travel to and from the small intestine. There are no major differences in external anatomy along the length of the small intestine. The inner surface of the ileum feels like velvet. The villi in the duodenum are more elongated than those in the ileum.
7. The cat does not have an appendix.

2. Rugae are not as well developed in humans. Cats do not have a uvula. The numerous filiform papillae are used by the cat for grooming and for removing flesh from bones.

Dissection Review

1. Compare the appearance of tongue papillae in cats and humans. _The cat has numerous sharp, bristly filiform papillae. Human filiform papillae are less numerous, blunted, and softer._

2. Compare the number of lobes of the liver in cats and humans. _The cat liver has five lobes; the human liver has four._

3. Does the cat have a uvula? _No_ An appendix? _No_

4. Give an explanation for the different adult dental formulas in cats and humans. _Cats are carnivores and need extra incisors for biting. They have a reduced need for grinding and thus have fewer molars._

5. How do the villi differ in the duodenum and the ileum? Explain.
The villi in the duodenum are more elongated and more numerous than those in the ileum. Villi contribute to the increase in surface area that is necessary for absorption of nutrients, especially in the duodenum. Most absorption occurs in the proximal portion of the small intestine.

Dissection of the Urinary System of the Cat

 Time Allotment: 1 hour.

 Multimedia Resources: See Appendix B for Guide to Multimedia Resource Distributors.

The Anatomy of the Cat (CBS: 85 minutes, DVD)
Cat Dissection (WNS: 46 minutes, DVD)
Practice Anatomy Lab™ 3.0 (PAL) (PE: DVD, website)

Laboratory Materials

Ordering information is based on a lab size of 24 students, working in groups of 4. A list of supply house addresses appears in Appendix A.

6–12 preserved double- or
    triple-injected cats
6–12 dissection trays
6–12 dissection kits with metric rulers

Paper towels
Disposable gloves
Safety glasses
Embalming fluid

Organic debris container
6–12 hand magnifying lenses

Advance Preparation:

1. See Dissection Exercise 1 for setup instructions.

Comments and Pitfalls

1. Emphasize the importance of clearing away the peritoneum and fat tissue. Once the kidneys have been isolated, there should be no difficulty identifying the ureters.

2. Remind the students that they are responsible for knowing both the male and the female urinary systems.

3. This dissection fits nicely with the dissection of the reproductive system.

Answers to Activity Questions

Activity 1: Identifying Organs of the Urinary System (pp. 755–758)

4. The ureters enter the bladder on the right and left lateral surfaces toward the posterior (caudal) end.

Dissection Review

1. a. How does the position of the kidneys in the cat differ from their position in humans?

   In humans, the left kidney is more superior. In the cat, the kidneys are located at the same level or the right

   kidney is more anterior.

   b. In what way is the position similar? _Both are retroperitoneal._

2. Distinguish between a ureter and the urethra.

   The ureter carries urine from the kidney to the urinary bladder. The urethra carries urine from the urinary bladder

   to the exterior.

3. How does the site of urethral emptying in the female cat differ from its termination point in the human female?

   Human: The urethra empties to the body exterior. Cat: Both the urethra and the vagina empty into the urogenital

   sinus, which then empties to the body exterior.

4. What is a urogenital sinus? _It is a common chamber into which the urethra and vagina enter._

5. What gland encircles the neck of the bladder in the male? _Prostate_ Is this part of the urinary

   system? _No_ What is its function? _The prostate is part of the male reproductive system. It_

   produces a secretion, which contributes to seminal fluid.

6. Compare the location of the adrenal glands in the cat to the location in humans.

   In humans the adrenal glands sit atop and attach to the kidneys. In the cat they are superior, separate, and medial to

   the kidneys, close to the inferior vena cava.

Dissection of the Reproductive System of the Cat

Time Allotment: 1^1/2–2 hours.

Multimedia Resources: See Appendix B for Guide to Multimedia Resource Distributors.

The Anatomy of the Cat (CBS: 85 minutes, DVD)
Cat Dissection (WNS: 46 minutes, DVD)
Practice Anatomy Lab™ 3.0 (PAL) (PE: DVD, website)

Laboratory Materials

Ordering information is based on a lab size of 24 students, working in groups of 4. A list of supply house addresses appears in Appendix A.

6–12 preserved double- or
   triple-injected cats
6–12 dissection trays
6–12 dissection kits with metric rulers

Paper towels
Disposable gloves
Safety glasses
Embalming fluid

Organic debris container
Bone cutters

Advance Preparation

1. See Dissection Exercise 1 for setup instructions.
2. Set out metric rulers and bone cutters.

Comments and Pitfalls

1. Students usually encounter some difficulty dissecting out the penis. It takes time, as the overlying skin is tightly attached in some places.
2. Caution students with male dissection animals to be careful when dissecting out the spermatic cord to avoid breaking it.
3. Remind students that they are responsible for doing both male and female dissections.
4. It is interesting to have at least one pregnant cat for dissection.
5. Students must use bone cutters to cut through the pubic region of the pelvis to complete the dissection. It is easiest if the cut is through the pubic symphysis.

Answers to Activity Questions

Activity 2: Identifying Organs of the Female Reproductive System (pp. 761–762)

4. The human female has separate openings for the vagina and the urethra.
6. The vagina is 2 to 3 centimeters long (will vary).

Dissection Review

1. The female cat has a(n) _bipartite_ uterus; that of the human female is _simplex_.

   Explain the difference in structure of these two uterine types.

   Cat: The uterus is Y-shaped with a central caudal chamber, the body, from which two horns extend. Human: The uterus

   is a pear-shaped chamber.

2. What reproductive advantage is conferred by the feline uterine type? _Cat fetuses develop in the horns of the_

   uterus. The long horns enable the cat to produce many offspring in each pregnancy.

3. Cite differences noted between the cat and the human relative to the following structures:

   Uterine tubes _Cat uterine tubes are smaller and much shorter than those in humans._

   Site of entry of ductus deferens into the urethra _The ductus deferens of the cat enters the urethra more distal to_

   the bladder.

   Location of the prostate _The cat prostate is smaller and more distal to the bladder._

   Seminal glands _Seminal glands are not present in the cat._

   Urethral and vaginal openings in the female _The cat urethra and vagina open into a common chamber, the_

   urogenital sinus. In humans, each organ opens independently to the body exterior.

Dissection and Identification of Fetal Pig Muscles

Time Allotment: Muscle dissection: 4 hours.

Multimedia Resources: See Appendix B for Guide to Multimedia Resource Distributors.

The Anatomy of the Fetal Pig (CBS: 62 minutes, DVD)
Fetal Pig Dissection (WNS: 26 minutes, DVD)
Practice Anatomy Lab™ 3.0 (PAL) (PE: DVD, website)

Solutions:

Carboglycerine solution
30 grams fungicide (Benomyl, Sigma-Aldrich)
250 milliliters glycerine
1 liter water
Mix together and store in a closed container.

Laboratory Materials

Ordering information is based on a lab size of 24 students, working in groups of 4. A list of supply house addresses appears in Appendix A.

6–12 preserved double- or triple-injected fetal pigs
6–12 dissection trays
6–12 dissection kits with metric rulers

6–12 name tags and large plastic storage bags
Paper towels
Disposable gloves

Safety glasses
Twine
Embalming fluid
Organic debris container

Advance Preparation

1. Make arrangements for appropriate storage, disposal, and cleanup of dissection materials. Check with the Department of Health or the Department of Environmental Protection, or their counterparts, for state regulations. Designate a disposal container for organic debris, set up a dishwashing area with hot soapy water and sponges, and provide lab disinfectant such as Wavicide-01 (Carolina) or 10% bleach solution for washing down the lab benches.

2. Set out disposable gloves, safety glasses, dissecting kits, dissection trays, plastic storage bags, twine, metric rulers, paper towels, and name tags.

3. Set out dissection animals (one per group of two to four students).

4. Set out *carboglycerine solution* or small plastic bags to hold embalming fluid.

Comments and Pitfalls

1. Emphasize the use of the blunt probe as a dissecting instrument, rather than the scalpel. Cut only when everyone in the group agrees that a cut should be made!
2. Muscle development may be poor in some fetal pig specimens if they are very young.
3. Students often "invent" muscles by tearing tissue apart. Emphasize that they should be separating muscles by breaking through the surrounding connective tissue.
4. Sometimes the dissection animal is in very poor condition, in which case the student should exchange it for a different specimen.
5. To prevent damage to muscles during skinning, separate skin from underlying tissues by inserting a blunt probe into the skin incision in the neck. Continue to use the probe to separate skin from underlying tissues before cutting the skin.

Answers to Activity Questions

Activity 3: Dissecting Trunk and Neck Muscles
Superficial Muscles of the Posterior Trunk and Neck (p. 712)

2. The acromiotrapezius and spinotrapezius muscles appear to have the same functions in the pig as in humans.

Activity 4: Dissecting Forelimb Muscles
Upper Forelimb Muscles (p. 715)

1. The triceps brachii has a similar function in pigs and humans.
3. The biceps brachii has only one head in the pig.

Activity 5: Dissecting Hindlimb Muscles
Muscles of the Posterolateral Hindlimb (pp. 716–717)

3. In humans the semimembranosus is also medial to and partially obscured by the semitendinosus. The human semimembranosus inserts on the tibia, but not on the femur.

Muscles of the Anteromedial Hindlimb (pp. 717–719)

2. The origin of the rectus femoris in humans is the anterior inferior iliac spine and just above the acetabulum.
3. The human gracilis muscle has a very similar origin and insertion.

Dissection Review

Many human muscles are modified from those of the pig (or any quadruped). The following questions refer to these differences.

1. How does the human trapezius muscle differ from the pig's? *The pig's trapezius is tripartite (clavo-, acromio-, and spino- portions); the human trapezius is a single muscle.*

2. How does the deltoid differ? *The pig's deltoid is a tripartite muscle; the human deltoid is a single muscle.*

3. How does the biceps brachii differ? *The biceps brachii has only one head in the pig.*

4. How do the size and orientation of the human sartorius muscle differ from that in the pig? *In humans, the sartorius is a thin, straplike muscle running obliquely across the anterior thigh. In the pig it is broad and flat and covers most of the anterolateral thigh. Its course is oblique, but appears less so because it is much larger.*

5. Explain these differences in terms of differences in function. *In humans the sartorius adducts and rotates the thigh. In addition to these functions, it also extends the knee in the pig.*

6. The human rectus abdominis is definitely divided by four transverse tendons (tendinous intersections). These tendons are absent or difficult to identify in the pig. How do these tendons help facilitate the human upright posture? *These tendons support the muscular abdominal wall so that the viscera are not allowed to become pendulous in the upright posture of humans.*

Dissection of the Spinal Cord and Spinal Nerves of the Fetal Pig

Time Allotment: 1¹/2 hours.

Multimedia Resources: See Appendix B for Guide to Multimedia Resource Distributors.

The Anatomy of the Fetal Pig (CBS: 62 minutes, VHS, DVD)
Fetal Pig Dissection (WNS: 26 minutes, DVD)

Laboratory Materials

Ordering information is based on a lab size of 24 students, working in groups of 4. A list of supply house addresses appears in Appendix A.

6–12 preserved double- or triple-
   injected fetal pigs
6–12 dissection trays
6–12 dissection kits with metric rulers

Paper towels
Disposable gloves
Safety glasses
Embalming fluid

Organic debris container
Bone cutters

Advance Preparation

1. See Dissection Exercise 1 for setup instructions.
2. Set out bone cutters.

Dissection Review

1. In what region (cervical, thoracic, lumbar, or sacral) of the spinal cord would you find the following special features?

   enlargements: _cervical and lumbar_

   cauda equina: _sacral_

2. As you trace a spinal nerve laterally, it divides into dorsal and ventral _rami_ (rami/roots).

3. Describe the appearance of the sympathetic trunk as seen in your dissection animal. _A white cord with_

   periodic enlargements

4. From anterior to posterior, put the nerves issuing from the brachial plexus of the pig (i.e., the median, radial, and ulnar nerves) in their proper order. _Radial, median, ulnar_

5. Just superior to the fetal pig's gastrocnemius muscle, the sciatic nerve divides into two main branches, the

   internal popliteal and the _external popliteal_ nerves.

323

Identification of Selected Endocrine Organs of the Fetal Pig

 Time Allotment: 1/2–1 hour.

 Multimedia Resources: See Appendix B for Guide to Multimedia Resource Distributors.

The Anatomy of the Fetal Pig (CBS: 62 minutes, VHS, DVD)
Fetal Pig Dissection (WNS: 26 minutes, DVD)
Practice Anatomy Lab™ 3.0 (PAL) (PE: DVD, website)

Laboratory Materials

Ordering information is based on a lab size of 24 students, working in groups of 4. A list of supply house addresses appears in Appendix A.

6–12 preserved double- or triple-
   injected fetal pigs
6–12 dissection trays
6–12 dissection kits with metric rulers

Paper towels
Disposable gloves
Safety glasses
Embalming fluid

Organic debris container
Bone cutters

Advance Preparation

1. See Dissection Exercise 1 for setup instructions.

Comments and Pitfalls

1. It is possible to leave identification of glands in the dissection animal until later dissections.

Dissection Review

1. How do the locations of the endocrine organs in the fetal pig compare with those in the human?

   They are similar, but in the pig the pancreas is more diffuse; the adrenal glands are medial rather than superior to

   the kidneys; and the thymus is much larger.

2. Name two endocrine organs located in the throat region. *Thyroid gland* and *thymus gland*

3. Name three endocrine organs located in the abdominopelvic cavity. *Pancreas*_____,

   *adrenal glands*_____, and *ovaries in female*_____

4. Given the assumption (not necessarily true) that human beings have more stress than adult pigs, which

   endocrine organs would you expect to be relatively larger in humans? *The adrenal glands*_____

5. Explain why the thymus gland in the fetal pig is so large relative to that in an adult pig. *During fetal*_____

   *development, T cells are rapidly dividing and maturing in the thymus gland.*_____

Dissection of the Blood Vessels and Main Lymphatic Ducts of the Fetal Pig

Time Allotment: 1¹/2–3 hours (depending on detail required in dissection).

Multimedia Resources: See Appendix B for Guide to Multimedia Resource Distributors.

The Anatomy of the Fetal Pig (CBS: 62 minutes, DVD)
Fetal Pig Dissection (WNS: 26 minutes, DVD)
Practice Anatomy Lab™ 3.0 (PAL) (PE: DVD, website)

Laboratory Materials

Ordering information is based on a lab size of 24 students, working in groups of 4. A list of supply house addresses appears in Appendix A.

6–12 preserved double- or triple- injected fetal pigs
6–12 dissection trays
6–12 dissection kits with metric rulers

Paper towels
Disposable gloves
Safety glasses
Twine

Embalming fluid
Organic debris container
Bone cutters

Advance Preparation

1. See Dissection Exercise 1 for setup instructions.

Comments and Pitfalls

1. As students dissect out the arteries and veins, caution them to avoid damaging other organs that will be studied in later exercises. *Especially caution them against cutting away the greater omentum.*

2. Students may want to forge ahead and do the entire dissection once the ventral body cavity has been opened. Remind them that the individual systems will be studied in detail at a later date.

3. If time is limited, the circulatory system may be studied in conjunction with the study of individual systems rather than as a separate exercise.

4. If desired by the instructor, a previously dissected animal may be put on demonstration.

5. If the specimen has been injected, frequently the right common carotid artery is damaged; therefore, tracing the common carotid artery to find the external and internal carotid arteries is more easily done by following the left common carotid artery.

Dissection Review

1. Is the fetal pig's lymphatic drainage pattern basically similar or dissimilar to that of humans?

   Similar

2. What is the role of the following?

   a.   thoracic duct   *It returns lymph from the lower body and upper left quadrant of the body to the left subclavian vein.*

   b.   right lymphatic duct   *It returns lymph to the right subclavian vein from the upper right quadrant of the body.*

3. What differences did you observe between the origin of the common carotid arteries in the pig and in the human?

   In the pig, the common carotid arteries may arise from the bicarotid trunk (a branch off the brachiocephalic trunk) or

   directly from the brachiocephalic artery. In humans, the right common carotid artery arises from the brachiocephalic

   artery; the left common carotid artery arises directly from the aortic arch.

4. How do the relative sizes of the external and internal jugular veins differ in the human and the pig?

   In the pig, the external jugular vein is larger. In humans, the internal jugular vein is larger.

5. How do the brachial veins of the pig differ from those of humans?   *In the pig, often there are two brachial*

   veins in each forelimb, which anastomose frequently along their course. In humans, the brachial vein is singular.

6. What differences did you note between the origin of the hepatic portal vein in the pig and in humans?

   Pig: from the union of the gastrosplenic and mesenteric veins

   Humans: from the union of the splenic and superior mesenteric veins

   between the origin of the internal and external iliac arteries?   *Pig: External iliac arteries issue directly from the*

   aorta. The internal iliac arteries are branches of the umbilical arteries at the aorta terminus.

   Humans: The external and internal iliac arteries arise from the division of the common iliac arteries, which are the

   final aorta branches.

7. Define the following terms.

   ascending aorta: *The aorta as it emerges from the heart and travels toward the head*

   aortic arch: *The aorta as it bends to travel caudally*

   descending thoracic aorta: *The aorta as it passes through the thoracic cavity*

   descending abdominal aorta: *The aorta as it passes through the abdominal cavity*

Dissection of the Respiratory System of the Fetal Pig

 Time Allotment: 1 1/2 hours.

 Multimedia Resources: See Appendix B for Guide to Multimedia Resource Distributors.

The Anatomy of the Fetal Pig (CBS: 62 minutes, DVD)
Fetal Pig Dissection (WNS: 26 minutes, DVD)
Practice Anatomy Lab™ 3.0 (PAL) (PE: DVD, website)

Laboratory Materials

Ordering information is based on a lab size of 24 students, working in groups of 4. A list of supply house addresses appears in Appendix A.

6–12 preserved double- or triple-injected fetal pigs	Disposable gloves	6–12 small beakers containing tap water
6–12 dissection trays	Safety glasses	Bone cutters (if thoracic cavity has not yet been opened)
6–12 dissection kits with metric rulers	Twine	
Paper towels	Embalming fluid	6–12 dissecting microscopes
	Organic debris container	

Advance Preparation

1. See Dissection Exercise 1 for setup instructions.
2. Set out dissecting microscopes and small beakers.

Answers to Activity Questions

Activity 1: Identifying Respiratory Organs of the Fetal Pig (pp. 739–742)

3. The mucosa helps warm and moisten the air entering the nasal cavity.

8. The segment of fetal lung tissue will sink to the bottom of the beaker of water. The lungs have never been inflated; therefore the tissue contains essentially no air and is dense. Lungs that have been inflated contain trapped air and will float.

Dissection Review

1. Are the cartilaginous rings in the pig trachea complete or incomplete? *Incomplete*

2. How does the number of lung lobes in the pig compare with the number in humans? *5 in humans; 7 in the pig*

3. Describe the appearance of lung tissue under the dissecting microscope. *Dense but spongy-looking*

Dissection of the Digestive System of the Fetal Pig

Time Allotment: 2 hours.

Multimedia Resources: See Appendix B for Guide to Multimedia Resource Distributors.

The Anatomy of the Fetal Pig (CBS: 62 minutes, DVD)
Fetal Pig Dissection (WNS: 26 minutes, DVD)
Practice Anatomy Lab™ 3.0 (PAL) (PE: DVD, website)

Laboratory Materials

Ordering information is based on a lab size of 24 students, working in groups of 4. A list of supply house addresses appears in Appendix A.

6–12 preserved double- or triple-injected fetal pigs	Paper towels	Embalming fluid
	Disposable gloves	Organic debris container
6–12 dissection trays	Safety glasses	6–12 hand lenses
6–12 dissection kits with metric rulers	Twine	Bone cutters

Advance Preparation

1. See Dissection Exercise 1 for setup instructions.
2. Set out bone cutters and hand lenses.

Comments and Pitfalls

1. In the pig, the large intestine will have a very different arrangement from that of the human.

Answers to Activity Questions

Activity 2: Identifying Digestive Organs in the Abdominal Cavity (pp. 745–747)

3. The stomach is a curved sac.

5. Blood vessels, lymphatics, and nerves are present in the mesenteries. The mesenteries provide a route for vessels and nerves to travel to and from the small intestine. The inner surface of the ileum feels like velvet. The villi in the duodenum are more elongated than those in the ileum.

6. The ileocecal valve prevents regurgitation of material from the cecum into the ileum. The pig does not have an appendix.

Dissection Review

1. The dental formula for the fetal pig is

$$\frac{3, 1, 4, 0}{3, 1, 4, 0} \times 2$$

Explain what this means.

There are 3 incisors, 1 canine, 4 premolars, and no molars. The extra incisors are for biting. The premolars provide

adequate surface for grinding; and since pigs have reduced need for fine grinding, they have no molars.

2. Several differences between pig and human digestive anatomy should have become apparent during the dissection. Note the pertinent differences between the human and the pig relative to the following structures.

Structure	Pig	Human
Number of liver lobes	*Five*	*Four*
Appendix	*Absent, cecum present*	*Present*
Appearance and distribution of colon	*Ascends and then forms a tight coil before descending*	*Basically an inverted U with ascending, transverse, and descending portions*
Presence of round ligament	*Absent. Umbilical vein is still present. It later becomes the round ligament.*	*Present*

Dissection of the Urinary System of the Fetal Pig

Time Allotment: 1 hour.

Multimedia Resources: See Appendix B for Guide to Multimedia Resource Distributors.

The Anatomy of the Fetal Pig (CBS: 62 minutes, DVD)
Fetal Pig Dissection (WNS: 26 minutes, DVD)
Practice Anatomy Lab™ 3.0 (PAL) (PE: DVD, website)

Laboratory Materials

Ordering information is based on a lab size of 24 students, working in groups of 4. A list of supply house addresses appears in Appendix A.

6–12 preserved double- or triple-injected fetal pigs	Paper towels	Embalming fluid
	Disposable gloves	Organic debris container
6–12 dissection trays	Safety glasses	
6–12 dissection kits with metric rulers	Twine or pins	

Advance Preparation

1. See Dissection Exercise 1 for setup instructions.

Comments and Pitfalls

1. Emphasize the importance of clearing away the peritoneum and fat tissue. Once the kidneys have been isolated there should be no difficulty identifying the ureters.

2. Remind the students that they are responsible for knowing both the male and the female urinary systems.

3. This dissection fits nicely with the dissection of the reproductive system.

Dissection Review

1. How do the structure and connectivity of the urinary bladder of the fetal pig differ from those of the urinary bladder of the human (or the adult pig, for that matter)?

   The fetal urinary bladder is very elongated and continues into the umbilical cord as the allantoic stalk. After birth, it

   is transformed into the adult urinary bladder, which empties into the urethra.

2. What differences in fetal elimination of nitrogenous wastes account for the structural differences described above?

Fetal elimination of nitrogenous waste occurs through the placenta. (The extraembryonic portion of the allantois

forms a part of the placenta.)

3. How does the site of urethral emptying in the female pig differ from the termination point in the human female?

The pig's urethra and vagina empty into a common chamber, the urogenital sinus. The human female's

urethra and vagina terminate independently at the body surface.

Dissection of the Reproductive System of the Fetal Pig

Time Allotment: 1 1/2–2 hours.

Multimedia Resources: See Appendix B for Guide to Multimedia Resource Distributors.

The Anatomy of the Fetal Pig (CBS: 62 minutes, DVD)
Fetal Pig Dissection (WNS: 26 minutes, DVD)
Practice Anatomy Lab™ 3.0 (PAL) (PE: DVD, website)

Laboratory Materials

Ordering information is based on a lab size of 24 students, working in groups of 4. A list of supply house addresses appears in Appendix A.

6–12 preserved double- or triple-
   injected fetal pigs
6–12 dissection trays

6–12 dissection kits with metric rulers
Paper towels
Disposable gloves

Safety glasses
Embalming fluid
Organic debris container

Advance Preparation

1. See Dissection Exercise 1 for setup instructions.
2. Set out metric rulers and bone cutters.

Comments and Pitfalls

1. Caution students with male dissection animals to be careful when dissecting out the spermatic cord to avoid breaking it.
2. Remind students that they are responsible for doing both male and female dissections.
3. Students must use bone cutters to cut through the pubic region of the pelvis to complete the dissection. It is easiest if the cut is through the pubic symphysis.

Answers to Activity Questions

Activity 2: Identifying Organs of the Female Reproductive System (pp. 755–756)

4. The human female has separate openings for the vagina and the urethra.
6. The vagina is 20 to 30 millimeters long (will vary).

Dissection Review

1. The female pig has a(n) _bipartite_ uterus; that of the human female is _simplex_.

   Explain the difference in structure of these two uterine types. _Pig: The uterus is Y-shaped with a central caudal chamber, the body, from which two horns extend. Human: The uterus is a pear-shaped chamber._

2. What reproductive advantage is conferred by the pig's uterine type? _Pig fetuses develop in the horns of the uterus. The long horns enable the pig to produce many offspring in each pregnancy._

3. Cite differences noted between the pig and the human relative to the following structures:

   Uterine tubes _They are very tiny and relatively much shorter in the pig._

   Urethral and vaginal openings in the female _In the pig, both open into a common chamber, the urogenital sinus. In humans, both structures empty independently to the body exterior._

   Location of the penis _In pigs, the penis lies internal to the urethral orifice on the ventral body surface. In human males, the penis is an external structure._

Cell Transport Mechanisms and Permeability

Advance Preparation/Comments

1. A "#" symbol after "rate" data indicates that equilibrium was not reached for that solute.

Answers to Questions/Experimental Data

Pre-lab Quiz in the Lab Manual

1. diffusion
2. b, contains more nonpenetrating solutes than the interior of the cell.
3. d, vesicular transport
4. phagocytosis
5. active

Activity 1: Simulating Dialysis (Simple Diffusion) (pp. PEx-4–PEx-6)

Predict Question 1: The correct prediction is "no." Urea is too large to diffuse through this membrane.

Predict Question 2: The correct prediction is that glucose will be able to diffuse through the membrane. Albumin, however, is too large and will not diffuse.

Chart 1: Dialysis Rates (average diffusion rate in mM/sec)

Solute	Membrane MWCO			
	20	50	100	200
Na⁺Cl⁻	0.0000	0.0150	0.0150	
		0.0300		
Urea	0.0000		0.0094	
Albumin				0.0000
Glucose				0.0040

Activity Questions:

1. No, none of the solutes tested passed through the 20 MWCO membrane. They were all too large.
2. Yes, Na⁺ Cl⁻ diffused through the 50 MWCO membrane.
3. Increasing the size of the solute slowed down the rate of diffusion.
4. Increasing the solute concentration increased the rate of diffusion.

Activity 2: Simulated Facilitated Diffusion (pp. PEx-6–PEx-8)

Predict Question 1: Increasing the number of protein carriers will increase the glucose transport rate.

Predict Question 2: Adding Na⁺Cl⁻ will have no effect on the glucose transport rate because the carrier is only transporting glucose through the membrane.

Chart 2: Facilitated Diffusion Results (glucose transport rate, m*M*/sec)

Glucose concentration	Number of glucose carrier proteins		
	500	700	100
2 m*M*	0.0008	0.0010	
8 m*M*	0.0023	0.0031	
10 m*M*			0.0017#
2 m*M* w/2.00 m*M* Na⁺Cl⁻		0.0010	

Activity Questions:

1. They are moving with their concentration gradient.

2. The rate of facilitated diffusion increased when the number of carriers was increased.

3. Equilibrium was not reached with 100 membrane carriers and 10 m*M* glucose because the carriers became saturated and unable to move the glucose across the membrane fast enough.

4. The membrane imbedded carrier in this simulation is only transporting glucose. It is not depending upon the cotransport of Na⁺Cl⁻, so the addition of Na⁺Cl⁻ had no effect.

Activity 3: Simulating Osmotic Pressure (pp. PEx-8–PEx-10)

Predict Question 1: Increasing the Na⁺Cl⁻ concentration will increase the osmotic pressure.

Predict Question 2: There will only be pressure above the left beaker because the albumin is too large to diffuse. The glucose will diffuse freely, generating no osmotic pressure.

Chart 3: Osmosis Results

Solute	Membrane (MWCO)	Pressure on left (mm Hg)	Diffusion rate (mM/sec)
Na⁺Cl⁻	20	170	0.0000
Na⁺Cl⁻	20	340	0.0000
Na⁺Cl⁻	50	0	0.0167
Glucose	100	136	0.0000
Glucose	100	0	0.0000
Glucose	200	0	0.0036
Albumin w/glucose	200	153	0.0044

Activity Questions:

1. The 20 MWCO membrane generated the most pressure. Na⁺Cl⁻ diffuses through the other membranes.

2. The osmostic pressure increases proportionally with increasing solute concentration.

3. No, if solutes diffuse, no osmotic pressure is generated.

4. The albumin can't diffuse, so osmotic pressure is generated on the left. The glucose is small enough to diffuse.

Activity 4: Simulating Filtration (pp. PEx-11–PEx-13)

Predict Question 1: The filtration rate should increase when the pore rate is increased.

Predict Question 2: Increasing the pressure above the beaker should increase the rate of filtration.

Chart 4: Filtration Results

		Membrane (MWCO)			
		20	50	200	200
Solute	Filtration rate (ml/min)	1.00	2.50	10.00	20.00
Na+Cl–	Filter concentration (mg/ml)	0.00	4.81	4.81	4.81
	Membrane residue	present	present	present	present
Urea	Filter concentration (mg/ml)	0.00	0.00	4.74	4.74
	Membrane residue	present	present	present	present
Glucose	Filter concentration (mg/ml)	0.00	0.00	4.34	4.34
	Membrane residue	present	present	present	present
Powdered charcoal	Filter concentration (mg/ml)	0.00	0.00	0.00	0.00
	Membrane residue	present	present	present	present

Activity Questions:

1. The solutes filtered were too large to pass through the 20 MWCO filter.

2. The two variables that affected the rate of filtration were the size of the pores in the membrane and the pressure applied to the filter.

3. The best way to increase the filtration rate in living membranes would be to increase the pressure applied. The powdered charcoal had the largest molecular weight because it was not able to pass through the filtration membrane.

Activity 5: Simulating Active Transport (pp. PEx-13–PEx-14)

Predict Question 1: No, sodium will not be transported because it must be cotransported with potassium. The sodium/potassium pump requires sodium and potassium on opposite sides of the membrane.

Predict Question 2: The addition of glucose carriers should not have an effect on the transport of sodium or potassium because the glucose carriers work independently of the sodium/potassium pump.

Activity Questions:

1. Some of the ions were transported, but there wasn't enough ATP to transport all of the ions. If no ATP were present, there wouldn't have been any movement of ions.

2. Sodium must be transported with potassium, so even though ATP was present, no sodium was transported.

3. When more pumps were added, the rate of transport of sodium and potassium increased proportionally.

4. Glucose is transported by its own carriers and is not dependent upon sodium or potassium. Nor is sodium or potassium dependent upon glucose, as evidenced from previous experimental runs.

NAME _____

LAB TIME/DATE _____

Cell Transport Mechanisms and Permeability

ACTIVITY 1   Simulating Dialysis (Simple Diffusion)

1. Describe two variables that affect the rate of diffusion. *Increasing the size of the solute decreases the rate of diffusion*

Increasing the concentration of a solute increases the rate of diffusion.

2. Why do you think the urea was not able to diffuse through the 20 MWCO membrane? How well did the results compare with

your prediction? *Urea was not able to diffuse because it was too large to fit through the pores. This matched the prediction made.*

Student predictions vary.

3. Describe the results of the attempts to diffuse glucose and albumin through the 200 MWCO membrane. How well did the

results compare with your prediction? *Glucose was able to diffuse through the 200 MWCO; the albumin, however, was too large.*

Student predictions vary.

4. Put the following in order from smallest to largest molecular weight: glucose, sodium chloride, albumin, and urea.

The following are put in order from smallest to largest: sodium chloride, urea, glucose, and albumin.

ACTIVITY 2   Simulated Facilitated Diffusion

1. Explain one way in which facilitated diffusion is the same as simple diffusion and one way in which it differs. *Similarities*

include: solutes move with their concentration gradient; the processes are both passive. A difference is that facilitated diffusion requires a carrier.

2. The larger value obtained when more glucose carriers were present corresponds to an increase in the rate of glucose

transport. Explain why the rate increased. How well did the results compare with your prediction? *With more carriers*

present, more glucose is able to be moved across the membrane. The correct prediction is that the rate increases.

3. Explain your prediction for the effect Na^+Cl^- might have on glucose transport. In other words, explain why you picked the

choice that you did. How well did the results compare with your prediction? *Na^+Cl^- should have no effect because it is not*

required for the transport of the glucose. The carrier is only moving glucose.

ACTIVITY 3   Simulating Osmotic Pressure

1. Explain the effect that increasing the Na^+Cl^- concentration had on osmotic pressure and why it has this effect. How well

did the results compare with your prediction? *Increasing the Na^+Cl^- concentration increased the osmotic pressure,*

because these variables are directly proportional to each other.

338

2. Describe one way in which osmosis is similar to simple diffusion and one way in which it is different. _Osmosis is similar_
because it is a passive process. It is different because it is the movement of water, rather than solutes.

3. Solutes are sometimes measured in milliosmoles. Explain the statement, "Water chases milliosmoles." _The net movement_
of water is with its concentration gradient. This means that it moves toward the higher concentration of solutes.

4. The conditions were 9 mM albumin in the left beaker and 10 mM glucose in the right beaker with the 200 MWCO membrane
in place. Explain the results. How well did the results compare with your prediction? _The osmotic pressure was generated by_
the albumin, which was too large to diffuse. The glucose diffused through the membrane.

ACTIVITY 4 Simulating Filtration

1. Explain in your own words why increasing the pore size increased the filtration rate. Use an analogy to support your statement. How well did the results compare with your prediction? _Increasing the pore size should proportionally increase_
the filtration rate.

2. Which solute did not appear in the filtrate using any of the membranes? Explain why. _The powdered charcoal did not_
appear in the filtrate because it was too large to go through.

3. Why did increasing the pressure increase the filtration rate but not the concentration of solutes? How well did the results
compare with your prediction? _At the lower pressure, all of the solutes were filtering through, so increasing the pressure just caused_
them to filter through faster.

ACTIVITY 5 Simulating Active Transport

1. Describe the significance of using 9 mM sodium chloride inside the cell and 6 mM potassium chloride outside the cell,
instead of other concentration ratios. _The concentration of the ions is significant because sodium and potassium are transported_
at a ratio of three to two, respectively, by the pump.

2. Explain why there was no sodium transport even though ATP was present. How well did the results compare with your
prediction? _Sodium and potassium are required to move these ions using the pump. If one is absent movement will not occur._

3. Explain why the addition of glucose carriers had no effect on sodium or potassium transport. How well did the results
compare with your prediction? _Glucose is not tied in any way to the movement of sodium or potassium in this simulation._
It is moving through its own carrie.

4. Do you think glucose is being actively transported or transported by facilitated diffusion in this experiment? Explain your
answer. _Glucose is moving with its concentration gradient through a carrier. This is facilitated diffusion._

Skeletal Muscle Physiology

Advance Preparation/Comments

1. Prior to the lab, suggest to the students that they become familiar with the exercise before coming to class. If students have a home computer, or access to a computer on campus, they can become familiar with the general operation of the simulations before coming to class.

2. You might do a short introductory presentation with the following elements:
   - Describe the basics of muscle contraction at the cellular level, focusing on the sarcomere. This explanation is especially important for the isometric part of the simulation.
   - Students often have problems distinguishing between in vivo stimulation via the nervous system versus the electrical stimulation we apply to whole skeletal muscle in an experiment. Mention that increasing the intensity of an electrical stimulus to the surface of whole muscle is not the same as stimulation via the nervous system, but that the outcome of increased force production is similar in both methods.
   - Encourage students to try to apply the concepts from the simulation to human skeletal muscles as they work through the program.
   - If a demonstration computer screen is available, briefly show students the basic equipment parts.

3. Keep in mind that many students in an introductory science course are deficient in their graphing skills. Reviewing the principles of plotting before the class begins may prove helpful.

4. Be prepared to help the students answer the more difficult "What if . . . " questions.

Answers to Questions/Experimental Data

Pre-lab Quiz in the Lab Manual

1. potential difference
2. c, influx of Na$^+$
3. repolarization
4. twitch
5. True
6. True
7. a, tetanus
8. a, oxygen deficit in the tissue after prolonged activity

Activity 1: The Muscle Twitch and the Latent Period (pp. PEx-18–PEx-20)

Predict Question 1: No, changes to the stimulus intensity will not change the duration of the latent period. The latent period is a chemical event initiated by the stimulus regardless of its intensity.

Chart 1: Latent Period Results

Voltage	Active force (g)	Latent period (msec)
0.0	0.00	
3.0	1.04	
4.0	1.32	3.20*
6.0	1.65	3.20*
8.0	1.81	3.20*
10.0	1.82	3.20*

* Students use a visual ruler to determine the latent period. A student who enters
2.80 msec as the latent period likely understood how to correctly measure the latent
period (the data points at 2.80 msec and 3.20 msec look very similar in the software).

Activity Questions:

1. A graph similar to the tracing generated in the simulation. See figure 2.3 in the simulation for comparison.

2. The events of the latent period include the events of excitation contraction coupling, most notably the release of calcium from the sarcoplasmic reticulum.

Activity 2: The Effect of Stimulus Voltage on Skeletal Muscle Contraction (pp. PEx-20–PEx-22)

6. 0.8 volts

Predict Question 1: The active force will first increase and then plateau at some maximal value as the stimulus voltage increases.

12. 8.5 volts

Chart 2: Effect of Stimulus Voltage on Skeletal Muscle Contraction

Voltage	Active force (g)	Voltage	Active force (g)
0.0	0.00	5.0	1.51
0.2	0.00	5.5	1.59
0.8	0.02	6.0	1.65
1.0	0.15	6.5	1.70
1.5	0.43	7.0	1.74
2.0	0.66	7.5	1.78
2.5	0.87	8.0	1.81
3.0	1.04	8.5	1.82
3.5	1.19	9.0	1.82
4.0	1.32	9.5	1.82
4.5	1.42	10.0	1.82

Activity Questions:

1. The active force produced by the muscle increased as the stimulus voltage was increased.

2. In the body this is achieved by motor unit recruitment. More muscle fibers are recruited to increase the force generated.

Activity 3: The Effect of Stimulus Frequency on Skeletal Muscle Contraction (PEx-22–PEx-23)

Predict Question 1: As the stimulus frequency increases, the muscle force generated by each successive stimulus will increase. There will be a limit to this increase.

Predict Question 2: The stimulus frequency will need to increase.

Chart 3: Effect of Stimulus Frequency on Skeletal Muscle Contraction

Voltage	Stimulus	Active force (g)
8.5	Single	1.83
8.5	Multiple	Variable, ≤2.42
8.5	Multiple	Variable, ≥2.42
8.5	Multiple	Variable, >2.42 and <5.20
10	Multiple	Variable, >2.42 and <5.20
8.5	Multiple	Variable, ≥5.20

Activity Questions:

1. Treppe is known as the staircase effect because the tracing looks like a staircase, with each subsequent wave higher than the previous wave.

2. More force is generated by the muscle with each successive twitch, thought to be due to increased availability of calcium.

3. When you increase the frequency of stimulation, the amount of force generated increases.

4. Wave summation occurs in the body when muscle fibers are stimulated before they have had a chance to completely relax.

Activity 4: Tetanus in Isolated Skeletal Muscle (pp. PEx-24–PEx-25)

Predict Question 1: As the stimulus frequency increases, the muscle force generated by each successive stimulus will increase. There will be a limit to this increase.

Chart 4: Tetanus in Isolated Skeletal Muscle

Stimuli/second	Active force (g)
50	5.12
130	5.88
140	5.91
142	5.94
144	5.94
146	5.95
148	5.95
150	5.95

Activity Questions:

1. A summation of force is occurring at a high frequency of stimulation to produce smooth muscle contraction.

2. "Lockjaw" is a pathological tetanus. Tetanus boosters are vaccines to prevent the development of tetanus, the disease.

Activity 5: Fatigue in Isolated Skeletal Muscle (pp. PEx-25–PEx-26)

Predict Question 1: The length of the rest period will proportionately increase the length of time for sustained muscle tension.

Chart 5: Fatigue Results

Rest period (sec)	Active force (g)	Sustained maximal force (sec)
0	5.86	10
0	5.86	10
Variable, 8–12	5.86	Variable, 0.2–1.8
Variable, 8–12	5.86	Variable, 4.2–5.8

Activity Questions:

1. Fatigue is still being investigated, but it is thought to involve the buildup of lactic acid, ADP, and inorganic phosphate, and possibly oxygen debt.

2. They best way to delay the onset of fatigue with intense exercise is to schedule brief periods of rest to allow muscle recovery.

Activity 6: The Skeletal Muscle Length-Tension Relationship (pp. PEx-26–PEx-28)

Predict Question 1: Total force can increase or decrease depending upon the starting resting length.

Chart 6: Skeletal Muscle Length-Tension Relationship

Length (mm)	Active force (g)	Passive force (g)	Total force (g)
75	1.82	0.00	1.82
70	1.75	0.00	1.75
65	1.55	0.00	1.55
60	1.21	0.00	1.21
55	0.73	0.00	0.73
50	0.11	0.00	0.11
80	1.75	0.02	1.77
90	1.21	0.25	1.46
100	0.11	1.75	1.86

Activity Questions:

1. Changes in the resting length of the sarcomere directly affect the amount of passive, active and total force that results as described by the length-tension relationship.

2. The dip in the total force curve is due to the fact that at a very short muscle length, there is too much overlap to generate a significant amount of active force. Additionally, there is no passive force at this muscle length.

Activity 7: Isotonic Contractions and the Load-Velocity Relationship (pp. PEx-28–PEx-29)

Predict Question 1: The latent period will increase, the shortening velocity will decrease, the distance will decrease, and the contraction duration will decrease.

Chart 7: Isotonic Contraction Results

Weight (g)	Velocity (cm/sec)	Twitch duration (msec)	Distance lifted (mm)
0.5	0.100	78.00	4.0
1.0	0.057	49.00	2.0
1.5	0.022	30.00	0.5
2.0	0.00	0.00	0.0

Activity Questions:

1. As the weight of the load increases, the initial velocity to move the weight decreases.

2. This is because a heavier weight will have a slower velocity for the repetitions, so it will take you longer to repeat the same number of repetitions of a heavier weight.

Skeletal Muscle Physiology

ACTIVITY 1   **The Muscle Twitch and the Latent Period**

1. Define the terms *skeletal muscle fiber, motor unit, skeletal muscle twitch, electrical stimulus, and latent period.* *See*
   definitions provided in the Introduction.

2. What is the role of acetylcholine in a skeletal muscle contraction? *Acetylcholine binds to receptors in the motor end plate,*
   initiating a change in ion permeability that results in the end-plate potential.

3. Describe the process of excitation-contraction coupling in skeletal muscle fibers. *Excitation-contraction coupling is the*
   release of calcium which binds to troponin, removing the blocking action of tropomyosin so that myosin can bind to actin.

4. Describe the three phases of a skeletal muscle twitch. *Latent period is the time preparing for contraction. Contraction is when*
   muscle tension peaks. The relaxation period is at the end of muscle contraction.

5. Does the duration of the latent period change with different stimulus voltages? How well did the results compare with your
   prediction? *The latent period did not change with changes in stimulus voltage.*

6. At the threshold stimulus, do sodium ions start to move into or out of the cell to bring about the membrane depolarization?
   Sodium would move into the cell to bring about membrane depolarization.

ACTIVITY 2   **The Effect of Stimulus Voltage on Skeletal Muscle Contraction**

1. Describe the effect of increasing stimulus voltage on isolated skeletal muscle. Specifically, what happened to the muscle
   force generated with stronger electrical stimulations and why did this change occur? How well did the results compare with
   your prediction? *The active force increased as predicted to the point in which it reached a plateau and was no longer able to increase.*

2. How is this change in whole-muscle force achieved in vivo? *This is achieved by the recruitment of more muscle fibers over*
   time.

3. What happened in the isolated skeletal muscle when the maximal voltage was applied? *All of the muscle fibers have been*
   recruited and so the maximal force has been achieved.

The Effect of Stimulus Frequency on Skeletal Muscle Contraction

1. What is the difference between stimulus intensity and stimulus frequency? *The stimulus intensity is the electrical changes that relate to the action potential. The frequency is the number of action potentials per minute.*

2. In this experiment you observed the effect of stimulating the isolated skeletal muscle multiple times in a short period with complete relaxation between the stimuli. Describe the force of contraction with each subsequent stimulus. Are these results called treppe or wave summation? *With complete relaxation, it would be treppe. This is the staircase effect, where you see an increase in the force/tension produced.*

3. How did the frequency of stimulation affect the amount of force generated by the isolated skeletal muscle when the frequency of stimulation was increased such that the muscle twitches did not fully relax between subsequent stimuli? Are these results called treppe or wave summation? How well did the results compare with your prediction? *The voltage needed to increase because the tension wasn't great enough at the lower voltage. This is consistent with wave summation.*

4. To achieve an active force of 5.2 g, did you have to increase the stimulus voltage above 8.5 volts? If not, how did you achieve an active force of 5.2 g? How well did the results compare with your prediction? *Yes, it was necessary to increase the voltage above 8.5 volts to achieve the active force of 5.2 grams.*

5. Compare and contrast frequency-dependent wave summation with motor unit recruitment (previously observed by increasing the stimulus voltage). How are they similar? How was each achieved in the experiment? Explain how each is achieved in vivo. *Frequency-dependent wave summation is dependent upon stimulation by the nervous system. The motor recruitment depends upon the number of motor fibers available.*

ACTIVITY 4 **Tetanus in Isolated Skeletal Muscle**

1. Describe how increasing the stimulus frequency affected the force developed by the isolated whole skeletal muscle in this activity. How well did the results compare with your prediction? *The force developed increases as the stimulus frequency increases—to a point.*

2. Indicate what type of force was developed by the isolated skeletal muscle in this activity at the following stimulus frequencies: at 50 stimuli/sec, at 140 stimuli/sec, and above 146 stimuli/sec. *At 50 stimuli/sec: 5.12 g. At 140 stimuli/sec: 5.91g. Above 146 stimuli/sec: 5.95g*

3. Beyond what stimulus frequency is there no further increase in the peak force? What is the muscle tension called at this frequency? *After 146 stimuli/sec there is no further increase in force. This is the maximal tetanic tension.*

ACTIVITY 5 Fatigue in Isolated Skeletal Muscle

1. When a skeletal muscle fatigues, what happens to the contractile force over time? *When skeletal muscle fatigues, the contractile force decreases over time.*

2. What are some proposed causes of skeletal muscle fatigue? *The buildup of lactic acid, ADP, and inorganic phosphate are thought to be involved in muscle fatigue.*

3. Turning the stimulator off allows a small measure of muscle recovery. Thus, the muscle will produce more force for a longer time period if the stimulator is briefly turned off than if the stimuli were allowed to continue without interruption. Explain why this might occur. How well did the results compare with your prediction? *When you increase the rest periods, you see an increase in the muscle tension produced.*

4. List a few ways that humans could delay the onset of fatigue when they are vigorously using their skeletal muscles. *They could periodically rest during vigorous exercise.*

ACTIVITY 6 The Skeletal Muscle Length-Tension Relationship

1. What happens to the amount of total force the muscle generates during the stimulated twitch? How well did the results compare with your prediction? *Total force can increase or decrease depending upon the starting resting length. This is due to the length-tension relationship of the sarcomere.*

2. What is the key variable in an isometric contraction of a skeletal muscle? *The length-tension relationship. The passive force is important in determining the active force produced.*

3. Based on the unique arrangement of myosin and actin in skeletal muscle sarcomeres, explain why active force varies with changes in the muscle's resting length. *The active forces vary with the number of crossbridges formed, which changes with the resting length of the muscle.*

4. What skeletal muscle lengths generated passive force? (Provide a range.) *The muscle lengths from 80–100 mm generated passive force.*

5. If you were curling a 7-kg dumbbell, would your bicep muscles be contracting isometrically? *No, it would be changing in length, so this would not be isometric contraction.*

1. If you were using your bicep muscles to curl a 7-kg dumbbell, when would your muscles be contracting isotonically?

   Yes, because your muscle is changing in length.

2. Explain why the latent period became longer as the load became heavier in the experiment. How well did the results compare with your prediction? *The latent period became longer because it takes more time to generate the force required.*

3. Explain why the shortening velocity became slower as the load became heavier in this experiment. How well did the results compare with your prediction? *It takes more time to generate the force required to lift the heavier load.*

4. Describe how the shortening distance changed as the load became heavier in this experiment. How well did the results compare with your prediction? *The shortening distance decreased with the heavier load.*

5. Explain why it would take you longer to perform 10 repetitions lifting a 10-kg weight than it would to perform the same number of repetitions with a 5-kg weight. *The velocity of shortening decreases with a heavier load, so the repetitions will take longer with a 10-kg weight.*

6. Describe what would happen in the following experiment: A 2.5-g weight is attached to the end of the isolated whole skeletal muscle used in these experiments. Simultaneously, the muscle is maximally stimulated by 8.5 volts and the platform supporting the weight is removed. Will the muscle generate force? Will the muscle change length? What is the name for this type of contraction? *The muscle will still generate force and change length. The type of contraction is isotonic.*

Neurophysiology of Nerve Impulses

Advance Preparation/Comments

Consider doing a short introductory presentation with the following elements:

- Explain how the resting membrane potential is established and maintained.
- Clearly distinguish between graded potentials and action potentials.
- Explain the importance of threshold and why an action potential is considered "all or none."
- Describe the relationship between stimulus strength and action potential frequency.
- Explain the factors that affect conduction velocity.

Answers to Questions/Experimental Data

Pre-lab Quiz in the Lab Manual

1. Conductivity
2. a, depolarization
3. b, K^+
4. absolute refractory period
5. a, gastrocnemius and sciatic

Activity 1: The Resting Membrane Potential (pp. PEx-36–PEx-39)

Predict Question 1: If the extracellular K^+ concentration is increased, the resting membrane will become less negative.

Chart 1: Resting Membrane Potential

Extracellular fluid (ECF)	Microelectrode position	Voltage (mV)
Control	Cell body, extracellular	0
Control	Cell body, intracellular	–70
Control	Axon, extracellular	0
Control	Axon, intracellular	–70
High K^+	Axon, intracellular	–40
High K^+	Axon, extracellular	0
High K^+	Cell body, extracellular	0
High K^+	Cell body, intracellular	–40
Low Na^+	Cell body, intracellular	–72
Low Na^+	Cell body, extracellular	0
Low Na^+	Axon, extracellular	0
Low Na^+	Axon, intracellular	–72

Activity Questions:

1. The resting membrane potential is the same because the permeability of the ions is the same in both locations.

2. If the sodium-potassium pump is blocked, sodium will flow in, depolarizing the membrane.

3. The resting membrane potential would become more negative because there would be more negative anions inside the cell.

Activity 2: Receptor Potential (pp. PEx-39–PEx-41)

Predict Question 1: The moderate intensity pressure modality will induce a receptor potential of the largest amplitude.

Predict Question 2: The moderate intensity chemical modality will induce a receptor potential of the largest amplitude.

Chart 2: Receptor Potential

Stimulus modality	Receptor potential (mV)		
	Pacinian (lamellar) corpuscle	Olfactory receptor	Free nerve ending
None	−70	−70	−70
Pressure			
Low	−60	−70	−70
Moderate	−45	−70	−70
High	−30	−70	−65
Chemical			
Low	−70	−64	−70
Moderate	−70	−58	−70
High	−70	−45	−70
Heat			
Low	−70	−70	−60
Moderate	−70	−70	−40
High	−70	−70	−20
Light			
Low	−70	−70	−70
Moderate	−70	−70	−70
High	−70	−70	−70

Activity Questions:

1. Graded receptor potentials can be depolarizing or hyperpolarizing. Since graded receptor potentials can be hyperpolarizing, they can make it more difficult to induce an action potential.

2. Membrane hyperpolarization is when the membrane becomes more negative than the resting potential.

3. The adequate stimulus for sensory receptors in the ear is a moderate intensity pressure stimulus. Intense pressure could inappropriately activate the sensory receptors in the ear.

Activity 3: The Action Potential: Threshold (pp. PEx-41–PEx-42)

Predict Question 1: The action potential will not change when the stimulus voltage is increased.

Chart 3: Threshold

Stimulus voltage (mV)	Peak value at R1 (µV)	Peak value at R2 (µV)	Action potential
10	0	0	No.
20	100	100	Yes
30	100	100	Yes
40	100	100	Yes
50	100	100	Yes

Activity Questions:

1. Each region of the neuron contains distinct membrane proteins that provide the basis for the threshold differences.

2. The action potential is regenerated by the influx of sodium which establishes local currents that depolarize adjacent sections of the membrane to threshold. The action potential must be regenerated at adjacent sections of the membrane.

3. The action potential is not graded. It is "all or none," so the peak value of the action potential doesnít change.

Activity 4: The Action Potential: Importance of Voltage-Gated Na⁺ Channels (pp. PEx-42–PEx-44)

Predict Question 1: If you apply TTX between recording electrodes R1 and R2, TTX will block the response at R2 but have no effect at R1.

Predict Question 2: If you apply lidocaine between recording electrodes

R1 and R2, lidocaine will block the response at R2 but have no effect at R1.

Chart 4: Effects of Tetrodotoxin and Lidocaine

Condition	Stimulus voltage (mV)	Electrodes	Peak value of response (µV)				
			2 sec	4 sec	6 sec	8 sec	10 sec
Control	30	R1	100	100	100	100	100
Control	30	R2	100	100	100	100	100
TTX	30	R1	100	100	100	100	100
TTX	30	R2	100	100	0	0	0
Lidocaine	30	R1	100	100	100	100	100
Lidocaine	30	R2	100	100	100	0	0

Activity Questions:

1. The sodium channels are voltage-gated sodium channels. Closure of the inactivation gate is a delayed response to the initial depolarization to threshold which closes the inactivation gate about 1 msec after sodium channels open.

2. Careful preparation of the pufferfish requires removal of the toxic portions that contain tetrodotoxin. The poison is most concentrated in the liver, ovaries, and skin of the fish.

3. Calcium channels could possibly substitute for sodium channels to provide an influx of cation.

Activity 5: The Action Potential: Measuring Its Absolute and Relative Refractory Periods (pp. PEx-44–PEx-45)

Predict Question 1: If you further decrease the interval between the stimuli, the threshold for the second action potential will be higher (requiring a larger depolarization).

Chart 5: Absolute and Relative Refractory Periods

Interval between stimuli (msec)	Stimulus voltage (mV)	Second action potential?
250	20	Yes
125	20	Yes
60	20	No
60	25	No
60	30	Yes
30	30	No
30	35	No
30	40	No
30	45	Yes
15	60	Yes
7.5	60	Yes
3.75	60	No

Activity Questions:

1. A refractory period is when the membrane is less excitable. When local currents develop, the action potential must move forward because the previous section is in the absolute refractory period.

2. A long absolute refractory period ensures that the muscle contracts fully.

3. The benefit of a relative refractory period in an axon of a sensory neuron is that it is easier to modify the intensity of the sensation by altering the frequency of stimulation.

Activity 6: The Action Potential: Coding for Stimulus Intensity (pp. PEx-46–PEx-47)

Predict Question 1: Increased stimulus intensity will increase the frequency of action potentials.

Chart 6: Frequency of Action Potentials

Stimulus voltage (mV)	Stimulus duration (msec)	ISI (msec)	Action potential frequency (Hz)
20	0.5	—	—
20	500	100*	10*
30	500	60*	16.6*
45	500	30*	33.3*

* The data in these columns are populated by student calculations.

Activity Questions:

1. The action potential frequency would be increased in the hot water when compared to the warm water.

2. The two determinants that are being overcome are the frequency of stimulation required to overcome the relative refractory period, and the greater than threshold stimulus required during the relative refractory period.

3. Two ways to overcome the relative refractory period are to increase the stimulus frequency and the strength of the stimulus. Pharmacologically, this would require timed release of the medication in bursts of increasing amounts.

Activity 7: The Action Potential: Conduction Velocity (pp. PEx-47–PEx-49)

Predict Question 1: The conduction velocity in the B fiber will be slower because the B fiber has a smaller diameter and less myelination.

Predict Question 2: The conduction velocity in the C fiber will be slower because the C fiber has a smaller diameter and less myelination.

Chart 7: Conduction Velocity

Axon type	Myelination	Stimulus voltage (mV)	Distance from R1 to R2 (m)	Time between action potentials at R1 and R2		Conduction velocity (m/sec)
				(msec)	(sec)	
A fiber	Heavy	30	.1	2	.002*	50*
B fiber	Light	30	.1	10	.01*	10*
C fiber	None	30	.1	100	.1*	1*

* The data in these columns are populated by student calculations.

Activity Questions:

1. The conduction velocity is dependent upon both myelination and the diameter of the axon. The large diameter of the squid axon contributes to its fast reaction.

2. The sharp immediate pain is probably carried by an A fiber with large diameter and heavy myelination. The slower dull pain is probably carried by a C fiber with small diameter and no myelination.

3. The mixture of axon types contributes to the variety of responses generated. Specifically, the rate with which a response is made can vary.

Activity 8: Chemical Synaptic Transmission and Neurotransmitter Release (pp. PEx-49–PEx-50)

Predict Question 1: There will be no neurotransmitter release if the extracellular calcium is removed.

Predict Question 2: When low amounts of calcium are added back to the extracellular solution, neurotransmitter release will increase a small amount.

Predict Question 3: There will be less neurotransmitter released when magnesium is added.

Activity Questions:

1. It is unlikely that sodium could substitute for calcium since the addition of magnesium blocked the calcium channels.

2. Botulinum toxin blocks the release of acetylcholine from the axon terminal. It is used in cosmetic procedures because it results in paralysis of the muscles that are contracting and causing the wrinkles.

Activity 9: The Action Potential: Putting It All Together (pp. PEx-50–PEx-52)

Predict Question 1: When you apply a very weak stimulus to the sensory receptor, small, depolarizing response will occur at R1, and no responses will occur at R2, R3, and R4.

Predict Question 2: When you apply a moderate stimulus to the sensory receptor, a larger, depolarizing response will occur at R1, and an action potential will be generated at R2 and maybe at R4.

Predict Question 3: When you apply a strong stimulus to the sensory receptor, a large, depolarizing response will occur at R1 and R3, and action potentials will occur at R2 and R4.

Chart 9: Putting It All Together

Stimulus	Peak value of response (mV)				
	Sensory neuron			Interneuron	
	Receptor	Axon	Axon terminal	Receptor	Axon
None	−70			−70	
Weak	−60	0	0	−70	0
Moderate	−40	16.6	4	−50	5
Strong	−25	33.3	6	−40	10

Activity Questions:

1. All action potentials are all or none. Threshold must be met, but once it is met, all action potentials are the same.

2. If the axons were unmyelinated, the peak value of the action potential wouldn't change.

Neurophysiology of Nerve Impulses

ACTIVITY 1 The Resting Membrane Potential

1. Explain why increasing extracellular K$^+$ reduces the net diffusion of K$^+$ out of the neuron through the K$^+$ leak channels.

   Increasing the extracellular potassium reduces the steepness of the concentration gradient and so less potassium diffuses out of the neuron.

2. Explain why increasing extracellular K$^+$ causes the membrane potential to change to a less negative value. How well did the results compare with your prediction? *The membrane potential became less negative because less potassium diffused out. If more potassium stays in, it is more positive or less negative.*

3. Explain why a change in extracellular Na$^+$ did not alter the membrane potential in the resting neuron. *There are less leakage sodium channels that leakage potassium channels, and more of the potassium channels are open.*

4. Discuss the relative permeability of the membrane to Na$^+$ and K$^+$ in a resting neuron. *The resting neuron is 4–5 times more permeable to potassium because of the increased number of leakage channels.*

5. Discuss how a change in Na$^+$ or K$^+$ conductance would affect the resting membrane potential. *A change in the potassium conductance would have a greater effect on the resting membrane potential than a change in sodium would.*

ACTIVITY 2 Receptor Potential

1. Sensory neurons have a resting potential based on the efflux of potassium ions (as demonstrated in Activity 1). What passive channels are likely found in the membrane of the olfactory receptor, in the membrane of the Pacinian corpuscle, and in the membrane of the free nerve ending? *The efflux of potassium ions is maintained by passive potassium channels.*

2. What is meant by the term graded potential? *Graded potentials are brief, localized changes in the membrane potential that can be either depolarizing or hyperpolarizing.*

3. Identify which of the stimulus modalities induced the largest amplitude receptor potential in the Pacinian corpuscle. How well did the results compare with your prediction? *The moderate intensity pressure modality induced a receptor potential of the largest amplitude in the Pacinian corpuscle.*

4. Identify which of the stimulus modalities induced the largest-amplitude receptor potential in the olfactory receptors. How well did the results compare with your prediction? *The moderate intensity chemical modality induced a receptor potential of the largest amplitude in the olfactory receptor.*

5. The olfactory receptor also contains a membrane protein that recognizes isoamyl acetate and, via several other molecules, transduces the odor stimulus into a receptor potential. Does the Pacinian corpuscle likely have this isoamyl acetate receptor protein? Does the free nerve ending likely have this isoamyl acetate receptor protein? *The Pacinian corpuscle and the free nerve ending are not likely to have the isoamyl acetate receptor because they did not respond to chemical stimuli.*

6. What type of sensory neuron would likely respond to a green light? *Photosensory neurons would respond to green light.*

ACTIVITY 3 **The Action Potential: Threshold**

1. Define the term *threshold* as it applies to an action potential. *Threshold is the voltage that must be reached in order to generate an action potential.*

2. What change in membrane potential (depolarization or hyperpolarization) triggers an action potential? *A depolarization in the membrane potential results in an action potential. The membrane potential must become less negative to generate an action potential.*

3. How did the action potential at R1 (or R2) change as you increased the stimulus voltage above the threshold voltage? How well did the results compare with your prediction? *The action potential didn't change as the stimulus voltage increased. This is because once threshold is met, the event is all or none, not graded.*

4. An action potential is an "all-or-nothing" event. Explain what is meant by this phrase. *This means that once threshold is met an action potential occurs. If the stimulus is too small an action potential does not occur.*

5. What part of a neuron was investigated in this activity? *The trigger zone was investigated. This is where the axon hillock and the initial segment come together.*

ACTIVITY 4 **The Action Potential: Importance of Voltage-Gated Na⁺ Channels**

1. What does TTX do to voltage-gated Na⁺ channels? *TTX blocks the diffusion of sodium through the voltage-gated sodium channels.*

2. What does lidocaine do to voltage-gated Na⁺ channels? How does the effect of lidocaine differ from the effect of TTX? *Lidocaine blocks the diffusion of sodium through the voltage-gated sodium channels.*

3. A nerve is a bundle of axons, and some nerves are less sensitive to lidocaine. If a nerve, rather than an axon, had been used in the lidocaine experiment, the responses recorded at R1 and R2 would be the sum of all the action potentials (called a compound action potential). Would the response at R2 after lidocaine application necessarily be zero? Why or why not? *With a compound action potential, the results would not necessarily be zero because some axons could remain unaffected.*

4. Why are fewer action potentials recorded at R2 when TTX is applied between R1 and R2? How well did the results compare with your prediction? *TTX blocked the sodium channels, preventing the propagation of the action potential from R1 to R2.*

5. Why are fewer action potentials recorded at R2 when lidocaine is applied between R1 and R2? How well did the results compare with your prediction? *Lidocaine blocked the sodium channels, preventing the propagation of the action potential from R1 to R2.*

6. Pain-sensitive neurons (called nociceptors) conduct action potentials from the skin or teeth to sites in the brain involved in pain perception. Where should a dentist inject the lidocaine to block pain perception? *Lidocaine should be applied to the receptors to prevent the generation of an action potential that would lead to the perception of pain.*

ACTIVITY 5 The Action Potential: Measuring Its Absolute and Relative Refractory Periods

1. Define *inactivation* as it applies to a voltage-gated sodium channel. *Voltage-gated sodium channels are inactivated when they no longer allow sodium to diffuse through.*

2. Define the absolute refractory period. *The absolute refractory period is the time in which no action potential can be generated regardless of the strength of the stimulus.*

3. How did the threshold for the second action potential change as you further decreased the interval between the stimuli? How well did the results compare with your prediction? *The threshold for the second action potential increased as the interval between the stimuli decreased as predicted.*

4. Why is it harder to generate a second action potential during the relative refractory period? *A greater stimulus is required because voltage-gated potassium channels that oppose depolarization are open during this time.*

ACTIVITY 6 The Action Potential: Coding for Stimulus Intensity

1. Why are multiple action potentials generated in response to a long stimulus that is above threshold? *The longer stimuli allow time for recovery and the above threshold allows the action potential to occur after the relative refractory period.*

2. Why does the frequency of action potentials increase when the stimulus intensity increases? How well did the results compare with your prediction? *Action potential can occur more frequently if there is a constant source of stimulation as long as the relative refractory period is reached.*

3. How does threshold change during the relative refractory period? *The threshold that must be achieved is higher than the original stimulus intensity during the relative refractory period.*

4. What is the relationship between the interspike interval and the frequency of action potentials? *The frequency of the action potentials is the reciprocal of the interspike interval with a conversion from milliseconds to seconds.*

ACTIVITY 7 The Action Potential: Conduction Velocity

1. How did the conduction velocity in the B fiber compare with that in the A fiber? How well did the results compare with your prediction? *The velocity of the B fiber was slower because it had a smaller diameter and was less myelinated.*

2. How did the conduction velocity in the C fiber compare with that in the B fiber? How well did the results compare with your prediction? *The conduction velocity of the C fiber was slower because it has no myelination and a smaller diameter.*

3. What is the effect of axon diameter on conduction velocity? *The larger the axon diameter, the greater the conduction velocity.*

4. What is the effect of the amount of myelination on conduction velocity? *The greater the myelination, the greater the conduction velocity.*

5. Why did the time between the stimulation and the action potential at R1 differ for each axon? *The time between the stimulation and the action potential at R1 differed for each axon because the diameter and the degree of myelination varied.*

6. Why did you need to change the timescale on the oscilloscope for each axon? *This is necessary in order to see the action potentials. The velocity changes so when it get very slow you need a longer time scale.*

ACTIVITY 8 Chemical Synaptic Transmission and Neurotransmitter Release

1. When the stimulus intensity is increased, what changes: the number of synaptic vesicles released or the amount of neurotransmitter per vesicle? *The number of synaptic vesicles released increases when the stimulus intensity increases.*

2. What happened to the amount of neurotransmitter release when you switched from the control extracellular fluid to the extracellular fluid with no Ca^{2+}? How well did the results compare with your prediction? *Without calcium present, no neurotransmitter was released because the exocytosis of the synaptic vesicles is dependent upon calcium.*

3. What happened to the amount of neurotransmitter release when you switched from the extracellular fluid with no Ca^{2+} to the extracellular fluid with low Ca^{2+}? How well did the results compare with your prediction? *When a small amount of calcium is added back, a small amount of synaptic vesicles are released.*

4. How did neurotransmitter release in the Mg^{2+} extracellular fluid compare to that in the control extracellular fluid? How well did the result compare with your prediction? *The neurotransmitter release was less when magnesium was added.*

5. How does Mg^{2+} block the effect of extracellular calcium on neurotransmitter release? *When magnesium is added to the extracellular fluid it blocks the calcium channels and inhibits the release of neurotransmitter.*

1. Why is the resting membrane potential the same value in both the sensory neuron and the interneuron? *The resting*

    membrane potential is the same value because this is the typical resting membrane potential regardless of the type of neuron.

2. Describe what happened when you applied a very weak stimulus to the sensory receptor. How well did the results compare

    with your prediction? *When you applied a very weak stimulus to the sensory receptor, a small, depolarizing response occurred at*

    R1, and no responses occurred at R2, R3, and R4.

3. Describe what happened when you applied a moderate stimulus to the sensory receptor. How well did the results compare

    with your prediction? *When you applied a moderate stimulus to the sensory receptor, a larger, depolarizing response occurred at R1,*

    and an action potential was generated at R2 and at R4.

4. Identify the type of membrane potential (graded receptor potential or action potential) that occurred at R1, R2, R3, and R4

    when you applied a moderate stimulus. (View the response to the stimulus.) *Action potentials occurred at R2 and R4 and*

    graded receptor potentials occurred at R1 and R3.

5. Describe what happened when you applied a strong stimulus to the sensory receptor. How well did the results compare with

    your prediction? *When you applied a strong stimulus to the sensory receptor, a large, depolarizing response occurred at R1 and R3,*

    and action potentials occurred at R2 and R4.

Endocrine System Physiology

Advance Preparation/Comments

Consider covering the following topics to prepare students for the simulation:

- Describe the regulation of thyroid hormone secretion.
- Explain the relationship between the hypophysis (pituitary gland) and the hypothalamus.
- Describe the synthesis of thyroid hormones, thyroxine and triiodothyronine.
- Explain disorders that result in goiter formation.
- Review the factors that contribute to bone density.
- Explain the regulation of blood glucose levels and the types of diabetes mellitus.
- Describe the regulation of glucocorticoid release from the adrenal gland.
- Describe the diseases associated with glucocorticoid imbalance.

Answers to Questions/Experimental Data

Pre-lab Quiz in the Lab Manual

1. Metabolism is defined as all of the chemical reactions that are necessary to maintain life.
2. Catabolism
3. Thyroid hormone
4. Control
5. b, increased in individuals with hyperthyroidism
6. c, oxygen
7. True
8. insulin

Activity 1: Metabolism and Thyroid Hormone (pp. PEx-60–PEx-64)

1h. 420–432 ml

1i. 1687–1734

Predict Question 1: The BMR of both remaining rats will be lower than the normal rat's BMR

Predict Question 2: The normal rat will become hyperthyroidic but will not develop a goiter.

Predict Question 3: The normal rat will become hyperthyroidic and develop a goiter.

Predict Question 4: The normal rat will become hypothyroidic and develop a goiter.

Chart 1: Effects of Hormones on Metabolic Rate

	Normal rat	Thyroidectomized rat	Hypophysectomized rat
Baseline			
Weight (g)	Variable, 249–251	Variable, 244–246	Variable, 244–246
ml O_2 used in 1 minute	Variable, 7.0–7.2	Variable, 6.2–6.4	Variable, 6.2–6.4
ml O_2 used per hour	420–432*	372–384*	372–384*
Metabolic rate	1673–1735 ml O_2/kg/hr*	1512–1574 ml O_2/kg/hr*	1512–1574 ml O_2/kg/hr*
Palpation results	No mass	No mass	No mass
With thyroxine			
Weight (g)	Same as baseline	Same as baseline	Same as baseline
ml O_2 used in 1 minute	Variable, 8.3–8.5	Variable, 7.7–7.9	Variable, 7.7–7.9
ml O_2 used per hour	498–510 ml	462–474 ml	462–474 ml
Metabolic rate	1984–2048 ml O_2/kg/hr	1878–1943 ml O_2/kg/hr	1878–1943 ml O_2/kg/hr
Palpation results	No mass	No mass	No mass
With TSH			
Weight (g)	Same as baseline	Same as baseline	Same as baseline
ml O_2 used in 1 minute	Variable, 7.9–8.1	Variable, 6.2–6.4	Variable, 7.7–7.9
ml O_2 used per hour	474–486 ml	372–384 ml	462–474 ml
Metabolic rate	1904 ml O_2/kg/hr	1512–1574 ml O_2/kg/hr	1878–1943 ml O_2/kg/hr
Palpation results	Mass	No mass	Mass
With propylthiouracil			
Weight (g)	Same as baseline	Same as baseline	Same as baseline
ml O_2 used in 1 minute	Variable, 6.2–6.4	Variable, 6.2–6.4	Variable, 6.2–6.4
ml O_2 used per hour	372–384 ml	372–384 ml	372–384 ml
Metabolic rate	1482–1542 ml O_2/kg/hr	1512–1574 ml O_2/kg/hr	1512–1574 ml O_2/kg/hr
Palpation results	Mass	No mass	No mass

* Data populated by student calculations.

Activity Questions:

1. The carbon dioxide is absorbed by the soda lime in the bottom of the glass chamber.
2. The fluid levels would increase due to the additional oxygen utilized for the exercising rat.
3. The hypothalamus secretes TRH which stimulates the release of TSH by the pituitary gland. TSH stimulates the thyroid gland to produce thyroxine.
4. A tropic hormone stimulates or inhibits another endocrine gland to secrete hormones.
5. Thyroidectomized rats could be treated with thyroxine to replace the hormone that is not available because the thyroid gland is missing.
6. The hypothalamus secretes TRH which stimulates the release of TSH.
7. TRH travels from the hypothalamus to the pituitary gland via the hypothalamic-pituitary portal system.
8. TSH has no effect on the thyroidectomized rat because the rat doesn't have a thyroid gland to stimulate.
9. The administration of PTU had no effect on the thyroidectomized and hypophysectomized rats because they lack the glands required for the production of thyroxine.
10. The buildup of the precursors to thyroxine can occur if there is no available iodine to complete the thyroxine formation. The lack of iodine can also result in goiter.

Activity 2: Plasma Glucose, Insulin, and Diabetes Mellitus (pp. PEx-64–PEx-67)

Predict Question 1: The optical density of the sample will be measured and the glucose concentration will be extrapolated from the glucose standard curve.

Chart 2.1 Glucose Standard Curve Results

Tube	Optical density	Glucose (mg/dl)
1	0.30	30
2	0.50	60
3	0.60	90
4	0.80	120
5	1.00	150

Chart 2.2 Fasting Plasma Glucose Results

Sample	Optical density	Glucose (mg/dl)
1	0.73	104
2	0.79	115
3	0.89	131
4	0.83	122
5	0.96	143

Activity Questions:

1. The optical density should be proportional to the concentration of glucose producing a roughly straight line. An aberrant glucose standard curve would not produce a straight line.

2. Some potential sources of variability include experimental error in measurement of the reagents and inherent variability of the spectrophotometer measurements.

3. Patients in the borderline range should be counseled to alter their diet and exercise. Their diet should limit the ingestion of simple sugars and their exercise level should be increased.

4. Our current diet trends are contributing to an increase in the prevalence of Type II diabetes in children.

Activity 3: Hormone Replacement Therapy (pp. PEx-67–PEx-69)

Predict Question 1: The saline injections will not change the rat's vertebral bone density (indicated by an unchanging T score).

Predict Question 2: The estrogen injections will increase the rat's vertebral bone density (indicated by a less-negative T score).

Predict Question 3: The calcitonin injections will not change the rat's vertebral bone density (indicated by an unchanging T score).

Chart 2.3 Hormone Replacement Therapy Results

Rat	T score
Control	Variable, –2.81 to –2.85
Estrogen	Variable, –1.52 to –1.74
Calcitonin	Variable, –2.05 to –2.35

Activity Questions:

1. Student's answers will vary depending upon their research. Possibly they will describe estrogen therapy and the risks associated with this therapy.

2. The dosage of hormone replacement will be determined by the current levels of hormones found in the body using blood tests.

Activity 4: Measuring Cortisol and Adrenocorticotropic Hormone (pp. PEx-69–PEx-70)

Chart 4: Measurement of Cortisol

Patient	Cortisol (mcg/dl)	Cortisol level	ACTH (pg/ml)	ACTH level
1	Variable, 3 ± 1	Low*	Variable, 18 ± 2	Low*
2	Variable, 35 ± 5	High*	Variable, 13 ± 2	Low*
3	Variable, 45 ± 5	High*	Variable, 86 ± 5	High*
4	Variable, 3 ± 1	Low*	Variable, 100 ± 5	High*
5	Variable, 50 ± 5	High*	Variable, 18 ± 2	Low*

* The entries in these columns are designated by the student in the software.

Activity Questions:

1. The benefits of glucocorticoid therapy include dilation of the airway. The drawbacks are the side effects associated with long-term treatment. These include high blood pressure, bone thinning, high blood sugar levels, suppression of the immune response, and weight gain.

2. Cushing's syndrome is primary hypercortisolism resulting from an adrenal gland tumor. Cushing's disease is secondary hypercortisolism resulting from a pituitary tumor.

Endocrine System Physiology

ACTIVITY 1 Metabolism and Thyroid Hormone

Part 1

1. Which rat had the fastest basal metabolic rate (BMR)? *The normal rat had the fastest basal metabolic rate because it was not missing its pituitary gland or its thyroid gland.*

2. Why did the metabolic rates differ between the normal rat and the surgically altered rats? How well did the results compare with your prediction? *The normal rat has the highest BMR because it has the glands required to stimulate and regulate the release of thyroid hormones.*

3. If an animal has been thyroidectomized, what hormone(s) would be missing in its blood? *For the thyroidectomized rats the hormones missing will be triiodothyronine and thyroxine.*

4. If an animal has been hypophysectomized, what effect would you expect to see in the hormone levels in its body? *For the hypophysectomized rat, the TSH will be missing due to the missing pituitary gland.*

Part 2

5. What was the effect of thyroxine injections on the normal rat's BMR? *The levels were a little off. The normal rat was hyperthyroidic because the thyroxine increases the metabolic rate but it did not develop goiter.*

6. What was the effect of thyroxine injections on the thyroidectomized rat's BMR? How does the BMR in this case compare with the normal rat's BMR? Was the dose of thyroxine in the syringe too large, too small, or just right? *The BMR increased for the thyroidectomized rat with thyroxine injections. The BMR was still a little bit below the normal rat's BMR with thyroxine. The dose was too low.*

7. What was the effect of thyroxine injections on the hypophysectomized rat's BMR? How does the BMR in this case compare with the normal rat's BMR? Was the dose of thyroxine in the syringe too large, too small, or just right? *The BMR increased for the hypophysectomized rat with thyroxine injections. The BMR was still a little bit below the normal rat's BMR with thyroxine. The dose was too low.*

Part 3

8. What was the effect of thyroid-stimulating hormone (TSH) injections on the normal rat's BMR? *The effect of TSH was to increase the normal rat's BMR.*

9. What was the effect of TSH injections on the thyroidectomized rat's BMR? How does the BMR in this case compare with the normal rat's BMR? Why was this effect observed? *There was no effect on the thyroidectomized rat's BMR with the injection of TSH because there was no thyroid gland to stimulate.*

10. What was the effect of TSH injections on the hypophysectomized rat's BMR? How does the BMR in this case compare with the normal rat's BMR? Was the dose of TSH in the syringe too large, too small, or just right? *The hypophysectomized rat BMR increased with TSH. The BMR was just below the normal rat but still lower. The syringe amount was a little too low.*

Part 4

11. What was the effect of propylthiouracil (PTU) injections on the normal rat's BMR? Why did this rat develop a palpable goiter? *The effect of PTU injections on the normal rat was to decrease the BMR. The palpable goiter was due to the buildup of the precursors to thyroxine.*

12. What was the effect of PTU injections on the thyroidectomized rat's BMR? How does the BMR in this case compare with the normal rat's BMR? Why was this effect observed? *The effect of PTU injections on the thyroidectomized rat was not visible because there was no thyroid gland to be affected.*

13. What was the effect of PTU injections on the hypophysectomized rat's BMR? How does the BMR in this case compare with the normal rat's BMR? Why was this effect observed? *The effect of PTU injections on the hypophysectomized rat was not visible because the rat is missing the pituitary gland.*

ACTIVITY 2   Plasma Glucose, Insulin, and Diabetes Mellitus

1. What is a glucose standard curve, and why did you need to obtain one for this experiment? Did you correctly predict how you would measure the amount of plasma glucose in a patient sample using the glucose standard curve? *The glucose standard curve correlates the intensity of the color obtained and measured on a spectrophotometer (optical density) to the glucose concentration.*

2. Which patient(s) had glucose reading(s) in the diabetic range? Can you say with certainty whether each of these patients has type 1 or type 2 diabetes? Why or why not? *Patients 3 and 5 had a fasting plasma glucose in the diabetic range. It is not possible to tell if they have type 1 or type 2 just from their fasting plasma glucose.*

3. Describe the diagnosis for patient 3, who was also pregnant at the time of this assay. *This would be described as gestational diabetes. The diabetes often disappears after the pregnancy.*

4. Which patient(s) had normal glucose reading(s)? _Patients 1 and 2 were in the normal range._

5. What are some lifestyle choices these patients with normal plasma glucose readings might recommend to the borderline impaired patients? _Limit the ingestion of simple sugars. Choose "good" carbohydrates such as whole wheat and fiber-based carbohydrate choices._

ACTIVITY 3   **Hormone Replacement Therapy**

1. Why were ovariectomized rats used in this experiment? How does the fact that the rats are ovariectomized explain their baseline T scores? _The ovaries produce estrogen and estrogen stimulates bone growth. Without estrogen bone growth is impaired and osteoporosis is a common result._

2. What effect did the administration of saline injections have on the control rat? How well did the results compare with your prediction? _The saline had no effect. The inclusion of the saline as a negative control is to insure that saline has no effect._

3. What effect did the administration of estrogen injections have on the estrogen-treated rat? How well did the results compare with your prediction? _The estrogen injections did increase the rat's vertebral bone density as predicted and as indicated by the negative T score._

4. What effect did the administration of calcitonin injections have on the calcitonin-treated rat? How well did the results compare with your prediction? _The calcitonin showed no change in the vertebral bone density. This is somewhat contradictory to what is expected. We do not know why._

5. What are some health risks that postmenopausal women must consider when contemplating estrogen hormone replacement therapy? _Health risks of estrogen therapy include an increased incidence of uterine cancer, breast cancer, and blood clots._

ACTIVITY 4   **Measuring Cortisol and Adrenocorticotropic Hormone**

1. Which patient would most likely be diagnosed with Cushing's disease? Why? _Patient 3 would be diagnosed with Cushing's disease because the levels of cortisol and ACTH are both high._

2. Which two patients have hormone levels characteristic of Cushing's syndrome? _Patients 2 and 5 both have high levels of cortisol and low ACTH. These levels are characteristic of Cushing's syndrome._

3. Patient 2 is being treated for rheumatoid arthritis with prednisone. How does this information change the diagnosis? _The diagnosis would change to iatrogenic or physician-induced Cushing's syndrome._

4. Which patient would most likely be diagnosed with Addison's disease? Why? _Patient 4 would be diagnosed with Addison's disease because the level of ACTH is high but the level of cortisol is low._

Cardiovascular Dynamics

Advance Preparation/Comments

Consider doing a short introductory presentation with the following elements:

- Describe the basics of peripheral resistance.
- Encourage students to try to apply the concepts from the simulation to the human as they work through the program.
- If a demonstration computer screen is available, show students both main screens of the simulation and describe the basic equipment parts.
- Explain how the simulated pump is similar to the left ventricle (or the right ventricle) of the heart.
- Point out the fact that the pump operates much like a syringe, with adjustable starting and ending volumes.
- It is often helpful to explain the basics of end diastolic and end systolic volumes and their relationship to the simulated pump.
- Indicate the analogies between the parts of the simulation and the parts of the human cardiovascular system.

Answers to Questions/Experimental Data

Pre-lab Quiz in the Lab Manual

1. diastole
2. b, cardiac cycle
3. True
4. b, 75
5. murmurs
6. c, pulse
7. radial artery
8. sphygmomanometer
9. 90, the number on the bottom
10. d, sounds of Korotkoff

Activity 1: Studying the Effect of Blood Vessel Radius on Blood Flow Rate (pp. PEx-76–PEx-78)

Predict Question 1: If the radius is increased, the flow rate will increase.

Predict Question 2: The graph of a plot of radius versus flow rate will not be linear.

Chart 1: Effect of Blood Vessel Radius on Blood Flow Rate

Flow (ml/min)	Radius (mm)
4.0	1.5
12.6	2.0
30.7	2.5
63.6	3.0
117.8	3.5
201.0	4.0
321.9	4.5
490.6	5.0

Activity Questions:

1. The radius and blood flow are directly proportional to each other. As the vessel radius increases, the blood flow also increases.

2. Depending upon the local needs of nutrients and oxygen by the tissues, blood vessels will increase or decrease their radii by altering the amount of contraction of the smooth muscle in the tunica media. The alteration of vessel diameter is controlled by the autonomic nervous system.

3. The plot is not linear. It is curved because blood flow varies directly in an exponential fashion to the radius.

4. Slower blood flow allows for more time for nutrient and gas exchange to occur between the blood and the surrounding cells.

Activity 2: Studying the Effect of Blood Viscosity on Blood Flow Rate (pp. PEx-78–PEx-79)

Predict Question 1: Increasing viscosity will result in a decrease in the fluid flow rate.

Chart 2: Effect of Blood Viscosity on Blood Flow Rate

Flow (ml/min)	Viscosity
490.6	1.0
245.3	2.0
163.5	3.0
122.7	4.0
98.1	5.0
81.8	6.0
70.1	7.0
61.3	8.0

Activity Questions:

1. As viscosity increases, the blood flow decreases. Viscosity and blood flow are inversely proportional to each other.

2. When viscosity increases, the blood is thicker and there is a greater resistance to flow. This results in a decrease in the flow rate.

3. Increasing the number of blood cells would increase the viscosity. This would result in a decrease in the flow rate due to the increased viscosity.

Activity 3: Studying the Effect of Blood Vessel Length on Blood Flow Rate (pp. PEx-79–PEx-80)

Predict Question 1: Increasing the flow tube length, will result in a decrease in the fluid flow rate.

Chart 3: Effect of Blood Vessel Length on Blood Flow Rate

Flow (ml/min)	Flow Tube length (mm)
90.8	10
60.6	15
45.4	20
36.3	25
30.3	30
26.0	35
22.7	40

Activity Questions:

1. The relationship between blood vessel length and fluid flow rate is that they are inversely proportional to each other.

2. Blood vessel diameter can vary more quickly than blood vessel length.

3. The resistance increases when the blood vessel length increases because there is more interaction between the blood and the blood vessel.

Activity 4: Studying the Effect of Blood Pressure on Blood Flow Rate (pp. PEx-80–PEx-82)

Predict Question 1: Increasing the pressure will result in an increase in fluid flow rate.

Predict Question 2: The graph should be linear because the relationship between pressure and blood flow is linear.

Chart 4: Effect of Blood Pressure on Blood Flow Rate

Flow (ml/min)	Pressure (mm Hg)
35.0	25
70.1	50
105.1	75
140.2	100
175.2	125
210.3	150
245.3	175
280.4	200

Activity Questions:

1. Increasing the driving pressure results in an increase in the blood flow rate.

2. The relationship between blood pressure and blood flow rate is directly proportional because if one variable is increased the other variable also increases and vice versa.

3. The cardiovascular system increases pressure by increasing the force of contraction of the heart.

4. Increases in blood pressure can cause problems since the blood vessels are not able to handle the blood delivered at increased force for long periods of time.

Activity 5: Studying the Effect of Blood Vessel Radius on Pump Activity (pp. PEx-82–PEx-83)

Predict Question 1: The pump rate will increase to maintain constant pressure.

Chart 5: Effect of Blood Vessel Radius on Pump Activity

Flow rate (ml/min)	Right radius (mm)	Pump rate (strokes/min)
6607.2	3.0	94.9
9423.9	3.5	134.6
11882.5	4.0	169.8
13798.3	4.5	197.1
15198.7	5.0	217.1

Activity Questions:

1. During diastole, the position of the pump is moving up. At the end of diastole, the pump is at the highest position.

2. During systole, the position of the pump is moving down. At the end of systole, the pump is at the lowest position.

3. As blood vessel radius increased, the flow rate increased.

4. When the radius was increased, the resistance decreased and the pump rate increased to maintain pressure.

Activity 6: Studying the Effect of Stroke Volume on Pump Activity (pp. PEx-84–PEx-85)

Predict Question 1: The pump rate will decrease to maintain cardiac output.

Chart 6: Effect of Stroke Volume on Pump Activity

Flow rate (ml/min)	Stroke volume (ml)	Pump rate (strokes/min)
5086.8	10	508.7
5086.8	20	254.3
5086.8	30	169.6
5086.8	40	127.2
5086.8	50	101.7
5086.8	60	84.8
5086.8	80	63.6
5086.8	100	50.8

Activity Questions:

1. With an increase in end diastolic volume, preload increases stretching the cardiac muscle more. In order to maintain cardiac output, the heart would increase contractility and stroke volume.

2. The pump rate decreased when the stroke volume increased. The heart doesn't have to pump as often to maintain cardiac output.

3. With increased cardiovascular conditioning, the heart is able to pump more forcefully resulting in a greater stroke volume. With increased stroke volume, the heart doesn't have to pump as often to maintain cardiac output.

Activity 7: Compensation in Pathological Cardiovascular Conditions (pp. PEx-86–PEx-88)

Predict Question 1: Decreasing the pressure in the right (destination) beaker should have the greatest effect.

Predict Question 2: If the pump pressure and the beaker pressure are the same, the flow will stop.

Chart 7: Compensation Results

Condition	Flow rate (ml/min)	Left radius (mm)	Right radius (mm)	Pump rate (strokes/min)	Pump pressure (mm Hg)	Right beaker pressure (mm Hg)
Normal	5086.8	3.0	3.0	72.7	40	40
Aortic stenosis	3310.0	3.0	2.5	47.3	40	40
Increased preload	3892.9	3.5	2.5	55.6	40	40
Increased preload	4256.7	4.0	2.5	60.8	40	40
Increased preload	4479.5	4.5	2.5	64.0	40	40
Increased contractility	3826.3	3.0	2.5	54.7	40	50
Increased contractility	4270.3	3.0	2.5	61.0	40	60
Decreased contractility	4656.3	3.0	2.5	66.5	40	70
Decreased afterload	3826.3	3.0	2.5	54.7	40	80
Decreased afterload	4270.3	3.0	2.5	61.0	40	60
Decreased afterload	4656.3	3.0	2.5	70	66.5	70

Activity Questions:

1. The thickness of the myocardium increases with athletes heart due to the increased demand placed on the heart with cardiovascular conditioning. In the diseased heart, the thickness increases to overcome the increased preload.

NAME _____

LAB TIME/DATE _____

Cardiovascular Dynamics

ACTIVITY 1 Studying the Effect of Blood Vessel Radius on Blood Flow Rate

1. Explain how the body establishes a pressure gradient for fluid flow. *The body establishes a pressure gradient for fluid flow due to the pressure difference between the two ends of the vessel.*

2. Explain the effect that the flow tube radius change had on flow rate. How well did the results compare with your prediction? *Increasing the flow tube radius resulted in an increase in the flow rate.*

3. Describe the effect that radius changes have on the laminar flow of a fluid. *Fully constricted vessels do not favor laminar flow because there is more blood in contact with the vessel wall and the blood does not flow as freely.*

4. Why do you think the plot was not linear? (Hint: Look at the relationship of the variables in the equation.) How well did the results compare with your prediction? *The plot of radius vs. blood flow is not linear because of the exponential relationship between the two variables.*

ACTIVITY 2 Studying the Effect of Blood Viscosity on Blood Flow Rate

1. Describe the components in the blood that affect viscosity. *The formed elements and plasma proteins affect viscosity. These include leukocytes, erythrocytes, platelets, and proteins such as albumin.*

2. Explain the effect that the viscosity change had on flow rate. How well did the results compare with your prediction? *Increasing the viscosity decreased the fluid flow rate because it made the blood effectively thicker and increased the resistance to flow.*

3. Describe the graph of flow versus viscosity. *The graph was not linear. It was exponential. It showed also that the relationship between viscosity and flow is inversely proportional.*

4. Discuss the effect that polycythemia would have on viscosity and on blood flow. *Polycythemia is an increase in the red blood cell numbers. This would result in an increase in viscosity and a corresponding decrease in blood flow.*

ACTIVITY 3 Studying the Effect of Blood Vessel Length on Blood Flow Rate

1. Which is more likely to occur, a change in blood vessel radius or a change in blood vessel length? Explain why. *A change in blood vessel radius is more likely to occur. These changes occur on a daily basis to accommodate homeostasis.*

2. Explain the effect that the change in blood vessel length had on flow rate. How well did the results compare with your prediction? *The fluid flow rate did decrease as the flow tube length increased. This is analogous to an increase in blood vessel length that would result in a decrease in fluid flow rate.*

3. Explain why you think blood vessel radius can have a larger effect on the body than changes in blood vessel length (use the blood flow equation). *The blood vessel radius varies to a power of four which is why the changes are greater than blood vessel length changes.*

4. Describe the effect that obesity would have on blood flow and why. *Obesity would decrease blood flow. The decrease is a result of increased blood vessel length generated to serve the increase in adipose.*

ACTIVITY 4 Studying the Effect of Blood Pressure on Blood Flow Rate

1. Explain the effect that pressure changes had on flow rate. How well did the results compare with your prediction? *The increase in pressure resulted in a corresponding increase in flow rate. A decrease in pressure would result in a decrease in flow rate.*

2. How does the plot differ from the plots for tube radius, viscosity, and tube length? How well did the results compare with your prediction? *The plot was linear. The other plots were curved.*

3. Explain why pressure changes are not the best way to control blood flow. *Diameter changes are much easier for the body to make. Pressure changes require the heart to beat harder which is difficult for the heart to sustain.*

4. Use your data to calculate the increase in flow rate in ml/min/mm Hg. *1.4 ml/min/mm Hg. To calculate divide the flow rate change by the change in pressure.*

ACTIVITY 5 Studying the Effect of Blood Vessel Radius on Pump Activity

1. Explain the effect of increasing the right flow tube radius on the flow rate, resistance, and pump rate. *As the right flow tube radius is increased, blood flow increases, resistance decreases, and the pump rate increases.*

2. Describe what the left and right beakers in the experiment correspond to in the human heart. *The left beaker simulates blood coming from the lungs. The right beaker simulates blood traveling to the systemic circuit.*

3. Briefly describe how the human heart could compensate for flow rate changes to maintain blood pressure. *If the flow rate increases, the heart must pump faster to maintain blood pressure.*

ACTIVITY 6 Studying the Effect of Stroke Volume on Pump Activity

1. Describe the Frank-Starling law in the heart. *This law states that, when more blood than normal is returned to the heart, the heart muscle will be stretched, resulting in a more forceful contraction of the ventricles.*

2. Explain what happened to the pump rate when you increased the stroke volume. Why do you think this occurred? How well did the results compare with your prediction? _With increased stroke volume, the pump rate will decrease to maintain cardiac output._

3. Describe how the heart alters stroke volume. _The heart alters stroke volume by altering contractility, the force of contraction. Increasing the force of contraction will increase stroke volume._

4. Describe the intrinsic factors that control stroke volume. _Intrinsic factors that control stroke volume are those that reside entirely within the heart. This includes the alteration of contractility._

ACTIVITY 7   Compensation in Pathological Cardiovascular Conditions

1. Explain how the heart could compensate for changes in peripheral resistance. _The heart can compensate for changes in peripheral resistance by increasing contractility._

2. Which mechanism had the greatest compensatory effect? How well did the results compare with your prediction?
Decreasing the pressure in the right-most beaker (the destination beaker) had the greatest effect because this decreases afterload.

3. Explain what happened when the pump pressure and the beaker pressure were the same. How well did the results compare with your prediction? _When the pump pressure and the beaker pressure were the same, the flow stopped._

4. Explain whether it would be better to adjust heart rate or blood vessel diameter to achieve blood flow changes at a local level (for example, in just the digestive system). _At a local level, it is best to adjust the blood vessel diameter. Therefore, the effects will only be seen locally. Adjustments to the heart rate would have systemic effects._

Cardiovascular Physiology

Advance Preparation/Comments

1. Suggest to the students that they become familiar with the exercise before coming to lab. If students have a home computer, or access to a computer on campus, they can become familiar with the general operation of the simulations.

2. A short introductory presentation with the following elements is often helpful:
   • Review the basics of heart anatomy and physiology, particularly the sequence of atrial to ventricular contraction.
   • Reinforce the concept of the electrical system of the heart, including the basics of electrical function at the cellular level.
   • Mention the sympathetic and parasympathetic connections to the heart, including the neurotransmitters and their functions.
   • Compare how this procedure is accomplished in a traditional wet lab to what they expect to see in the simulation.

Answers to Questions/Experimental Data

Pre-lab Quiz in the Lab Manual

1. True
2. b, rhythmicity
3. b, three
4. True
5. an extra contraction of the ventricles that occurs after normal systole
6. b, digitalis
7. d, vagus
8. vagal escape
9. True
10. c, Histamine

Activity 1: Investigating the Refractory Period of Cardiac Muscle (pp. PEx-94–PEx-95)

1. Variable, ~59

Predict Question 1: When you increase the frequency of the stimulation, the amplitude will not change.

Predict Question 2: Neither wave summation nor tetanus will occur at 20 stimuli per second.

Activity Questions:

1. The frog heart has only three chambers, two atria and a single incompletely divided ventricle. The human heart has four discreet chambers.

2. The extrasystole corresponds to an extra contraction of the ventricles. It was produced by administering a series of single stimuli in rapid succession.

3. Wave summation and tetanus do not occur in cardiac muscle because the flow of blood through the heart is dependent upon the atria contracting fully and the ventricles contracting fully. Summation would prevent the heart from pumping properly.

Activity 2: Examining the Effect of Vagus Nerve Stimulation (pp. PEx-95–PEx-96)

1. Variable, ~62

3. Variable, ~62

Predict Question 1: If you apply multiple stimuli to the heart via the vagus nerve, the heart rate will decrease and the heart will stop.

Activity Questions:

1. Stimulation of the vagus nerve decreases the heart rate.

2. The sympathetic nervous system increases the heart rate and also increases the force of contraction of the heart.

3. The resumption of the heartbeat is referred to as vagal escape and can be the result of sympathetic reflexes or initiation of a rhythm by the Purkinje fibers.

4. The heart rate would increase if the vagus nerve was cut.

Activity 3: Examining the Effect of Temperature on Heart Rate (pp. PEx-96–PEx-98)

Predict Question 1: Decreasing the temperature of the Ringer's solution will result in a decrease in heart rate.

Predict Question 2: Increasing the temperature of the Ringer's solution will result in an increase in heart rate.

Chart 3: Effect of Temperature on Heart Rate

Solution	Heart rate (beats/min)
23°C Ringer's	Variable, ~62
5°C Ringer's	Variable, ~52
32°C Ringer's	Variable, ~72

Activity Questions:

1. Ringer's solution consists of essential electrolytes required for the spontaneous action potentials of the heart.

2. Decreasing the temperature of the Ringer's solution resulted in a decrease in heart rate.

3. Fever would increase the internal body temperature and therefore increase the heart rate.

Activity 4: Examining the Effects of Chemical Modifiers on Heart Rate (pp. PEx-98–PEx-99)

Predict Question 1: Pilocarpine will decrease heart rate.

Predict Question 2: Atropine will increase heart rate.

Chart 4: Effects of Chemical Modifiers on Heart Rate

Solution	Heart rate (beats/min)
—	Variable, ~62
Epinephrine	Variable, ~82
Pilocarpine	Variable, ~47
Atropine	Variable, ~73
Digitalis	Variable, ~43

Activity Questions:

1. If a modifier works in the same fashion it is an agonist, for example, pilocarpine is an acetylcholine agonist. If the modifier works in the opposite direction, it is an antagonist, for example, atropine is an acetylcholine antagonist.

2. Epinephrine increases the heart rate and also increases the force of contraction of the heart.

3. Atropine increases the heart rate because it is an acetylcholine antagonist.

4. Digitalis decreases the heart rate and increases the force of contraction.

Activity 5: Examining the Effects of Various Ions on Heart Rate (pp. PEx-99–PEx-101)

Predict Question 1: Calcium should be positive inotropic (increasing the force of contraction) and positive chronotropic (increasing the heart rate).

Predict Question 2: The initial effect of potassium should be to decrease the heart rate.

Chart 5: Effects of Various Ions on Heart Rate

Solution	Heart rate (beats/min)
—	Variable, ~59
Calcium	Variable, ~69
Sodium	Variable, ~34 then erratic
Potassium	Variable, ~28 then erratic

Activity Questions:

1. Modifiers that affect heart rate are chronotropic, and modifiers that affect the force of contraction are inotropic.

2. The addition of calcium ions to the frog heart increased the heart rate.

3. Calcium channel blockers reduce the force of contraction of the heart which would decrease blood pressure. Additionally, calcium channel blockers reduce the amount of calcium that flows into vascular smooth muscle which in turn lowers vasomotor tone and decreases peripheral resistance.

4. The initial effect of potassium ion addition was to decrease the heart rate.

NAME _____

LAB TIME/DATE _____

Cardiovascular Physiology

ACTIVITY 1 Investigating the Refractory Period of Cardiac Muscle

1. Explain why the larger waves seen on the oscilloscope represent ventricular contraction.

The ventricles are larger chambers therefore, when they contract they generate more force thus producing a larger wave.

2. Explain why the amplitude of the wave did not change when you increased the frequency of the stimulation. (Hint: Relate your response to the refractory period of the cardiac action potential.) How well did the results compare with your prediction?

The amplitude did not change because of the long absolute refractory period of cardiac muscle tissue which insures that the extrasystole doesn't occur during contraction.

3. Why is it only possible to induce an extrasystole during relaxation? *The extrasystole did not occur until relaxation and so we could not achieve wave summation or tetanus.*

4. Explain why wave summation and tetanus are not possible in cardiac muscle tissue. How well did the results compare with your prediction? *Wave summation and tetanus are not possible because relaxation must complete before the next contraction can begin due to the long absolute refractory period.*

ACTIVITY 2 Examining the Effect of Vagus Nerve Stimulation

1. Explain the effect that extreme vagus nerve stimulation had on the heart. How well did the results compare with your prediction?
The heart rate decreased and stopped temporarily.

2. Explain two ways that the heart can overcome excessive vagal stimulation. *The heart can overcome excessive vagal stimulation through sympathetic reflexes and the initiation of a rhythm by the Purkinje fibers.*

3. Describe how the sympathetic and parasympathetic nervous systems work together to regulate heart rate. *The sympathetic and parasympathetic branches can take turns dominating depending upon what is going on in the body.*

4. What do you think would happen to the heart rate if the vagus nerve was cut? *The heart rate would speed up. It would go back to the 100 bpm, the intrinsic rate.*

ACTIVITY 3 Examining the Effect of Temperature on Heart Rate

1. Explain the effect that decreasing the temperature had on the frog heart. How do you think the human heart would respond? How well did the results compare with your prediction? *Decreasing the temperature of the frog heart decreased the heart rate. This effect would not be seen in humans because we are not poikilothermic animals.*

2. Describe why Ringer's solution is required to maintain heart contractions. *Ringer's solution includes the ions that are*

required for the spontaneous contractions and autorhythmicity.

3. Explain the effect that increasing the temperature had on the frog heart. How do you think the human heart would respond? How well did the results compare with your prediction? *Increasing the temperature of the frog heart increased the heart rate.*

This effect would not be seen in humans because we are not poikilothermic animals.

ACTIVITY 4 **Examining the Effects of Chemical Modifiers on Heart Rate**

1. Describe the effect that pilocarpine had on the heart and why it had this effect. How well did the results compare with your prediction? *Pilocarpine decreased the heart rate because it is an acetylcholine agonist. It decreased the frequency of action*

potentials.

2. Atropine is an acetylcholine antagonist. Does atropine inhibit or enhance the effects of acetylcholine? Describe your results and how they correlate with how the drug works. How well did the results compare with your prediction? *As an*

acetylcholine antagonist, atropine would increase the heart rate working in opposition to acetylcholine.

3. Describe the benefits of administering digitalis. *Digitalis decreases the heart rate and increases the force of contraction thus*

increasing stroke volume.

4. Distinguish between cholinergic and adrenergic chemical modifiers. Include examples of each in your discussion. *Cholinergic*

modifiers affect acetylcholine action such as pilocarpine and atropine. Adrenergic modifiers affect epinephrine action such as

epinephrine itself.

ACTIVITY 5 **Examining the Effects of Various Ions on Heart Rate**

1. Describe the effect that increasing the calcium ions had on the heart. How well did the results compare with your prediction? *The addition of calcium ions to the frog heart increased the heart rate.*

2. Describe the effect that increasing the potassium ions initially had on the heart in this activity. Relate this to the resting membrane potential of the cardiac muscle cell. How well did the results compare with your prediction? *The initial effect of*

potassium ion addition was to decrease the heart rate. Excess potassium decreases the resting potential of the plasma membrane.

3. Describe how calcium channel blockers are used to treat patients and why. *Calcium channel blockers reduce the force of*

contraction of the heart which would decrease blood pressure.

Respiratory System Mechanics

Advance Preparation/Comments

1. Demonstrate the mechanics of the lungs during respiration if a bell jar and balloon lungs are available.

2. Prior to the lab, suggest to the students that they become familiar with the exercise before coming to class. If students have a home computer, or access to a computer on campus, they can become familiar with the general operation of the simulations before coming to class. In particular, they should understand the lung volumes.

3. A short introductory presentation with the following elements is often helpful:

   - Review the basics of respiratory anatomy, particularly the inspiratory and expiratory sequence.
   - Reinforce the fact that there are no fibrous or muscular connections between the lungs and the thoracic wall when doing the bell jar demonstration. Students often remember this demonstration more than most others.
   - Mention that normal inspiration requires muscle action but that normal expiration is passive.
   - If a demonstration computer and bell jar lungs are available, compare the operation of the onscreen lungs with the balloon lungs in the bell jar.
   - A pair of microscope slides with a thin film of water between makes an excellent demonstration of the concept of water tension.
   - Briefly explain the idea of carbon dioxide retention in the blood during hypoventilation and its removal from the blood by hyperventilation.
   - Review Boyle's Law.
   - h. Remind students that the respiratory center in the brain is more sensitive to Pco_2 than to Po_2.

Answers to Questions/Experimental Data

Pre-lab Quiz in the Lab Manual

1. Expiration
2. c, inspiratory muscles relax
3. False
4. b, 500 ml
5. Vital capacity
6. False
7. aortic and carotid bodies
8. c, 7.4 ± 0.02
9. Acids
10. False

Activity 1: Measuring Respiratory Volumes and Calculating Capacities (pp. PEx-106–PEx-109)

6. ~7485

Predict Question 1: When airway radius is decreased, FEV_1 will decrease proportionately.

11. 73.9% (3541/4791 × 100%)

12. 70% (436/621 × 100%)

Chart 1: Respiratory Volumes and Capacities

Radius (mm)	Flow (ml/min)	TV (ml)	ERV (ml)	IRV (ml)	RV (ml)	VC (ml)	FEV_1 (ml)	TLC (ml)
5.00	7485	499	—	—	—	—	—	—
5.00	7500	500	1200	3091	1200	4791	3541	5991
4.50	4920	328	787	2028	1613	3143	2303	4756
4.00	3075	205	492	1266	1908	1962	1422	3871
3.50	1800	120	288	742	2112	1150	872	3262
3.00	975	65	156	401	2244	621	436	2865

Activity Questions:

1. Residual volume is the air remaining in the airways and the lungs which prevents the alveoli from collapsing.

2. The helium dilution method is used to calculate the residual volume.

3. Prior to a cough, the respiratory rate will be regular on the spirogram. During a cough, the respiratory rate becomes irregular and there are more pronounced expiratory events.

Activity 2: Comparative Spirometry (pp. PEx-109–PEx-112)

Predict Question 1: The lung values that should change with emphysema include ERV, IRV, RV, FVC, FEV_1, and FEV_1 (%).

Predict Question 2: The lung values that should change with a patient suffering from an acute asthma attack include TV, ERV, IRV, RV, FVC, FEV_1, and FEV1 (%).

Predict Question 3: The lung values that change back when the asthma patient uses an inhaler include TV, ERV, and FEV_1 (%).

Predict Question 4: The lung value that should change more with moderate exercise is IRV.

Chart 2: Spirometry Results

Patient type	TV (ml)	ERV (ml)	IRV (ml)	RV (ml)	FVC (ml)	TLC (ml)	FEV_1 (ml)	FEV_1 (%)
Normal	500	1500	2000	1000	5000	6000	4000	80%
Emphysema	500	750	2000	2750	3250	6000	1625	50%
Acute Asthma Attack	300	750	2700	2250	3750	6000	1500	40%
Plus Inhaler	500	1500	2800	1200	4800	6000	3840	80%
Moderate Exercise	1875	1125	2000	1000	ND	6000	ND	ND
Heavy Exercise	3650	750	600	1000	ND	6000	ND	ND

Activity Questions:

1. With emphysema the lungs lose their elasticity resulting in more air remaining in the alveoli which increases the residual volume.

2. During an acute asthma attack, bronchiole smooth muscle spasms and, thus, the airways become restricted. The medication in the inhaler will partially dilate the airways, but the underlying cause for the asthma is still present.

3. The breathing rate and increase in tidal volume are more pronounced in the heavy exerciser than in the moderate exerciser.

Activity 3: Effect of Surfactant and Intrapleural Pressure on Respiration (pp. PEx-112–PEx-113)

Predict Question 1: Airflow will further increase with the addition of surfactant.

Predict Question 2: The lung will remain collapsed with the valve closed.

Chart 3: Effect of Surfactant and Intrapleural Pressure on Respiration

Surfactant	Intrapleural pressure left (atm)	Intrapleural pressure right (atm)	Airflow left (ml/min)	Airflow right (ml/min)	Total airflow (ml/min)
0	−4	−4	49.69	49.69	99.38
2	−4	−4	69.56	69.56	139.13
4	−4	−4	89.44	89.44	178.88
0	−4	−4	49.69	49.69	99.38
0	0.00	−4	0.00	49.69	49.69
0	0.00	−4	0.00	49.69	49.69
0	−4	−4	49.69	49.69	99.38

Activity Questions:

1. Premature infants have difficulty with normal breathing because they lack sufficient surfactant which decreases the surface tension in the alveoli.

2. The presence of air in the pleural cavity is referred to as a pneumothorax. When air is present in the pleural cavity, it can lead to the collapse of a lung, atelectasis.

Respiratory System Mechanics

ACTIVITY 1 **Measuring Respiratory Volumes and Calculating Capacities**

1. What would be an example of an everyday respiratory event the ERV button simulates? *The ERV button simulates a*

   forced expiration.

2. What additional skeletal muscles are utilized in an ERV activity? *In forced expiration, abdominal-wall muscles and the*

   internal intercostal muscles contract.

3. What was the FEV_1 (%) at the initial radius of 5.00 mm? *The FEV_1 (%) at a radius of 5 mm is 73.9% (3541/4791 × 100%).*

4. What happened to the FEV_1 (%) as the radius of the airways decreased? How well did the results compare with your prediction?

   The FEV_1 (%) decreased proportionally as the radius decreased.

5. Explain why the results from the experiment suggest that there is an obstructive, rather than a restrictive, pulmonary problem.

   The FEV_1 (%) decreased proportionally as the radius decreased, which is characteristic of an obstructive pulmonary problem.

ACTIVITY 2 **Comparative Spirometry**

1. What lung values changed (from those of the normal patient) in the spirogram when the patient with emphysema was

   selected? Why did these values change as they did? How well did the results compare with your prediction? *The values that*

   change for the patient with emphysema are ERV, IRV, RV, FVC, FEV_1 and the FEV_1 (%). These changes are due to the loss of elastic recoil.

2. Which of these two parameters changed more for the patient with emphysema, the FVC or the FEV_1? *The FEV_1 decreased*

   significantly more than the FVC for the patient with emphysema.

3. What lung values changed (from those of the normal patient) in the spirogram when the patient experiencing an acute asthma

   attack was selected? Why did these values change as they did? How well did the results compare with your prediction?

   The values that changed for the patient with the acute asthma attack are TV, ERV, IRV, RV, FVC, FEV_1, and the FEV_1 (%). These

   changes are due to the restriction of the airways.

4. How is having an acute asthma attack similar to having emphysema? How is it different? *Both are similar because they are*

   obstructive diseases characterized by increased airway resistance. It is more difficult to exhale with emphysema than with asthma.

5. Describe the effect that the inhaler medication had on the asthmatic patient. Did all the spirogram values return to "normal"? Why do you think some values did not return all the way to normal? How well did the results compare with your prediction?

The values that returned to normal were TV, ERV, FEV_1 (%). The smooth muscles in the bronchioles didn't return to normal plus

mucus still blocks the airway.

6. How much of an increase in FEV_1 do you think is required for it to be considered significantly improved by the medication?

A significant improvement would be at least 10–15% improvement. Student answers will vary on this response.

7. With moderate aerobic exercise, which changed more from normal breathing, the ERV or the IRV? How well did the results compare with your prediction? _The lung value that changed more with moderate exercise was IRV._

8. Compare the breathing rates during normal breathing, moderate exercise, and heavy exercise. _The breathing rate increased_ _with moderate and heavy exercise. A greater increase in breathing rate was seen with heavy exercise._

ACTIVITY 3   **Effect of Surfactant and Intrapleural Pressure on Respiration**

1. What effect does the addition of surfactant have on the airflow? How well did the results compare with your prediction?

The surfactant addition further increased airflow because the surface tension in the alveoli decreased allowing the alveoli to

expand more.

2. Why does surfactant affect airflow in this manner? _Surfactant serves to decrease the surface tension._

3. What effect did opening the valve have on the left lung? Why does this happen?

It caused the lung to collapse because the pressure in the pleural cavity is less than the intrapulmonary pressure. Air flows from the

lungs causing the collapse of the lung.

4. What effect on the collapsed lung in the left side of the glass bell jar did you observe when you closed the valve? How well did the results compare with your prediction? _The lung did remain collapsed and did not reinflate after the valve was closed._

5. What emergency medical condition does opening the left valve simulate? _Opening the left valve simulates a pneumothorax._

6. In the last part of this activity, you clicked the Reset button to draw the air out of the intrapleural space and return the lung to its normal resting condition. What emergency procedure would be used to achieve this result if these were the lungs in a living person? _Emergency professionals will insert a chest tube to pull a partial vacuum out of the intrapleural space to return it to_

a value below atmospheric pressure.

7. What do you think would happen when the valve is opened if the two lungs were in a single large cavity rather than separate cavities? _Both lungs would collapse if the lungs were not separated. Breathing would stop and the person would die._

Chemical and Physical Processes of Digestion

Advance Preparation/Comments

1. Suggest to the students that they become familiar with the exercise before coming to class. If students have a home computer or access to a computer on campus they can become familiar with the general operation of the simulations before coming to class.

2. A short introductory presentation with the following elements is often helpful:

   a. Describe the basics of enzymatic hydrolysis, mentioning how the enzyme-substrate interaction puts stress on the chemical bonds within the substrate to aid in the hydrolytic action.

   b. Students need to clearly understand why the different control tubes are necessary. Explain this concept with plenty of examples.

   c. Because enzymes work as well in vitro as they do in vivo, encourage students to apply what they see in the simulation to what must occur in the lumen of the digestive system.

   d. If a demonstration computer screen is available, briefly show students the basic equipment parts.

3. As the lab progresses, ask students questions directing them to think about the logic of the experiment. For example, if a group of students makes the statement: "Amylase digests starch to maltose," try asking some of the following questions as the opportunity arises:

   • How do you know that the amylase preparation was not contaminated with maltose?
   • How do you know that the buffer was not contaminated with maltose?
   • How do you know that the water was not contaminated with maltose?
   • How do you know that you even started with starch and that the starch was not contaminated with maltose?

4. Be prepared to help the students answer the more difficult "What if . . . " questions.

Answers to Questions/Experimental Data

Pre-lab Quiz in the Lab Manual

1. catalysts
2. control
3. salivary amylase (students could also put simply amylase)
4. True
5. blue to black
6. trypsin
7. pancreatic lipase
8. True
9. Segmental

Activity 1: Assessing Starch Digestion by Salivary Amylase (pp. PEx-121–PEx-123)

Predict Question 1: Boiling an enzyme should denature the protein and render it inactive. Freezing the enzyme will have no effect on the enzyme activity because it has little to no effect on enzyme structure.

Chart 1: Salivary Amylase Digestion of Starch

Tube No.	1	2	3	4	5	6	7	8
Additives	Amylase Starch pH 7.0 buffer	Amylase Starch pH 7.0 buffer	Amylase Starch pH 7.0 buffer	Amylase Deionized water pH 7.0 buffer	Deionized water Starch pH 7.0 buffer	Deionized water Maltose pH 7.0 buffer	Amylase Starch pH 2.0 buffer	Amylase Starch pH 9.0 buffer
Incubation condition	Boil first, then incubate at 37°C for 60 minutes	Freeze first, then incubate at 37°C for 60 minutes	37°C 60 minutes	37°C 60 minutes	37°C 60 minutes	37°C 60 minutes	37°C 60 minutes	37°C 60 minutes
IKI test	+	−	−	−	+	−	+	+
Benedict's test	−	++	++	−	−	++	+	+

Activity Questions:

1. The enzyme was no longer active after boiling. Heat denatures enzymes. Freezing had no effect on the activity of the enzyme.

2. The purpose of including tube 3 is to observe the activity of the enzyme at neutral pH. The enzyme is very active at this pH.

3. The optimum pH is obtained by comparing the results from tubes 3, 7, and 8.

4. The amylase would not be very active in the stomach because the pH is about 2 and amylase was not very active at this pH.

Activity 2: Exploring Amylase Substrate Specificity (pp. PEx-123–PEx-125)

Predict Question 1: Test tube 3 should not show a positive Benedict's test because cellulose is not the substrate for amylase.

Chart 2: Enzyme Digestion of Starch and Cellulose

Tube No.	1	2	3	4	5	6
Additives	Amylase Starch pH 7.0 buffer	Amylase Glucose pH 7.0 buffer	Amylase Cellulose pH 7.0 buffer	Deionized water Cellulose pH 7.0 buffer	Peptidase Starch pH 7.0 buffer	Bacteria Cellulose pH 7.0 buffer
Incubation condition	37°C 60 minutes	37°C 60 minutes	37°C 60 minutes	37°C 60 minutes	37°C 60 minutes	37°C 60 minutes
IKI test	−	−	+	+	+	−
Benedict's test	++	++	−	−	−	++

Activity Questions:

1. No, amylase doesn't use cellulose as a substrate. Starch is the substrate for amylase.

2. The bacteria were able to digest the cellulose because they produce the enzyme cellulase.

3. The peptidase had no effect on the starch because the substrate for peptidase is peptides and proteins.

4. The smallest subunit that starch can be broken down into is glucose.

Activity 3: Assessing Pepsin Digestion of Protein (pp. PEx-125–PEx-126)

Predict Question 1: It should be pH 2 because pepsin is most active in the stomach.

Chart 3: Pepsin Digestion of Protein

Tube No.	1	2	3	4	5	6
Additives	Pepsin BAPNA pH 2.0 buffer	Pepsin BAPNA pH 2.0 buffer	Pepsin Deionized water pH 2.0 buffer	Deionized water BAPNA pH 2.0 buffer	Pepsin BAPNA pH 7.0 buffer	Pepsin BAPNA pH 9.0 buffer
Incubation condition	Boil first, then incubate at 37°C for 60 minutes	37°C 60 minutes	37°C 60 minutes	37°C 60 minutes	37°C 60 minutes	37°C 60 minutes
Optical density	0.00	0.40	0.00	0.00	0.03	0.00

Activity Questions:

1. The optimum pH matches the pH secreted by gastric glands. Gastric juice is also about pH 2.

2. Since the pH of the mouth is closer to neutrality, you would expect pepsin to be slightly active but not as active as it is in the stomach at pH 2.

3. The subunit products of digestion are peptides and amino acids.

4. The control tube 4 is present to make certain that the BAPNA is not breaking down due to the low pH.

Activity 4: Assessing Lipase Digestion of Fat (pp. PEx-127–PEx-128)

Predict Question 1: Test tube 1 should have the highest activity because the pH is closest to the pH of the small intestine.
Note: Some students might choose pH 9.0 but the intestine is closer to 8.0 and the enzyme is not active at such high alkalinity.

Chart 4: Pancreatic Lipase Digestion of Triglycerides and the Action of Bile

Tube No.	1	2	3	4	5	6
Additives	Lipase Vegetable oil Bile salts pH 7.0 buffer	Lipase Vegetable oil Deionized water pH 7.0 buffer	Lipase Deionized water Bile salts pH 9.0 buffer	Deionized water Vegetable oil Bile salts pH 7.0 buffer	Lipase Vegetable oil Bile salts pH 2.0 buffer	Lipase Vegetable oil Bile salts pH 9.0 buffer
Incubation condition	37°C 60 minutes	37°C 60 minutes	37°C 60 minutes	37°C 60 minutes	37°C 60 minutes	37°C 60 minutes
pH	6.21	6.72	9.00	7.00	2.00	8.97

Activity Questions:

1. Lipase activity is measured by a decrease in pH through the release of fatty acids.

2. The pH in tube 5 is pH 2.0. The pH is too low to be able to see if any fatty acids have been released.

3. Pancreatic lipase would be active in the mouth since the pH of the mouth is close to 7.0 and the enzyme is most active at this pH.

4. Fat globules are separated into droplets by bile salts through an emulsification process which is physical not chemical.

NAME _____

LAB TIME/DATE _____

Chemical and Physical Processes of Digestion

1. List the substrate and the subunit product of amylase. *The substrate of amylase is animal starch and the product is maltose and glucose.*

2. What effect did boiling and freezing have on enzyme activity? Why? How well did the results compare with your prediction? *The boiling denatured the enzyme and inactivated it as predicted. The freezing has no effect on the enzyme.*

3. At what pH was the amylase most active? Describe the significance of this result. *Amylase was most active at pH 7.0. This is significant because this is the same pH as the mouth.*

4. Briefly describe the need for controls and give an example used in this activity. *Controls are necessary to validate the results of the experiment. Tube 5 is an example where the enzyme that tests for contaminating glucose in the starch or the buffer is absent.*

5. Describe the significance of using a 37°C incubation temperature to test salivary amylase activity. *The 37°C incubation is significant because it is the same temperature as body temperature so it should be ideal for the enzyme.*

1. Describe why the results in tube 1 and tube 2 are the same. *In tube 1 the amylase is hydrolyzing the starch to glucose and in tube 2 the glucose is already present in the hydrolyzed form.*

2. Describe the result in tube 3. How well did the results compare with your prediction? *The correct prediction is "no." Tube 3 should not be positive for the Benedict's test because amylase should not digest cellulose.*

3. Describe the usual substrate for peptidase. *The usual substrate for peptidase is peptides and proteins.*

4. Explain how bacteria can aid in digestion. *Bacteria can aid in digestion by breaking down cellulose, which do not produce cellulase.*

ACTIVITY 3   Assessing Pepsin Digestion of Protein

1. Describe the effect that boiling had on pepsin and how you could tell that it had that effect. _Boiling inactivated the pepsin._

This is evidenced by the fact that no activity was seen with tube 1. However, the enzyme was very active in tube 2.

2. Was your prediction correct about the optimal pH for pepsin activity? Discuss the physiological correlation behind your results.

The correct prediction is pH 2.0. This is because pepsin is most active at the pH of gastric juice which is about pH 2.0.

3. What do you think would happen if you reduced the incubation time to 30 minutes for tube 5? _If the incubation time were_

reduced, it is possible that no digestion of protein would be seen since only a small amount is seen.

ACTIVITY 4   Assessing Lipase Digestion of Fat

1. Explain why you can't fully test the lipase activity in tube 5. _Measurement of lipase activity uses a decrease in pH. Since the_

pH in tube 5 is already very low, it is difficult to tell if fatty acids are released.

2. Which tube had the highest lipase activity? How well did the results compare with your prediction? Discuss possible reasons

why it may or may not have matched. _The correct prediction is tube 1, pH 7.0, which approximates the pH of the small intestine._

3. Explain why pancreatic lipase would be active in both the mouth and the intestine. _Since the activity of pancreatic lipase is_

highest at pH 7.0, the enzyme should be active in the mouth and the small intestine.

4. Describe the process of bile emulsification of lipids and how it improves lipase activity. _Bile serves to mechanically break up_

large globules of fat and produce small droplets that effectively increases the surface area of the lipids.

Renal System Physiology

Advance Preparation/Comments

1. Prior to the lab, suggest to the students that they become familiar with the exercise before coming to class. If students have a home computer, or access to a computer on campus, they can become familiar with the general operation of the simulations before coming to class. In particular, they should examine the structure of the nephron in the textbook.

2. A good working knowledge of diffusion, filtration, and osmosis is important in understanding renal function. Suggest to the students that they review those concepts before coming to class.

3. A short introductory presentation with the following elements is often helpful:
   - Review the basics of nephron anatomy and basic renal physiology, focusing on the major concepts such as glomerular filtration and the movement of substances due to passive and active forces.
   - Reinforce the idea of how changing the arteriole diameter influences the filtration pressure in the glomerulus.
   - Use the analogy of a coffee filter when describing the filtration that takes place in the glomerulus.
   - If the students have not been exposed to the concept of carrier transport, a short introduction using glucose as an example might be helpful.
   - Encourage students to make the transition from what they see in the simulation to what they see under microscopic examination.
   - Remind students that they are manipulating a single nephron that represents the function of the entire kidney, but that the living kidney contains many nephrons.

Answers to Questions/Experimental Data

Pre-lab Quiz in the Lab Manual

1. urochrome
2. 6.0
3. False
4. Albumin
5. Hematuria
6. bilirubinuria
7. Casts
8. A precipitate is an insoluble substance that forms.

Activity 1: The Effect of Arteriole Radius on Glomerular Filtration (pp. PEx-132–135)

Predict Question 1: When the radius of the afferent arteriole is decreased, the pressure and filtration rate will both decrease.

Predict Question 2: When the radius of the afferent arteriole is increased, the pressure and filtration rate will both increase.

Predict Question 3: When the radius of the efferent arteriole is decreased, the pressure and filtration rate will both increase.

Chart 1: Effect of Arteriole Radius on Glomerular Filtration

Afferent arteriole radius (mm)	Efferent arteriole radius (mm)	Glomerular capillary pressure (mm Hg)	Glomerular filtration rate (ml/min)
0.50	0.45	55.08	124.99
0.45	0.45	51.54	81.06
0.40	0.45	48.52	43.66
0.35	0.45	46.16	14.35
0.55	0.45	58.94	172.86
0.60	0.45	62.88	221.69
0.50	0.45	55.08	124.99
0.50	0.40	56.10	137.69
0.50	0.35	56.84	146.82
0.50	0.30	57.34	152.96

Activity Questions:

1. Activation of the sympathetic nerves serves to decrease the radius of the afferent arteriole.

2. The benefit is that urine output will decrease. The kidneys are a blood filter so slowing down the rate of filtration for long periods could lead to abnormal blood composition.

Activity 2: The Effect of Pressure on Glomerular Filtration (pp. PEx-135–PEx-137)

Predict Question 1: Glomerular capillary pressure and filtration rate will increase when you increase the beaker pressure.

Predict Question 2: If you close the one-way valve, pressure will increase in the Bowman's capsule and filtration rate will decrease.

Chart 2: Effect of Arteriole Radius on Glomerular Filtration

Blood pressure (mm Hg)	Valve (open or closed)	Glomerular capillary pressure (mm Hg)	Glomerular filtration rate (ml/min)	Urine volume (ml)
70		49.72	58.57	161.76
80		52.40	91.78	186.23
90		55.08	124.99	200.44
100		57.76	158.20	209.72
70	open	49.72	58.57	161.76
70	closed	49.72	31.97	0
100	closed	57.76	114.20	0
100	open	57.76	158.20	209.72

Activity Questions:

1. Based upon this activity, increased blood pressure should increase the glomerular filtration rate.

2. High blood pressure can damage the blood vessels in the kidneys leading to reduced kidney function and kidney failure.

Activity 3: Renal Response to Altered Blood Pressure (pp. PEx-137–PEx-139)

Predict Question 1: If both arteriole radii changes are implemented (increasing the afferent and decreasing the efferent), glomerular filtration rate and pressure will rise above baseline values.

Chart 3: Renal Response to Altered Blood Pressure

Afferent arteriole radius (mm)	Efferent arteriole radius (mm)	Blood pressure (mm Hg)	Glomerular capillary pressure (mm Hg)	Glomerular filtration rate (ml/min)
0.50	0.45	90	55.08	124.99
0.50	0.45	70	49.72	58.57
0.60	0.45	70	54.25	114.72
0.50	0.35	70	51.24	77.41
0.60	0.35	70	55.58	131.15

Activity Questions:

1. Increased blood pressure can be a result of increased blood volume. For this reason, an increase in urine volume would stabilize blood volume.

2. Diuretics increase the amount of urine output thus decreasing the blood volume. A decrease in blood volume should result in a corresponding decrease in blood pressure.

Activity 4: Solute Gradients and Their Impact on Urine Concentration (pp. PEx-139–PEx-140)

Predict Question 1: When the solute concentration gradient in the interstitial space is increased, the urine volume will decrease and the concentration of the urine will increase.

Chart 4: Solute Gradients and Their Impact on Urine Concentration

Urine volume (ml)	Urine concentration (mOsm)	Concentration gradient (mOsm)
80.57	300	300
40.28	600	600
26.86	900	900
16.86	1200	1200

Activity Questions:

1. Since desert rats have limited water supply, their urine volume will decrease due to an increased solute gradient thus concentrating their urine significantly.

2. Diuretics could work by inhibiting ADH or by altering the solute gradient.

Activity 5: Reabsorption of Glucose via Carrier Proteins (pp. PEx-140–PEx-142)

Predict Question 1: As glucose carriers are added, the glucose concentration in the bladder will increase.

Chart 5: Reabsorption of Glucose via Carrier Proteins

Glucose concentration (mM)			
Bowman's capsule	Distal convoluted tubule	Urinary bladder	Glucose carriers
6.00	6.00	6.00	0
6.00	4.29	4.29	100
6.00	2.57	2.57	200
6.00	0.86	0.86	300
6.00	0.00	0.00	400

Activity Questions:

1. A physician might taste urine to detect increased glucose in the urine which could indicate diabetes mellitus.

Activity 6: The Effect of Hormones on Urine Formation (pp. PEx-142–PEx-143)

Predict Question 1: When aldosterone is added, the urine volume will decrease.

Predict Question 2: When ADH is added, the urine volume will increase.

Predict Question 3: In the presence of ADH and aldosterone, urine volume will decrease and the concentration will increase.

Chart 6: The Effect of Hormones on Urine Formation

Potassium concentration (mM)	Urine volume (ml)	Urine concentration (mOsm)	Aldosterone	ADH
6.25	201.00	100	absent	absent
10.42	180.90	100	present	absent
62.37	16.86	1200	absent	present
65.37	12.67	1200	present	present

Activity Questions:

1. Ethanol is a diuretic that works by inhibiting ADH. Inhibition of ADH increases urine output.

2. ACE catalyzes the conversion of angiotensin I to angiotensin II. Angiotensin II has a variety of effects that all result in an increase in blood volume and decreased urine output. Therefore, inhibiting this enzyme would increase urine output.

Renal System Physiology

ACTIVITY 1 — The Effect of Arteriole Radius on Glomerular Filtration

1. What are two primary functions of the kidney? *The two primary functions of the kidney are excretion and regulation.*

2. What are the components of the renal corpuscle? *The two components of the renal corpuscle are the Bowman's capsule and the glomerular capillaries (glomerulus).*

3. Starting at the renal corpuscle, list the components of the renal tubule as they are encountered by filtrate. *1. Proximal convoluted tubule, 2. loop of Henle, 3. Distal convoluted tubule*

4. Describe the effect of decreasing the afferent arteriole radius on glomerular capillary pressure and filtration rate. How well did the results compare with your prediction? *When the radius of the afferent arteriole was decreased, the pressure and filtration rate both decreased.*

5. Describe the effect of increasing the afferent arteriole radius on glomerular capillary pressure and filtration rate. How well did the results compare with your prediction? *When the radius of the afferent arteriole was increased, the pressure and filtration rate both increased.*

6. Describe the effect of decreasing the efferent arteriole radius on glomerular capillary pressure and filtration rate. How well did the results compare with your prediction? *When the radius of the efferent arteriole was decreased, the pressure and filtration rate both increased.*

7. Describe the effect of increasing the efferent radius on glomerular capillary pressure and filtration rate. *When the radius of the efferent arteriole was increased, the pressure and filtration rate both decreased.*

ACTIVITY 2 — The Effect of Pressure on Glomerular Filtration

1. As blood pressure increased, what happened to the glomerular capillary pressure and the glomerular filtration rate? How well did the results compare with your prediction? *When you increase the blood pressure, glomerular capillary pressure and filtration rate will increase.*

2. Compare the urine volume in your baseline data with the urine volume as you increased the blood pressure. How did the urine volume change? *As the pressure increased, the urine volume increased proportionally.*

3. How could the change in urine volume with the increase in blood pressure be viewed as being beneficial to the body?

Increased blood pressure can be a result of increased blood volume. For this reason, an increase in urine volume would stabilize blood volume.

4. When the one-way valve between the collecting duct and the urinary bladder was closed, what happened to the filtrate pressure in Bowman's capsule (this is not directly measured in this experiment) and the glomerular filtration rate? How well did the results compare with your prediction? _If you close the one-way valve, pressure will increase in the Bowman's capsule and filtration rate will decrease._

5. How did increasing the blood pressure alter the results when the valve was closed? _With increased pressure and the valve closed, the filtration rate decreased but the glomerular pressure stayed the same. Urine output was zero._

ACTIVITY 3 Renal Response to Altered Blood Pressure

1. List the several mechanisms you have explored that change the glomerular filtration rate. How does each mechanism specifically alter the glomerular filtration rate? _Both increasing the afferent arteriole radius and decreasing the efferent arteriole resulted in an increase in glomerular filtration rate._

2. Describe and explain what happened to the glomerular capillary pressure and glomerular filtration rate when _both_ arteriole radii changes were implemented simultaneously with the low blood pressure condition. How well did the results compare with your prediction? _When both arteriole radii changes were implemented, glomerular filtration rate and pressure rose above baseline values._

3. How could you adjust the afferent or efferent radius to compensate for the effect of reduced blood pressure on the glomerular filtration rate? _Increasing the afferent radius or decreasing the efferent would compensate for lowered blood pressure._

4. Which arteriole radius adjustment was more effective at compensating for the effect of low blood pressure on the glomerular filtration rate? Explain why you think this difference occurs. _Increasing the afferent radius had a greater effect than decreasing the efferent radius because there was a greater increase in glomerular pressure._

5. In the body, how does a nephron maintain a near-constant glomerular filtration rate despite a constantly fluctuating blood pressure? _Intrinsic and extrinsic mechanisms result in changes to the afferent and efferent arterioles to maintain glomerular filtration rate._

1. What happened to the urine concentration as the solute concentration in the interstitial space was increased? How well did the results compare to your prediction? _When the solute concentration gradient in the interstitial space was increased, the urine volume decreased._

2. What happened to the volume of urine as the solute concentration in the interstitial space was increased? How well did the results compare to your prediction? _When the solute concentration gradient in the interstitial space was increased, the concentration of the urine increased._

3. What do you think would happen to urine volume if you did not add ADH to the collecting duct? _The urine volume will increase in the absence of ADH in the collecting duct._

4. Is most of the tubule filtrate reabsorbed into the body or excreted in urine? Explain. _Most of the tubular filtrate is reabsorbed to prevent fluid loss and maintain homeostasis._

5. Can the reabsorption of solutes influence water reabsorption from the tubule fluid? Explain. _Yes, the reabsorption of solutes affects water reabsorption because water will follow the solutes by osmosis._

ACTIVITY 5 Reabsorption of Glucose via Carrier Proteins

1. What happens to the concentration of glucose in the urinary bladder as the number of glucose carriers increases? _As glucose carriers were added, the glucose concentration in the bladder increased._

2. What types of transport are utilized during glucose reabsorption and where do they occur? _Glucose is first reabsorbed by secondary active transport at the apical membrane of PCT cells and then via facilitated diffusion along the basolateral membrane._

3. Why does the glucose concentration in the urinary bladder become zero in these experiments? _When the number of glucose carriers becomes great enough all of the glucose is reabsorbed._

4. A person with type 1 diabetes cannot make insulin in the pancreas, and a person with untreated type 2 diabetes does not respond to the insulin that is made in the pancreas. In either case, why would you expect to find glucose in the person's urine? _The absence of insulin or decreased sensitivity to the hormone, leads to excess glucose in the blood so the carriers reach their maximum transport levels._

1. How did the addition of aldosterone affect urine volume (compared with baseline)? Can the reabsorption of solutes influence water reabsorption in the nephron? Explain. How well did the results compare with your prediction? _When aldosterone was added, the urine volume decreased. Aldosterone results in increased sodium and water reabsorption and increased potassium secretion._

2. How did the addition of ADH affect urine volume (compared with baseline)? How well did the results compare with your prediction? Why did the addition of ADH also affect the concentration of potassium in the urine (compared with baseline)? _When ADH was added, the urine volume increased. The addition of ADH resulted in the potassium being more concentrated because the volume of urine decreased._

3. What is the principal determinant for the release of aldosterone from the adrenal cortex? _Aldosterone release is stimulated by production of angiotensin II which is under control of the body's renin-angiotensin system._

4. How did the addition of both aldosterone and ADH affect urine volume (compared with baseline)? How well did the results compare with your prediction? _When ADH was added, the urine volume increased._

5. What is the principal determinant for the release of ADH from the posterior pituitary gland? Does ADH favor the formation of dilute or concentrated urine? Explain why. _An increase in body fluid osmolarity will stimulate the release of more ADH. ADH favors dilute urine._

6. Which hormone (aldosterone or ADH) has the greater effect on urine volume? Why? _ADH has the greater effect on urine volume. ADH is responsible for fluid retention. Aldosterone is primarily increasing sodium uptake and potassium secretion._

7. If ADH is not available, can the urine concentration still vary? Explain your answer. _The urine concentration will not vary in the absence of ADH._

8. Consider this situation: you want to reabsorb sodium ions but you do not want to increase the volume of the blood by reabsorbing large amounts of water from the filtrate. Assuming that aldosterone and ADH are both present, how would you adjust the hormones to accomplish the task? _In order to reabsorb sodium without affecting urine volume, you would need to increase the amount of aldosterone and decrease ADH._

Acid-Base Balance

Advance Preparation/Comments

1. Spend time reviewing acid and base as well as the equation:

$$H_2O + CO_2 \leftrightarrow H_2CO_3 \leftrightarrow H^+ + HCO_3^-.$$

2. Describe how the body can compensate for acid/base imbalances.

Answers to Questions/Experimental Data

Pre-lab Quiz in the Lab Manual

1. acid
2. b, pH
3. d, the digestive system
4. True
5. carbon dioxide
6. carbonic acid
7. b, acidosis
8. False
9. respiratory (not fixed in manu)

Activity 1: Hyperventilation (pp. PEx-150–PEx-151)

Predict Question 1: With hyperventilation, pH will increase and P_{CO_2} will decrease.

Chart 1: Hyperventilation Breathing Patterns

Condition	Minimum P_{CO_2}	Maximum P_{CO_2}	Minimum pH	Maximum pH
Normal	40	40	7.40	7.40
Hyperventilation	19.7*	40	Variable, 7.39–7.40	Variable, 7.43–7.72
Hyperventilation	35.3*	40	Variable, 7.38–7.40	Variable, 7.43–7.46
* These results will vary if the student waits for slightly shorter or longer periods than instructed.				

Activity Questions:

1. Respiratory alkalosis is classified as a blood pH greater than 7.45.
2. The renal system can compensate for alkalosis by retaining H^+ and excreting bicarbonate icons to lower the blood pH levels back to the normal range.
3. The tidal volume increased with hyperventilation.
4. Hyperventilation can be brought on by fever, panic attack, or anxiety.

Activity 2: Rebreathing (pp. PEx-151–PEx-152)

Predict Question: During rebreathing, pH will decrease and P_{CO_2} will increase.

Chart 2: Normal Breathing Patterns

Condition	Minimum P_{CO_2}	Maximum P_{CO_2}	Minimum pH	Maximum pH
Normal	40	40	7.39	7.39
Hyperventilation	40	53.95*	Variable, 7.22–7.39	Variable, 7.41–7.46

* This result will vary if the student waits for slightly shorter or longer periods than instructed.

Activity Questions:

1. Yes, with rebreathing the pH changed. During rebreathing the pH decreased.

2. Too much carbon dioxide in the blood results in a decrease in pH.

3. The tidal volumes increased with rebreathing.

4. Too much carbon dioxide in the blood is a result of hypoventilation. The causes of impaired respiration include airway obstruction, depression of the respiratory center in the brain stem, lung disease (such as emphysema and chronic bronchitis), and drug overdose.

Activity 3: Renal Responses to Respiratory Acidosis and Respiratory Alkalosis (PEx-152–PEx-154)

Predict Question 1: Lowering the P_{CO_2} will result in a decrease in $[H^+]$ and an increase in $[HCO_3^-]$.

Predict Question 2: Raising the P_{CO_2} will result in an increase in $[HCO_3^-]$.

Chart 3: Renal Responses to Respiratory Acidosis and Respiratory Alkalosis

P_{CO_2}	Blood pH	$[H^+]$ in urine	$[HCO_3^+]$ in urine
40	Variable, 7.38–7.42	normal	normal
30	Variable, 7.28–7.59	decreased	elevated
60	Variable, 7.28–7.32	elevated	decreased

Activity Questions:

1. The renal system can compensate for respiratory acidosis by elimination H^+ and retaining bicarbonate ion to raise the pH levels back to normal.

2. Respiratory acidosis is characterized by a pH less than 7.35.

3. The renal system can compensate for respiratory alkalosis by retaining H^+ and excreting bicarbonate ions to lower the blood pH levels back to the normal range.

4. Respiratory alkalosis is characterized by a pH greater than 7.45.

Activity 4: Respiratory Responses to Metabolic Acidosis and Metabolic Alkalosis
(pp. PEx-154–PEx-156)

Predict Question 1: When the metabolic rate is increased to 80 kcals/hr, metabolic acidosis will occur.

Predict Question 2: When the metabolic rate is decreased to 20 kcals/hr, breaths per minute will increase.

Chart 4: Respiratory Responses to Metabolic Acidosis and Metabolic Alkalosis

Metabolic rate	BPM (breaths/min)	Blood pH	P_{CO_2}	[H+] in blood	[HCO$_3$+] in blood
50	15	Variable, 7.40–7.44	40	40	24
60	17	Variable, 7.35–7.39	45	47	20
80	21	Variable, 7.23–7.29	55	63	14.50
40	13	Variable, 7.42–7.48	37	38	26
20	9	Variable, 7.50–7.55	31	32	30

Activity Questions:

1. With an increase in metabolism, carbon dioxide increases and pH decreases.

2. The respiratory response to metabolic acidosis is hyperventilation, an increase in the rate and depth of breathing.

3. The pH values will increase when the respiratory system responds to metabolic acidosis.

4. The respiratory response to metabolic alkalosis is hypoventilation, slow shallow breathing.

Acid-Base Balance

ACTIVITY 1 Hyperventilation

1. Describe the normal ranges for pH and carbon dioxide in the blood. *The normal pH range is between 7.35 and 7.45.*

   The partial pressure of carbon dioxide is between 35 and 45 mm Hg.

2. Describe what happened to the pH and the carbon dioxide levels with hyperventilation. How well did the results compare with your prediction? *The pH increased and the carbon dioxide decreased. The lack of carbon dioxide shifted the equilibrium so there was less acid potential increasing the pH.*

3. Explain how returning to normal breathing after hyperventilation differed from hyperventilation without returning to normal breathing. *With the second hyperventilation, there was a period where the breath was held and this was instrumental in retaining carbon dioxide to return the pH and carbon dioxide levels to normal.*

4. Describe some possible causes of respiratory alkalosis. *The possible causes of respiratory alkalosis are traveling to high altitude and hyperventilation, which could be brought on by fever, anxiety, or panic attacks.*

ACTIVITY 2 Rebreathing

1. Describe what happened to the pH and the carbon dioxide levels during rebreathing. How well did the results compare with your prediction? *During rebreathing, pH decreased and P_{CO_2} increased.*

2. Describe some possible causes of respiratory acidosis. *Respiratory acidosis is the result of hypoventilation. The causes of hypoventilation include airway obstruction, brain stem injury, lung disease, and drug overdose.*

3. Explain how the renal system would compensate for respiratory acidosis. *In the body, the kidneys would compensate for respiratory acidosis by elimination H^+ and retaining bicarbonate ion to restore the pH.*

ACTIVITY 3 Renal Responses to Respiratory Acidosis and Respiratory Alkalosis

1. Describe what happened to the concentration of ions in the urine when the P_{CO_2} was lowered. How well did the results compare with your prediction? *Lowering the carbon dioxide resulted in a decrease in $[H^+]$ and an increase in $[HCO_3^-]$.*

2. What condition was simulated when the P_{CO_2} was lowered? *When the carbon dioxide level lowered, this simulated respiratory alklaosis.*

3. Describe what happened to the concentration of ions in the urine when the P_{CO_2} was raised. How well did the results compare with your prediction? *Raising the carbon dioxide increases the acid potential and so the body has to get rid of H^+ ions in the urine. Therefore H^+ in the urine increased.*

4. What condition was simulated when the P_{CO_2} was raised? *Raising the carbon dioxide level simulates respiratory acidosis. The pH decreases.*

ACTIVITY 4 **Respiratory Responses to Metabolic Acidosis and Metabolic Alkalosis**

1. Describe what happened to the blood pH when the metabolic rate was increased to 80 kcal/hr. What body system was compensating? How well did the results compare with your prediction? *When the metabolic rate increased to 80 kcal/hr, the blood pH decreased to 7.23. The respiratory system can compensate for metabolic acidosis.*

2. List and describe some possible causes of metabolic acidosis. *Poisoning from aspirin or ingestion of too much alcohol, strenuous activity, extreme diarrhea as well as diabetes mellitus can all cause metabolic acidosis.*

3. Describe what happened to the blood pH when the metabolic rate was decreased to 20 kcal/hr. What body system was compensating? How well did the results compare with your prediction? *When the metabolic rate decreased to 20 kcal/hr, the blood pH increased to 7.52. The respiratory system is compensating by decreasing the rate of breathing.*

4. List and describe some possible causes of metabolic alkalosis. *Causes of metabolic alkalosis include vomiting, ingestion of too much alkali, and constipation.*

EXERCISE

Blood Analysis

Advance Preparation, Comments, and Pitfalls

Consider doing a short introductory presentation with the following elements:

- Describe what happens to whole blood when it is centrifuged.
- Explain the importance of erythropoietin in regulating erythropoiesis.
- Describe the shape of red blood cells and how they settle in a test tube.
- Show students the structure of hemoglobin and explain its function.
- Describe the ABO and Rh blood groups.
- Explain why total cholesterol determination is an important diagnostic tool.

Answers to Questions/Experimental Data

Pre-lab Quiz in the Lab Manual

1. c, platelets
2. erythrocytes
3. c, monocyte
4. a, Basophils
5. hematocrit
6. antigens
7. True

Activity 1: Hematocrit Determination (pp. PEx-162–PEx-164)

Predict Question 1: The hematocrits of the Denver residents will be higher than those of the Boston residents.

Chart 1: Hematocrit Determination

	Total height of column of blood (mm)	Height of red blood cell layer (mm)	Height of buffy coat (mm)	Hematocrit	% WBC
Sample 1 (healthy male living in Boston)	100 mm	48 mm	1 mm	48	1
Sample 2 (healthy female living in Boston)	100 mm	44 mm	1 mm	44	1
Sample 3 (healthy male living in Denver)	100 mm	55 mm	1 mm	55	1
Sample 4 (healthy female living in Denver)	100 mm	53 mm	1 mm	53	1
Sample 5 (male with aplastic anemia)	100 mm	19 mm	0.5 mm	19	0.5
Sample 6 (female with iron-deficiency anemia)	100 mm	32 mm	1 mm	32	1

Activity Questions:

1. The hematocrit is calculated by dividing the height of the RBC layer by the total height of the blood and multiplying by 100%. The resulting percentage is the portion of the blood that contains RBCs.

2. The buffy coat contains a layer of white blood cells, which are lighter than the red blood cells and therefore end up in between the red blood cells and the plasma after centrifugation.

3. The individual described has a hematocrit that is slightly higher than normal. Given the effects of testosterone, this individual probably has higher than normal levels of testosterone for her gender.

Activity 2: Erythrocyte Sedimentation Rate (pp. PEx-164–PEx-165)

Predict Question 1: The sedimentation rate for sample 6 will be the same as sample 1.

Chart 2: Erythrocyte Sedimentation Rate

Blood sample	Distance RBCs have settled (mm)	Elapsed time	Sedimentation rate
Sample 1 (healthy individual)	5 min	60 mm	5 mm/hr
Sample 2 (menstruating female)	15 min	60 mm	15 mm/hr
Sample 3 (individual with sickle cell anemia)	0 min	60 mm	0 mm/hr
Sample 4 (individual with iron-deficiency anemia)	30 min	60 mm	30 mm/hr
Sample 5 (individual suffering a myocardial infarction)	40 min	60 mm	40 mm/hr
Sample 6 (individual with angina pectoris)	5 min	60 mm	5 mm/hr

Activity Questions:

1. ESR can be used to follow the progression of certain diseases. When the disease worsens, the ESR increases.

2. An accelerated ESR can be caused by certain disease conditions where the RBCs clump together, stack up, and form a dark red column (rouleaux formation) which is heavier and settles faster.

Activity 3: Hemoglobin Determination (pp. PEx-165–PEx-167)

Predict Question 1: The hemoglobin levels for the female Olympic athlete will be greater than those for the healthy female.

Chart 3: Hemoglobin Determination

Blood sample	Hb in grams per 100 ml of blood	Hematocrit (PCV)	Ratio of PCV to Hb
Sample 1 (healthy male)	16	48	3:1
Sample 2 (healthy female)	14	44	3.14:1
Sample 3 (female with irondeficiency anemia)	8	40	5:1
Sample 4 (male with polycythemia)	20	60	3:1
Sample 5 (female Olympic athlete)	22	60	2.73:1

Activity Questions:

1. Individuals living at higher elevation need a greater oxygen carrying capacity because there is less oxygen at higher elevations. Increased hemoglobin levels would provide a greater oxygen carrying capacity.

2. The more oxygen that the blood is carrying the brighter the red color. Blood that is poorly oxygenated has a dull brick-red appearance.

Activity 4: Blood Typing (pp. PEx-167–PEx-169)

Predict Question 1: If the patient's blood type is AB−, the appearance would be A, clumpy; B, clumpy; Rh, unclumped.

Chart 4: Blood Typing Results

Blood sample	Agglutination with anti-A serum	Agglutination with anti-B serum	Agglutination with anti-Rh serum	Blood type*
1	positive	negative	positive	A+
2	negative	positive	positive	B+
3	positive	positive	negative	AB−
4	negative	negative	negative	O−
5	positive	positive	positive	AB+
6	negative	positive	negative	B−

* The entries in this column are designated by the student.

Activity Questions:

1. For blood type AB−, antigens present would be A and B. Antibodies present would be none. (Note Rh antibodies only occur with prior sensitization.)
   For blood type O+, Rh antigens present. Antibodies present would be anti-A and anti-B.
   For blood type B−, B antigens present. Antibodies present would be anti-A.
   For blood type A+, A and Rh antigens present. Antibodies present would be anti-B.

2. The recipients blood type changes to that of the bone marrow donor.

Activity 5: Blood Cholesterol (pp. PEx-169–PEx-171)

Predict Question 1: Based upon his dietary preference, you anticipate his total cholesterol level to be abnormally high.

Chart 5: Total Cholesterol Determination

Blood sample	Approximate total cholesterol (mg/dL)	Cholesterol level
1	150	desirable*
2	300	elevated*
3	150	desirable*
4	225	borderline elevated*

* The entries in this column are designated by the student.

Activity Questions:

1. The arteries are subject to greater pressure, which can lead to damage to the endothelium. This damage results in plaques.

2. Phytosterols stop or slow absorption of dietary cholesterol and cholesterol made by the liver, which should lower the amount of LDLs in the blood.

NAME _____

LAB TIME/DATE _____

Blood Analysis

ACTIVITY 1 **Hematocrit Determination**

1. List the hematocrits for the healthy male (sample 1) and female (sample 2) living in Boston (at sea level) and indicate whether they are normal or whether they indicate anemia or polycythemia. *The healthy male hematocrit was 48% and the healthy female hematocrit was 44%. They were both normal for their respective gender.*

2. Describe the difference between the hematocrits for the male and female living in Boston. Why does this difference between the sexes exist? *The hematocrit for the female living in Boston was lower than the male. The difference is because males have more testosterone, which promotes RBC production.*

3. List the hematocrits for the healthy male and female living in Denver (approximately one mile above sea level) and indicate whether they are normal or whether they indicate anemia or polycythemia. *The hematocrits for the male and female livinig in Denver are 55% and 53% respectively. Both values indicate polycythemia, an adaption to living at high altitude.*

4. How did the hematocrit levels of the Denver residents differ from those of the Boston residents? Why? How well did the results compare with your prediction? *The hematocrits for the Denver residents were higher as predicted. This is because there is less oxygen in the air at higher elevation.*

5. Describe how the kidneys respond to a chronic decrease in oxygen and what effect this has on hematocrit levels. *The kidneys respond to a decrease in oxygen by releasing more EPO (erythropoietin), which stimulates the production of red blood cells.*

6. List the hematocrit for the male with aplastic anemia (sample 5) and indicate whether it is normal or abnormal. Explain your response. *The hematocrit for the male with aplastic anemia is 19%, below the acceptable range. Aplastic anemia can result from the destruction of RBCs or the inhibition of red marrow.*

7. List the hematocrit for the female with iron-deficiency anemia (sample 6) and indicate whether it is normal or abnormal. Explain your response. *The iron-deficient female has a hematocrit of 32%, abnormally low. Iron-deficiency is often accompanied by a low hematocrit.*

Erythrocyte Sedimentation Rate

1. Describe the effect that sickle cell anemia has on the sedimentation rate (sample 3). Why do you think that it has this effect?

The sedimentation rate was dramatically lower in the sickle cell anemia sample. This is because of the abnormal shape of the RBCs.

They do not form stacks of cells.

2. How did the sedimentation rate for the menstruating female (sample 2) compare with the sedimentation rate for the healthy

individual (sample 1)? Why do you think this occurs? *The sedimentation rate for the menstruating female was faster than the*

healthy individual probably due to the fact that she is anemic.

3. How did the sedimentation rate for the individual with angina pectoris (sample 6) compare with the sedimentation rate for

the healthy individual (sample 1)? Why? How well did the results compare with your prediction? *The sedimentation rate*

was the same. The sedimentation rate was not elevated because the individual hasn't had a myocardial infarction.

4. What effect does iron-deficiency anemia (sample 4) have on the sedimentation rate? *Iron-deficieny results in an increase in*

the sedimentation rate.

5. Compare the sedimentation rate for the individual suffering a myocardial infarction (sample 5) with the sedimentation

rate for the individual with angina pectoris (sample 6). Explain how you might use this data to monitor heart conditions.

The sedimentation rate for the individual suffering an MI is increased but is normal for the individual with angina. Elevated ESR can

be indicative of an MI event.

Hemoglobin Determination

1. Is the male with polycythemia (sample 4) deficient in hemoglobin? Why? *No, the male with polycythemia is not deficient in*

hemoglobin. His ratio of PCV to hemoglobin is 3:1, normal.

2. How did the hemoglobin levels for the female Olympic athlete (sample 5) compare with the hemoglobin levels for the

healthy female (sample 2)? Is either person *deficient* in hemoglobin? How well did the results compare with your prediction?

The hemoglobin levels for the female Olympic athlete were higher than the healthy female. Neither person is deficient in hemoglobin.

3. List conditions in which hemoglobin levels would be expected to decrease. Provide reasons for the change when possible.

Hemoglobin levels decrease in patients with anemia, hyperthyroidism, cirrhosis of the liver, renal disease, systemic lupus

erythematosus, and severe hemorrhage.

4. List conditions in which hemoglobin levels would be expected to increase. Provide reasons for the change when possible.

Hemoglobin levels increase in patients with polycythemia, congestive heart failure, chronic obstructive pulmonary disease (COPD),

and when living at high altitudes.

5. Describe the ratio of hematocrit to hemoglobin for the healthy male (sample 1) and female (sample 2). (A normal ratio of hematocrit to grams of hemoglobin is approximately 3:1.) Discuss any differences between the two individuals. *Both ratios*

are approximately 3:1, which is normal. The ratio for the female was 3.14:1, slightly higher than the male ratio of 3:1.

6. Describe the ratio of hematocrit to hemoglobin for the female with iron-deficiency anemia (sample 3) and the female Olympic athlete (sample 5). (A normal ratio of hematocrit to grams of hemoglobin is approximately 3:1.) Discuss any differences between the two individuals. *The ratio for the iron-deficient female was 5:1, which is not normal. The ratio for the female Olympic*

athlete was 3:1.

ACTIVITY 4 **Blood Typing**

1. How did the appearance of the A, B, and Rh samples for the patient with AB− blood type compare with your prediction?

With blood type is AB−, the appearance was A, clumpy; B, clumpy; Rh, unclumped.

2. Which blood sample contained the rarest blood type? *Sample 3 contains the rarest blood type, AB−. If you have this*

blood type the blood banks have you on speed dial.

3. Which blood sample contained the universal donor? *Sample 4 contained the universal donor, O−.*

4. Which blood sample contained the universal recipient? *Sample 5 contains the universal recipient, AB+. It is the universal*

recipient because all of the antigens are present on the surface of the RBCs.

5. Which blood sample did not agglutinate with any of the antibodies tested? Why? *Sample 4 did not agglutinate with any of*

the antibodies tested. This is because none of the antigens were present.

6. What antibodies would be found in the plasma of blood sample 1? *Antibodies against the B antigens because the blood type*

for sample 1 is A+.

7. When transfusing an individual with blood that is compatible but not the same type, it is important to separate packed cells from the plasma and administer only the packed cells. Why do you think this is done? (Hint: Think about what is *in plasma* versus what is *on RBCs*.) *The plasma contains antibodies that will react with the individual's RBCs if they do not have the exact*

same blood type.

8. List the blood samples in this activity that represent people who could donate blood to a person with type B+ blood.

The following samples could donate: sample 2 because it is B+, sample 4 because it is O–, the universal donor and sample 6

because it is B–.

ACTIVITY 5   **Blood Cholesterol**

1. Which patient(s) had desirable cholesterol level(s)? *Patients 1 and 3 had desireable cholesterol levels because they were both*

approximately 150 mg/dL.

2. Which patient(s) had elevated cholesterol level(s)? *Patient 2 had elevated cholesterol at 300 mg/dL.*

3. Describe the risks for the patient(s) you identified in question 2. *Patient 2 is at risk for heart disease since elevated cholesterol*

can lead to blocking of the path of blood to the heart.

4. Was the cholesterol level for patient 4 low, desirable, or high? How well did the results compare with your prediction? What

advice about diet and exercise would you give to this patient? Why? *Patient 4 was in the range of borderline elevated. It is not*

in the desireable range but not quite elevated. So, his diet should be modified to limit fat intake.

5. Describe some reasons why a patient might have abnormally low blood cholesterol. *One reason for low blood cholesterol is*

an overactive thyroid gland. Other reasons are thought to be linked to mood and the neurotransmitter serotonin.

Serological Testing

Advance Preparation/Comments

1. Consider doing a short introductory presentation with the following elements:
   - Explain the principles of how antigens and antibodies can be used to detect disease. Clearly differentiate between antigens and antibodies.
   - Briefly describe the serological tests used in this exercise; direct fluorescent antibody technique, Ouchterlony double diffusion, the indirect ELISA and the Western blotting technique.
   - Stress the difference between direct tests that test for the presence of antigen and indirect tests that test for the presence of antibodies.
   - Describe the basic structure of antibodies.
   - Explain the meaning of seroconversion and how it relates to diagnostic tests that use antibodies to detect disease.
   - Introduce the term epitope (antigenic determinant) and distinguish epitope from antigen.

Answers to Questions/Experimental Data

Pre-lab Quiz in the Lab Manual

1. True
2. b, excess tissue fluid that has filtered out of the capillaries
3. True
4. b, Lymph nodes
5. True
6. b, specificity
7. T cells
8. cellular
9. True

Activity 1: Using Direct Fluorescent Antibody Technique to Test for Chlamydia (pp. PEx-178–PEx-180)

Chart 1: Direct Fluorescent Antibody Technique Results

Sample	Number of elementary bodies	Chlamydia result
Patient A	0	Negative
Patient B	16*	Positive**
Patient C	1*	Negative**
Positive control	19*	Positive**
Negative control	0*	Negative**

* The data in this column is populated by student entries.

** The entries in this column are designated by the student.

Activity Questions:

1. The antigen is found on the patient sample. Since the test is a direct test, it detects antigen. The antigens detected are the elementary bodies.

2. The antigen is the entire foreign particle whereas the epitope is the specific binding site on the antigen that antibodies bind to. Antigens can have multiple epitopes with different structures.

3. Patient sample C displayed some nonspecific binding that was not removed by the washing steps.

Activity 2: Comparing Samples with Ouchterlony Double Diffusion (pp. PEx-180–PEx-181)

Predict Question 1: Human serum albumin and bovine serum albumin will have partial identity.

Chart 2: Ouchterlony Double Diffusion Results

Wells	Identity
2 and 5	Partial*
2 and 3	Identity*
3 and 4	Partial*
4 and 5	Identity*

* The entries in this column are designated by the student.

Activity Questions:

1. The unknown and human serum albumin expressed identity. This means that the two antigens are identical.

2. The center well contains the antibodies that are prepared in goats against the two types of serum albumin, human and bovine.

3. The precipitate is very faint. If the agar was cloudy, it would be impossible to detect the precipitate.

4. Albumin is a key protein in maintaining osmotic pressure in the blood as well as a blood buffer.

Activity 3: Indirect Enzyme-Linked Immunosorbent Assay (ELISA) (pp. PEx-181–PEx-184)

Chart 3: Indirect ELISA Results

Sample	Optical density	HIV test result
Patient A	0.054	Negative*
Patient B	0.432	Indeterminate*
Patient C	1.990	Positive*
Positive control	1.624	Positive*
Negative control	0.154	Negative*

* The entries in this column are designated by the student.

Activity Questions:

1. In this indirect ELISA we are testing for the presence of antibodies in the patient sample. The antibodies are a result of the presence of antigen.

2. The secondary antibody binds to the constant region of the primary antibody. It is specifically prepared to do this so that it can detect the presence of the primary antibody in the patient sample.

3. Seroconversion is when a patient sample contains antibodies against a particular antigen. We say the serum has converted from not containing the antibody to a condition where it does contain the antibody.

Activity 4: Western Blotting Technique (pp. PEx-184–PEx-186)

Chart 4: Western Blot Results

Sample	gp160	gp120	p55	p31	p24	HIV test result
Patient A	no	no	no	no	no	Negative*
Patient B	no	no	yes	no	yes	Indeterminate*
Patient C	yes	yes	yes	no	yes	Positive*
Positive control	yes	yes	yes	yes	yes	Positive*
Negative control	no	no	no	no	no	Negative*

* The entries in this column are designated by the student.

Activity Questions:

1. Gel electrophoresis uses electrical current to separate proteins on the basis of size and charge.

2. In this application of the Western blot, antibodies are detected in the patient sample when they bind to the separated antigens on the nitrocellulose strips.

Serological Testing

ACTIVITY 1   Using Direct Fluorescent Antibody Technique to Test for Chlamydia

1. Describe the importance of the washing steps in the direct antibody fluorescence test. *The washing steps are to remove any nonspecific binding between antigen and antibodies that might occur.*

2. Explain where the epitope (antigenic determinant) is located. *The epitope is a subpart of the antigen. Antigens are large. The epitope is the small part of the antigen where the antibody specifically binds.*

3. Describe how a positive result is detected in this serological test. *A positive result is detected when fluorescently labeled antibodies bind to the epitope regions found on the elementary bodies when they are present.*

4. How would the results be affected if a negative control gave a positive result? *If the negative control gave a positive result it would invalidate all of the results. It could be a result of not enough washing.*

ACTIVITY 2   Comparing Samples with Ouchterlony Double Diffusion

1. Describe how you were able to determine what antigen is in the unknown well. *Since human serum albumin was in well 4 and wells 4 and 5 were identical, this meant that the unknown well (well 5) was human serum albumin as well.*

2. Why does the precipitin line form? *The precipitin line forms because antibodies and antigens diffuse toward each other. When the optimum ratio is present, a precipitate forms.*

3. Did you think human serum albumin and bovine serum albumin would have epitopes in common? How well did the results compare with your prediction? *Human serum albumin and bovine serum albumin did have partial identity because they had a single spur form. This indicated that they had epitopes in common.*

ACTIVITY 3   Indirect Enzyme-Linked Immunosorbent Assay (ELISA)

1. Describe how the direct and indirect ELISA are different. *The direct ELISA tests directly for antigens whereas the indirect ELISA tests for the result of the presence of antigens, antibodies.*

2. Discuss why a patient might test indeterminate. *The patient might test indeterminate if they have not yet seroconverted or if they have not yet produced enough antibodies to yield a positive result.*

3. How would your results have been affected if your negative control had given an indeterminate result? *If the negative control is positive, this invalidates the results. It could be due to not enough washing in the washing steps to remove nonspecific binding.*

4. Briefly describe the basic structure of antibodies. *Antibodies are made up of amino acids. They have a constant region that is the same within an Ig class and a variable region that acts as the binding site for epitope.*

A C T I V I T Y   4   Western Blotting Technique

1. Describe why the HIV Western blot is a more specific test than the indirect ELISA for HIV. *The Western blot is more specific because you are looking at separated antigens and specifically how they react with antibodies rather than a mixture of antibodies.*

2. Explain the procedure for a patient with an indeterminate HIV Western blot result. *A patient that is indeterminate would be retested and monitored.*

3. Briefly describe how the nitrocellulose strips were prepared before the patient samples were added to them. *The antigens are separated by size and charge using electrophoresis and then transferred to nitrocellulose, which is easier to work with than agar.*

4. Describe the importance of the washing steps in the procedure. *The washing steps are to remove nonspecific binding that could lead to a false positive result.*

List of Supply Houses

This is a partial list of suppliers of equipment, animals, and chemicals, and should not be considered a recommendation for these companies. Many supply companies have regional addresses. Only one address is listed below.

American Scientific LLC
6450 Fiesta Drive
Columbus, OH 43235
888-490-9002/614-764-9002
www.american-scientific.com

BIOPAC® Systems, Inc.
42 Aero Camino
Goleta, CA 93117
805-685-0066
www.biopac.com

Carolina Biological Supply Company
2700 York Road
Burlington, NC 27215
800-334-5551
www.carolina.com

Craig Medical Distribution, Inc.
1185 Park Center Drive, Building P
Vista, CA 92081
760-598-7170
www.craigmedical.com

CSI Forensic Supply
P.O. Box 16
Martinez, CA 94553
800-227-6020
www.csiforensic.com

EDVOTEK, Inc.
P.O. Box 341232
Bethesda, MP 20827-1232
800-338-6835/202-370-1501
www.edvotek.com

Fisher Scientific
300 Industry Drive
Pittsburgh, PA 15275
800-766-7000
www.fishersci.com

Fotodyne, Inc.
950 Walnut Ridge Drive
Hartland, WI 53029
800-362-3686/262-369-7000
www.fotodyne.com

ICN Biochemicals
Sold by LabSource, Inc.
1186 Arbor Dr.
Romeoville, IL 60446
800-545-8823
www.LabSource.com

Immucor, Inc.
3130 Gateway Drive
P.O. Box 5625
Norcross, GA 30091-5625
855-466-8267/770-441-2051
www.immucor.com

Intelitool® (Phipps & Bird)
P.O. Box 7475
Richmond, VA 23221-0475
800-955-7621
www.intelitool.com

LabChem, Inc.
200 William Pitt Way
Pittsburgh, PA 15238
412-826-5230
www.labchem.net

Modern Biology, Inc.
3710 East 700 South
Lafayette IN 47909
800-733-6544
www.modernbio.com

Nasco
901 Janesville Avenue
P.O. Box 901
Fort Atkinson, WI 53538-0901
800-558-9595
www.enasco.com

Sigma-Aldrich®
P.O. Box 14508
St. Louis, MO 63178
800-325-3010
www.sigma-aldrich.com

Sirchie® Finger Print Laboratories
100 Hunter Place
Youngsville, NC 27596
800-356-7311
www.sirchie.com

Triarch, Inc.
P.O. Box 98
Ripon. WI 54971
800-848-0810
www.triarchmicroslides.com

VWR International, Inc.
2039 Center Square Road
Bridgeport, NJ 08014
800-932-5000
www.us.vwr.com

WARD'S Natural Science
5100 West Henrietta Road
P.O. Box 92912
Rochester, NY 14692-9012
800-962-2660
www.wardsci.com